# FATIGUE OF METALS

# Fatigue of Metals

by

P. G. FORREST, B.Sc.(Eng.), Ph.D., M.I.Mech.E.

Head of Queen's Award to Industry Branch,
Ministry of Technology

1966

PERGAMON PRESS

OXFORD · LONDON · EDINBURGH · NEW YORK
TORONTO · SYDNEY · PARIS · BRAUNSCHWEIG

Pergamon Press Ltd., Headington Hill Hall, Oxford
4 & 5 Fitzroy Square, London W.1

Pergamon Press (Scotland) Ltd., 2 & 3 Teviot Place, Edinburgh 1

Pergamon Press Inc., Maxwell House, Fairview Park, Elmsford,
New York 10523

Pergamon of Canada Ltd., 207 Queen's Quay West, Toronto 1

Pergamon Press (Aust.) Pty. Ltd., 19a Boundary Street,
Rushcutters Bay, N.S.W. 2011, Australia

Pergamon Press S.A.R.L., 24 rue des Écoles, Paris 5e

Vieweg & Sohn GmbH, Burgplatz 1, Braunschweig

08 009729 4

*Printed in Great Britain by Page Bros. (Norwich) Ltd., Norwich
and reprinted lithographically by A. Wheaton & Co., Exeter*

# CONTENTS

vi

# PREFACE

FATIGUE of metals is a subject of great practical importance because most of the material failures in engineering components and structures are fatigue failures. This importance is reflected by the many technical papers published on the subject and by the number of conferences held in recent years to discuss it. Yet, despite this activity, no comprehensive British book on fatigue, as distinct from reports of conferences, has been published during the last 30 years. It therefore seemed that there was a need to provide a general account of the present knowledge of fatigue and this I have tried to do.

The book is written primarily for engineers and metallurgists. It is intended to serve as an introduction to the subject and also as a reference book and I hope that it will prove useful to students, to designers and to those working in research on strength of materials. The subject matter has, accordingly, been arranged to suit the reader unfamiliar with the subject, but a considerable amount of data and a fairly extensive bibliography are included.

I wish particularly to record my thanks to Mr. H. L. Cox, whose many comments and criticisms have been invaluable. I would not have attempted the task without his help. I wish also to thank Mr. B. E. Hopkins for reading the book and making many helpful comments and Mr. J. G. Hayes for reading the section on statistical methods. I am indebted to Mr. G. A. Cottell, Mr. A. J. Fenner, Mr. P. J. E. Forsyth and Dr. N. Thompson for providing photographs and to the many industrial firms who provided fatigue data or details of fatigue testing machines.

P. G. FORREST

## CHAPTER I

# INTRODUCTION

FAILURE of metals by fatigue results from loads which are varied or repeated and the maximum load required to cause failure in this way is much less than the static breaking load. In service many components and structures are subject to varying loads and, although the average stresses are often low, local concentrations of stress, which do not much reduce the static strength, may often lead to failure by fatigue. Indeed, by far the greater number of failures in service are by fatigue and relatively few by static failure.

The most striking characteristic of fatigue failures is the lack of deformation in the region of the fractures, even in materials like mild steel, which are quite ductile when broken by a static load. This is one of the dangers of fatigue, for there is generally no prior indication of impending failure. Fatigue cracks are usually fine and difficult to detect and once they have grown to macroscopic size they may spread and cause complete fracture in a short time. The detection of fatigue cracks, therefore, presents a serious problem to those responsible for the inspection and maintenance of engineering plant.

It is usually found that fatigue cracks originate at some surface discontinuity. This is because any change in section, such as a hole, a change in shaft diameter, a groove, a keyway, or even a tool mark, gives rise to a concentration of stress. The static strength is little affected by such changes in section because the stress concentrations are relieved by plastic deformation. Under fatigue loading, however, much less plastic deformation occurs; consequently the range of stress remains considerably higher at stress concentrations than in the surrounding material, resulting in a reduced fatigue strength. For example, in a flat bar with a small transverse hole, subjected to a tensile load, the stress at the side of the hole under elastic conditions is equal to about three times the average stress in the bar. For a ductile metal, the tensile strength of such a bar would be scarcely affected by the presence of the hole, whereas the resistance to fatigue failure might be reduced by a factor of two or more.

The magnitude of the stress at a stress concentration increases with the curvature of the surface. In other words, the smaller the radius of a fillet at a change of diameter in a shaft, the greater is the stress concentration.

1

It is, therefore, important in the design of parts to withstand dynamic stresses to assess the stress concentration at each change in section and to ensure that an adequate radius is provided. Except in the few cases in which the variation of load in service is very small, it is most unwise to base design on the static strength and to rely on a factor of safety as a safeguard against fatigue. This procedure, still widely adopted, leads to the use of excessively large factors of safety with a consequent increase in the weight of the whole component. By attention to detail in design and the adjustment of the dimensions in relation to the local concentrations of stress, the component can be made lighter without incurring any danger of fatigue.

Of the many factors which affect fatigue resistance, that of local concentrations of stress is the most important and this alone renders design against fatigue more difficult than design for static stress. At the same time, fatigue resistance is affected by the size of a component, by the relative magnitude of static and fluctuating loads and by the number of load reversals. Furthermore, fatigue resistance is adversely affected by corrosion to a much greater extent than is static strength and particularly by fretting corrosion, which results from small repeated relative movements between two parts in contact. The influence of these factors on fatigue behaviour is discussed in detail in the following chapters, and design procedures for avoiding fatigue are considered in Chapter X.

Fatigue fractures are usually associated with many thousands or millions of stress reversals, but they can and do occur after hundreds or even tens of cycles. For example, gun springs sometimes fail by fatigue as a result of the stresses induced each time the gun is fired. Such failures are usually accompanied by considerable plastic deformation and appear to result from progressive distortion.

Fatigue is not confined only to metals, but also occurs in non-metallic materials. These include wood, plastics, concrete and even human bone and in many ways the fatigue behaviour of these materials is similar to that in metals. Fatigue of non-metallic materials is discussed briefly in Chapter XII.

## Characteristics of fatigue fractures

If a component is repeatedly subjected to loads of sufficient magnitude, a fatigue crack, or cracks, will eventually be formed in some highly stressed region, usually at the surface, and will gradually progress through the metal until complete fracture results. The fractured surfaces of parts that have failed by fatigue generally have a characteristic appearance by which they may be recognised.

There are usually two or three zones which can be identified on each fractured surface. Round the region of origin of the crack the surface often has a smooth appearance showing conchoidal or beach markings; this is the area over which the fatigue crack has spread relatively slowly. A second, less smooth zone can sometimes be distinguished across which the crack has extended more rapidly, perhaps in several places at once, so that the fracture surface is irregular. The third zone is the area on which the final fracture occurred when the section was reduced so much that the metal was unable to withstand the last application of load. This zone may have either a crystalline appearance indicating that the final fracture has occurred in a brittle manner, or a fibrous appearance indicating a final ductile fracture.

If a fractured part has been subjected to compressive loads, some of the detail in the fracture surfaces may be lost as a result of a repeated hammering together of the cracked surface before complete fracture occurs; this action produces a polished appearance. Another characteristic of a fatigue failure is staining or oxidation of part of the fractured surfaces indicating that a crack has been present for some time. These features are often useful in identifying fatigue failures. There is usually little difficulty with ductile materials but in cast metals, particularly cast iron, it is often difficult to distinguish between fatigue and static fractures. The same problem may occur in steels that have failed in an intergranular manner, but such failures are rather unusual.

Much information can be obtained from a study of fatigue fracture surfaces and this may be invaluable in diagnosing the cause of a service failure. [1, 2] The conchoidal markings on the first zone are particularly useful in this respect because these represent stages in crack propagation. Some features of fracture surfaces are illustrated by photographs of typical service failures in Figs. 1 to 4.

Figure 1 shows the fracture surface of a motor car rear axle shaft in which the three zones of failure can be clearly distinguished. The first zone covers more than half the section and the beach markings show the way in which the crack has spread. It started at the stress concentration caused by the keyway and has spread in an asymmetrical manner which is typical of fatigue fractures in rotating shafts. There is a tendency for the crack to extend preferentially in a direction opposite to that of rotation, from which it may be deduced that the shaft, as viewed in Fig. 1, had rotated in a clockwise direction. This can be confirmed by the author, for the shaft was from his own car (the final fracture occurring at 6.0 a.m. just after setting out on holiday). The second zone of more rapid crack propagation covers most of the rest of the section and shows the characteristic rougher appearance. The final fracture occurred in a ductile manner on a thin region, appearing mostly as a dark area on the right hand side of the photograph. The relatively small area covered by this third zone is an indication that the applied stresses were fairly low.

FIG. 1. Fatigue fracture of a motor car rear axle shaft. (*By courtesy of N.P.L.*)

The two zones of relatively slow and fast crack propagation are also clearly illustrated in Fig. 2, which shows the fractured surface of a coil spring. The fatigue crack started at a surface flaw and developed initially on a diagonal plane on which the direct stress was a maximum and then changed direction and propagated on a plane of high shear stress. The dark markings running parallel to the direction of crack propagation in the second zone indicate the presence of several cracks in different planes, which joined up at a later stage to cause complete fracture.

FIG. 2. Fatigue fracture of a coil spring. (*By courtesy of N.P.L.*)

Figure 3 shows a fatigue fracture of a crankshaft, which has propagated from the stress concentration at the junction of the journal and the web. Dark lines parallel to the direction of crack propagation are present in the first zone of this fracture, indicating that failure originated from several independent cracks. This is characteristic of fatigue failures that have spread from extensive regions of high stress concentration. Crankshafts are subjected in service to a combination of bending and torsional loads, but the failure shown can be attributed primarily to bending loads because the crack has spread approximately in a direction tangential to the journal. If torsional loads are predominant the cracks tend to extend round the fillet and sometimes show a saw-tooth formation [1]. Less commonly, fatigue cracks propagate from the oil hole in the journal.

FIG. 3. Fatigue fracture of a crankshaft. (*By courtesy of N.P.L.*)

The coil spring, shown in Fig. 4 has fractured by fatigue in two places as a result of fretting corrosion produced by the rubbing together under load of adjacent coils. Fretting produces characteristic oxidation products and the dark zone at the bottom of the fracture surface shows the staining that these have caused.

An example of a fatigue fracture in an aluminium alloy, broken in the laboratory, is illustrated in Fig. 91 and two corrosion fatigue fractures are shown in Figs. 100 and 101.

### Detection of fatigue cracks

There is always a danger of fatigue fracture in parts subjected to fluctuating stress and inspection is necessary if failures are to be avoided. Clearly, inspection would be more effective if damage could be detected at an early stage in the fatigue process, and it would be of great value if a method were available for detecting fatigue damage before cracking occurred. Unfortunately, although changes in certain physical properties can be detected in laboratory fatigue specimens before cracking occurs,

Fig. 4. Fatigue fracture of a coil spring as a result of fretting corrosion.
(*By courtesy of N.P.L.*)

none affords a reliable indication of imminent failure in service. At present it is, therefore, necessary to rely on the detection of fatigue cracks. Even this presents considerable practical difficulties, for a crack less than about $\frac{1}{4}$ inch long cannot readily be detected unless its presence is suspected.

Many different methods are available for the detection of cracks, each having advantages for particular applications. The most useful methods are magnetic, penetrant, electrical and ultrasonic. A brief description of each of these methods is given in the next few pages; more detailed reviews of the detection of fatigue cracks have been written [3, 4], and many reviews of crack detection in general are available [5, 6].

The operation of magnetic crack detectors depends on the distortion of a magnetic field in the neighbourhood of a crack or flaw, on account of the local change in permeability. The equipment provides a suitable magnetizing arrangement and a means of detecting field distortion. The distortion is greatest when the field crosses the crack at right angles. For the detection of transverse cracks, therefore, the part to be examined is

B

magnetized longitudinally, usually by placing it between the poles of an electromagnet. For the detection of longitudinal cracks the part can be magnetized circumferentially by passing a heavy current (usually a.c.) through it. To detect the field distortion produced by cracks, a finely divided magnetic powder, suspended in paraffin, is applied to the part, either by complete immersion or by pouring or spraying. The magnetic particles tend to bridge the narrow gaps formed by cracks and are held there by the magnetic field. The particles then appear as a line which shows the position of the cracks.

The method can be adapted for use on large engineering parts which cannot be dismantled, and has the advantage of being sensitive and relatively easy to use. The limitations are that it can only be used on magnetic metals and that only cracks at, or close to, the surface can be detected. The second limitation is not usually a serious one, for nearly all fatigue cracks are formed at the surface. A number of magnetic crack detectors are available commercially, for example from A.E.I. (Manchester), and Fel Electric Ltd., Sheffield.

Most penetrant methods of crack detection are based on one of two simple principles; one depends on the spreading of a liquid from the crack and the other on the deposit of a fluorescent material, which enhances the contrast and makes the crack visible to the naked eye. The simplest method and one which has been used for many years is to immerse the part to be examined in hot oil and then to clean the surface and cover it with French chalk. As the oil exudes from the crack it stains the chalk. Better results can be obtained with dyes which have been specially developed for this purpose. One disadvantage of using dyes is that they tend to clog the crack and make it more difficult to use other methods subsequently. Fluorescent materials are more sensitive than dye, but they need to be viewed in ultra-violet light, which is not always convenient. Equipment for these methods of crack detection can be obtained from Fel Electric Ltd., Sheffield, A.E.I. (Manchester) and from Hanovia Ltd., Slough.

The main advantage of penetrant methods is their simplicity. For ferrous materials, however, better results are usually obtained with magnetic methods. Penetrant methods may fail to reveal cracks which are sealed by internal stresses or by corrosion, or which have been "peened over" by the action of machining. They are, of course, of no use for detecting cracks below the surface.

There are two advantages of using electrical methods of crack detection instead of magnetic or penetrant methods; firstly, defects below the surface can be detected, and secondly, the test can be carried out much more quickly, particularly on long lengths of bar, tube or rail.

The electromagnetic method of crack detection was originally developed in the U.S.A. for detecting cracks in rails while in service. A high direct current is passed through the rails inducing a magnetic field, which is cut by a search coil situated between the rails. The presence of a crack alters the flux and a current is induced in the search coil. The whole apparatus is carried in a special truck, known as a Sperry wagon, thus giving a rapid and effective method of detecting cracks, both on and under the surface [7]. It is also possible to use alternating current methods where the specimen acts as the core of a transformer whose efficiency is impaired by a crack or other discontinuity. Measurement of electrical resistance can also be used; alternating current is more effective for detecting surface cracks and direct current for cracks some distance below the surface.

Detection of cracks by ultrasonics depends on the transmission or reflection of elastic waves in the metal, which can be produced by means of piezo-electricity or magnetostriction. In transmission testing, an ultrasonic beam is emitted by a transducer applied to one side of the part to be examined and is received by a second transducer on the other side of the part. If the beam intersects a crack or flaw, some of its energy will be lost by reflection and diffusion, and this will be apparent from the output of the second transducer. In testing by reflection, a transducer is used to emit short high-frequency pulses. These are reflected from the opposite surface of the part under examination and also from any crack or flaw in the material. The reflected pulse is received either by the same or by a second transducer, and is displayed on a cathode ray oscillograph. It is sometimes difficult to interpret the signals received, but with experience and by repeating the tests with the emitters and receivers in a number of different positions, small fatigue cracks can be detected and their positions determined. Furthermore, the equipment can be portable and there is no limit to the thickness of the part that can be tested. The method is becoming increasingly popular and has been used successfully to detect fatigue cracks in a wide range of components [8]. An alternative technique, using ultrasonic surface waves, has recently been developed, which is particularly suitable for detecting fatigue cracks in parts of complex shape. By this means, fatigue cracks have been detected in compressor and turbine blades without removing the blades, and a high sensitivity is claimed [9]. Suitable equipment can be obtained from Ultrasonoscope, Ltd., Brixton Hill, London, and Kelvin & Hughes Ltd., Wembley, Middlesex.

Radiography, using either X-rays or $\gamma$-rays, is widely used for detecting flaws, but is not sufficiently sensitive to be a reliable method for detecting fatigue cracks. Cracks can be detected by etching the surface with a suitable acid and examining it under a low-powered microscope; the acid reveals the crack by preferentially attacking its edges. The method can be effective and is sometimes used on non-ferrous metals but it cannot be regarded as wholly non-destructive.

A method of detecting fatigue cracks with bonded wires has been used successfully in the investigation of the fatigue strength of full-scale aircraft wing structures [10]. Insulated annealed copper wires, 0·002 in. in diameter, were cemented to the structure where fatigue failures were likely to occur. A fatigue crack passing underneath the wire was sufficient to break it and, by means of an electric circuit, a break in a detector wire actuated a warning system. It was found possible in this way to detect cracks not visible to the naked eye and sometimes not even visible under a microscope with a magnification of twenty.

The frequency with which inspection for fatigue cracks should be undertaken is dependent on the rate at which fatigue cracks can be expected to propagate under service conditions. The factors influencing crack propagation are discussed in Chapter V. Once a fatigue crack has been detected in a component it is almost always the wisest policy to remove the part from service. Attempts are sometimes made to repair a cracked part or to prevent a fatigue crack from propagating. Probably the simplest method is to drill a small hole at the end of the crack. This may prevent further propagation of the crack by alleviating, to some extent, the stress concentration. If this method is used, the hole should be drilled at some distance ahead of the advancing crack, leaving a gap between the end of the crack and the hole because the material ahead of the crack may be damaged. Other possible ways of preventing crack propagation are to reinforce the part in some way or to repair the damage by welding. A welding repair may be satisfactory if the part is built up by welding in a longitudinal direction, but adverse residual stresses may be introduced and there is a danger that cracking will occur in the parent metal adjacent to the weld during cooling or subsequent stressing. Moreover, the weld metal may contain stress concentrations, such as inclusions and blow holes, from which fatigue cracks may propagate [11, 12]. All these methods must be regarded as temporary expedients which should be used only if the damage resulting from complete failure is not likely to be serious.

There are certain circumstances, however, when the presence of short fatigue cracks may not be dangerous. If a very sharp notch is introduced into a material, the fluctuating load required to form a crack at the root of the notch may be appreciably lower than the load required to propagate it once it has spread beyond the immediate vicinity of the notch. This results in the presence of "non-propagating cracks", which are often found, for example, in locomotive crankpins at the press-fit with the wheel. These are caused by a combination of the high stress concentration induced by the press-fit and fretting corrosion. Horger and Cantley [13] showed that these non-propagating cracks still occurred when the crankpins were tested in the laboratory at a constant stress range. The depth to which the cracks grew depended on the applied stress, the maximum depth of a non-propagating crack being about 1/10 in. The subject has been investigated subsequently at the National Engineering Laboratory and the results are discussed in Chapter V (see page 146).

## CHAPTER II

# FATIGUE TESTING

To obtain a quantitative measure of resistance to fatigue it is necessary to carry out tests under controlled conditions and for this purpose a wide variety of fatigue testing machines is available. Many different methods of fatigue testing can be adopted, from laboratory tests on smooth specimens under the simplest stress conditions, to tests on full-scale components and structures under conditions simulating those occurring in practice. Tests on laboratory specimens are used primarily for determining the influence on fatigue resistance of such factors as alloy content, heat-treatment or surface finish, because the results can be obtained quickly and economically. Such tests can be made on smooth or notched specimens, if necessary at a high or low temperature, or under corrosive conditions. To provide data for design, however, fatigue tests on actual parts are usually more valuable. For this purpose, special testing facilities are sometimes required, but many small components can be accommodated and tested in standard fatigue machines.

## Notation

During a fatigue test the stress cycle is usually maintained constant so that the applied stress conditions can be written $S_m \pm S_a$, where $S_m$ is the static or mean stress, and $S_a$ is the alternating stress, equal to half the stress range. The positive sign is used to denote a tensile stress and the negative sign, a compressive stress. Some of the possible combinations of $S_m$ and $S_a$ are illustrated in Fig. 5. When $S_m = 0$ (Fig. 5a) the maximum tensile stress is equal to the maximum compressive stress and this is called an alternating stress, or a completely reversed stress. When $S_m = S_a$ (Fig. 5b) the minimum stress of the cycle is zero, and this is termed a pulsating or repeated tensile (or compressive) stress. Any other combination is known as a fluctuating stress which may be a fluctuating tensile stress (Fig. 5c), a fluctuating compressive stress or may fluctuate from a tensile to a compressive value (Fig. 5d). The stress conditions may, alternatively, be defined in terms of the maximum and minimum stress in the cycle, $S_{max}$ and $S_{min}$. The algebraic ratio $S_{min}/S_{max}$ is called the stress ratio, $R$.

When the loading conditions are such that the stress in the specimen

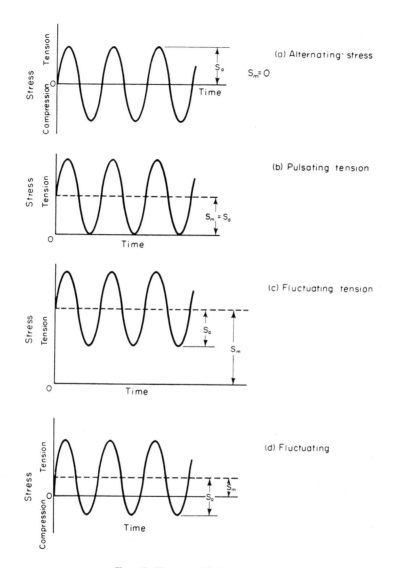

FIG. 5. Types of fatigue stress.

is not uniformly distributed, it is usual to present the results in terms of the nominal stress $S$, which is the stress calculated by simple theory without taking into account the variations in stress conditions caused by geometrical discontinuities such as holes, grooves and fillets.

## Fatigue strength and fatigue limit

The usual procedure for determining fatigue strength is to test a number of similar specimens, subjecting each to a particular range of fluctuating or alternating load until it breaks, so that a relation is obtained between the fluctuating load or stress $S$, and the number of cycles to fracture $N$. A typical stress–endurance ($S$–$N$) curve is shown in Fig. 6. $N$ is usually

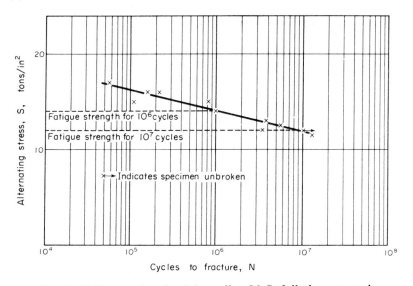

FIG. 6. $S$–$N$ curve for aluminium alloy 26-S, fully heat-treated.

plotted on a logarithmic scale because the value may range from a few thousand to many million. The stress may also be plotted on a logarithmic scale and it has been claimed that the results can often be represented by a straight line if the double log method of plotting is used. The claim is not well supported by experimental data, however, particularly if results at very long endurances are included.

A feature of fatigue behaviour which is illustrated in Fig. 6 is the scatter in the results of fatigue tests. Some of the scatter may arise from experimental errors, such as misalignment of the specimen or inaccurate determination of the stress range, but there is little doubt that scatter is an inherent feature of fatigue behaviour. It is, therefore, necessary to carry out a large number of tests if the $S$–$N$ curve is to be determined accurately. Eight tests should normally be regarded as a minimum and more should be carried out if possible. In Fig. 6 the line drawn is the one which appears, by eye, to be the best fit of the experimental results. For most purposes this method is sufficiently accurate, but an analytical method such as the "least squares" can be used, if required, to fit a line or a curve of chosen shape. The problem of scatter and the use of statistical methods in fatigue testing are discussed later in the chapter (see page 44).

The fatigue strength is defined as the maximum alternating (or fluctuating) stress which a material will withstand without failure for a given number of cycles. This is illustrated in Fig. 6; the fatigue strength for failure after $10^6$ cycles is equal to about 14 tons/in² and for failure after $10^7$ cycles is equal to about 12 tons/in². As the value of the fatigue strength depends on the number of cycles to failure, this number should be given when fatigue strengths are quoted.

$S$–$N$ curves are usually determined over a range from about $10^5$ to $10^8$ cycles. The fatigue strength for endurances of less than $10^4$ cycles are required only for some special applications and the $S$–$N$ curve is seldom investigated between $N = 1$ and $N = 10^4$. For many practical applications the fatigue strength for $10^9$ or $10^{10}$ cycles is required, but to continue fatigue tests to these endurances takes a very long time using conventional fatigue machines which usually operate at speeds between 1000 and 10,000 cycles per minute. Fortunately, $S$–$N$ curves usually tend to flatten out at long endurances so that they can be extrapolated with some degree of confidence.

There are some materials for which failures seldom occur after endurances greater than a million or so cycles, even if the fatigue test is continued for as many as $10^8$ or $10^9$ cycles. The $S$–$N$ diagram is then drawn as a sloping line through the specimens which fractured and a horizontal line above those which remained unbroken. The stress at which the curve becomes horizontal is known as the fatigue limit or endurance limit. Figure 7 shows the $S$–$N$ curve for a material with a fatigue limit of about 19·5 tons/in².

The metals which show a fatigue limit include cast and wrought iron, low and medium strength steels, stainless steel, aluminium–magnesium alloys and some titanium alloys. It is often thought that this is the normal behaviour, but this is not so, for the majority of metals and probably all non-metals do not show a fatigue limit. The misconception has arisen because most of the early investigations and a great many of the more recent ones have been made on steels. It has resulted in too wide a use of the term fatigue limit, which should be used only for those metals whose $S$–$N$ curves become horizontal. The occurrence of a fatigue limit can be explained if a gradual change in the metal structure is induced by cyclic stress which more than counterbalances the damaging effect of the stress. In iron and steel this is thought to be strain ageing and this is discussed further in Chapter XI (see page 344).

It is sometimes the practice, particularly when testing large engineering parts, to apply a low stress range to the specimen and if it does not fail in a given number of cycles to raise the stress range and to test again and

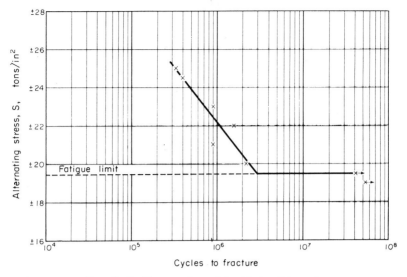

FIG. 7. *S–N* curve for cold-rolled mild steel.

to repeat this procedure until failure does occur. This method has the merit of conserving specimens but the result should always be checked by another test at higher stress on a virgin specimen because some metals, particularly carbon steels, can be strengthened appreciably by this procedure, with the result that an optimistic value of the fatigue strength might be obtained.

### The relation between stress and strain during fatigue

Although fatigue fractures usually appear to have occurred in a brittle manner, observation of the metal structure or measurement of both the stress and the strain during a fatigue test often show that some plastic deformation occurs. The relation between the stress and the strain during an alternation of stress in which plastic deformation occurs is illustrated in Fig. 8. On the first loading in tension, a curve of the form OC is obtained (Fig. 8a) similar to a static stress–strain curve. At low stresses the strain is wholly elastic and the curve follows the elastic line OB, but beyond the elastic limit plastic deformation occurs and increases with the stress. On unloading, the strain follows the line CD, which for metals at air temperature is usually found to be parallel to the elastic line OB. On loading in compression, plastic strain begins in the opposite direction at a low value of compressive stress, giving the curve DE. (The reduction of the elastic limit in compression, resulting from preload in tension, is known as the Bauschinger effect.) On unloading from compression, the line EF is obtained, again, parallel to the elastic line; then reloading in tension gives the curve FG. If the stress alternates between equal tension and compression, the tensile strain will be mostly cancelled by the compressive strain and after a few stress cycles a closed loop will be obtained, as shown in Fig. 8b. The occurrence of stress–strain loops results from the strain lagging behind the stress and they are therefore known as hysteresis loops. The range of strain during a stress cycle is equal to the sum of the elastic strain and the plastic strain. Provided that the unloading lines CD and EF are parallel to the elastic line, then the width of the hysteresis loop FD is equal to the plastic strain range.

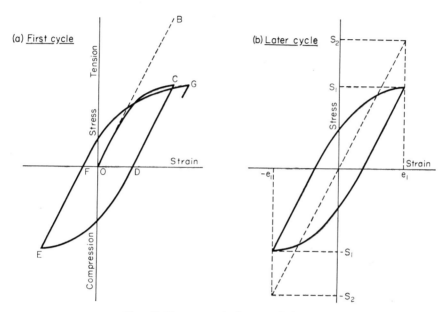

FIG. 8. Stress–strain hysteresis loops.

During a fatigue test at constant stress range the amount of plastic strain occurring in each cycle may vary during the course of the test, as illustrated for a number of materials in Fig. 9. The amount of plastic strain occurring depends markedly on the stress; this can be illustrated by plotting the alternating stress against the alternating strain to give a dynamic stress–strain curve. Such curves are shown in Fig. 10; these were obtained by plotting the alternating stress against the average value of the alternating strain during the course of a fatigue test. On each of these curves the alternating stresses corresponding to failure in $10^5$, $10^6$ and $10^7$ cycles are indicated. Some materials, notably mild steel and austenitic steel, show considerable plastic strain in every cycle, even at stress ranges below their

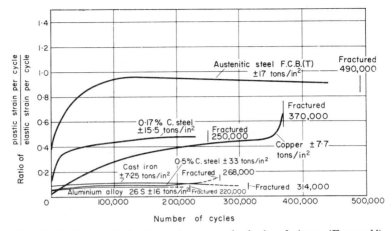

FIG. 9. Variation of plastic strain per cycle during fatigue. (Forrest[14])

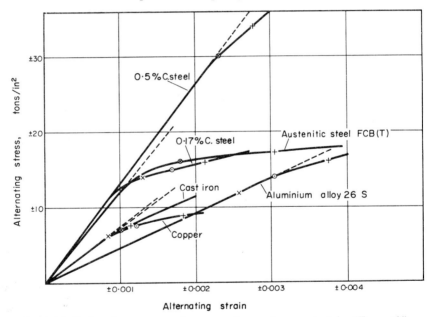

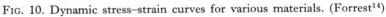

FIG. 10. Dynamic stress–strain curves for various materials. (Forrest[14])

+—Stress for failure in $10^5$ cycles
○—Stress for failure in $10^6$ cycles
× —Stress for failure in $10^7$ cycles
⊗—Stress for failure in $10^6$ and $10^7$ cycles

fatigue limits, while other materials, for example, high strength alloy steels
and aluminium alloys, show no detectable plastic strain unless the stress
is above the range for failure in $10^5$ or $10^6$ cycles.

The area of a hysteresis loop represents the work done on the material during the stress cycle. A very small proportion of this work may be stored in the material as a result of permanent distortion of the structure, but almost all of it is dissipated as heat. When fatigue testing metals which show considerable hysteresis, the dissipation of heat may result in an appreciable rise in temperature of the specimen, particularly at high stress ranges in direct stress fatigue machines, where the whole of the test section is subjected to the maximum stress range. Since the fatigue strength of the material is affected by temperature, some means of cooling are required in these circumstances and the temperature of the specimen should be measured. The area of a hysteresis loop is also a measure of the damping capacity of the metal. This can be an important property in applications where fatigue failure may result from resonant vibrations (see page 322). The ability of a material to deform plastically without failing by fatigue also renders the material less sensitive to the effect of notches (see page 134).

## Types of fatigue test and their correlation

Fatigue testing machines can be classified by the type of straining action that is applied to the specimen, that is direct or axial stress, bending, torsion, and combined or complex stress. In direct stress machines the specimen is subjected to tension–compression stresses; for a plain specimen with no stress concentrations and well-designed transition curves between the test section and the enlarged ends, the stress across the test section is uniform (provided there is no misalignment) and is calculated simply by dividing the applied load by the area of cross section. Bending fatigue machines are of two types, one in which the specimen is rotated, and the other in which it is repeatedly bent to and fro. In the rotating bending machine, the specimen is supported as a cantilever or a beam and loaded by dead weights applied through bearings, which permit the specimen to rotate. As the specimen rotates, each point on the circumference of the test section is subjected to an alternating stress that varies sinusoidally from tension to equal compression. For bending fatigue tests the nominal stress $S$ is calculated from the applied bending moment $M$ by the equation:

$$S = \frac{My}{I}, \tag{1}$$

where $y = $ distance from the neutral axis to the outermost fibre and $I = $ second moment of area of the test section; this becomes:

$$S = \frac{32M}{\pi d^3} \tag{2}$$

for a round solid specimen of diameter $d$.

Shear stresses are usually obtained by the application of an alternating

torque to the specimen and complex stresses are most easily obtained
either by combining torsion and bending, or by subjecting a tubular
specimen to fluctuating internal pressure. For a fatigue test carried out in
torsion, the nominal shear stress $S_s$ is calculated from the applied torque
$T$, by the equation:

$$S_s = \frac{Ty}{\mathcal{J}} \tag{3}$$

where $\mathcal{J}$ is the polar moment of inertia and this becomes:

$$S_s = \frac{16T}{\pi d^3} \tag{4}$$

for a round solid specimen of diameter $d$.

The stresses calculated from the above equations are denoted as "nominal stresses" to indicate that elastic conditions are assumed, no account
being taken of plastic deformation. If repeated plastic strain does occur in
the highly stressed region of the specimen at and near the surface in the
way illustrated in Fig. 8, then the value of the maximum stress will be less
than the calculated nominal stress.

Before attempting to correlate the results obtained from different types
of fatigue machine, it is necessary to consider the way in which the applied
stress is controlled in each. This leads to a different classification and in
this respect most fatigue machines can be classified in one of three cate-
gories:

1. Constant range of load.
2. Constant range of displacement.
3. Constant range of moment.

Direct stress machines usually operate at a constant range of load. This
can be obtained, of course, by applying an axial force of constant amplitude to the specimen, but it can also be achieved by applying a constant
range of displacement to an assembly consisting of the specimen mounted
in series with an elastic spring of much lower stiffness than the specimen.
In reversed bending machines the specimen is often subjected to a constant range of displacement and under these conditions the addition of a
spring in series with the specimen results approximately in a range of
constant bending moment. The specimens in rotating bending machines
are usually subjected to a range of constant bending moment and in torsion machines to a range of constant torque.

The influence of plastic strain on the range of stress obtained in a plain
specimen subjected to a constant range of displacement can be illustrated
with reference to Fig. 8b. If a strain of $\pm e_1$ were applied to the material,
the resulting stress range would actually be $\pm S_1$, as shown by the stress–
strain loop, while the nominal stress, calculated from the elastic bending

relation would be $\pm S_2$. The distinction between constant range of load and constant range of displacement is often not important when fatigue resistance to many millions of cycles is required, particularly for high strength materials which show little or no plastic deformation under these conditions. It is important, however, for applications where high stresses can be permitted because the number of stress reversals is small; in these circumstances the ability of a material to withstand repeated plastic strain without breaking may be more important than its fatigue strength (see page 89). A further feature of testing under a constant range of displacement is that the stage of crack propagation may be appreciably prolonged, because once cracks occur, the range of load required to maintain the same amplitude is reduced. There is little effect on hard materials but in some soft materials, for example, lead and rubber, complete failure may not occur and the test must be discontinued at some arbitrary stage of crack propagation.

Provided that the alternating plastic strain is small, a constant range of moment is approximately equivalent to a constant range of displacement and this is one reason why the fatigue strengths of plain specimens in rotating bending are usually higher than in direct stress. Attempts have been made to estimate the actual maximum stress range during a bending fatigue test from dynamic stress–strain curves [15, 16] and hence to correlate the results of fatigue tests in bending with those in direct stress. (It must be emphasised that a static stress–strain curve cannot be used for this purpose, because the stress–strain relation in the first loading seldom bears any relation to that which develops during a fatigue test.) These attempts have been only partially successful and this is because there are other factors which give rise to differences between the two types of test.

A comparison of fatigue strengths in bending and direct stress show that results in bending are almost always higher than those in direct stress, sometimes by as much as 25%. One important factor contributing to the difference is the influence of the stress gradient in bending. The bending fatigue strength is found to decrease with increase in diameter of the specimen, that is, with a decrease in the stress gradient across the specimen section. In a direct stress fatigue test there is no stress gradient across the specimen and in this respect it corresponds to a bending specimen of infinite diameter. The size or stress gradient effect is discussed in detail in Chapter V. Another factor is that additional stresses arising from misalignment of the specimen are likely to be higher in direct stress than in bending.

The importance of ensuring axial alignment in direct stress fatigue tests is often emphasised, but there is little direct experimental evidence to show how much results are affected by misalignment. The errors are likely to be greatest under conditions where plastic deformation is very restricted, as for example, when testing notched specimens of high strength alloys. In these circumstances, particular care is therefore required to reduce misalignment to a minimum; the use of specimens with threaded ends should be avoided if possible.

A number of investigations have been made to determine the influence of the shape of a specimen on the fatigue strength [17–20]. These have mostly been made in reversed (vibratory) bending and have included tests on round, square, rectangular and diamond sections. The fatigue strength of rectangular or square section specimens of steel averaged about 10% lower than for round specimens [17, 19], while for aluminium alloys the differences were between 20 and 30% [18, 20]. The behaviour was attributed partly to the smaller volume of material subjected to the maximum stress in the round specimens and partly to the effect of the sharp corners in the square and rectangular specimens.

A comparison of the fatigue strength of metals in bending and torsion and the effects of complex stress are discussed in Chapter IV.

## Rapid methods of determining fatigue strength

To determine the $S–N$ curve for a metal up to an endurance of $10^8$ cycles requires a minimum of 8 tests, the longest of which will last for about two weeks if the speed of the machine is 5000 cycles per minute. The total time required, if only one fatigue machine is available, will be 8 or 10 weeks. It is not surprising, therefore, that many attempts have been made to devise rapid methods for determining fatigue strength [21]. None of these methods has proved entirely satisfactory; a close approximation is often obtained for the majority of the materials tested, but there are always a few materials for which the methods fail and for these the discrepancies may be 10 or 20%. Attempts have been made to relate fatigue strength to other mechanical properties but the correlation is not close enough to render fatigue testing unnecessary: this is discussed in the next chapter.

The early investigators, realizing that fatigue was closely associated with plastic deformation, looked for some relation between the two. Bauschinger [22], in effect, identified the fatigue limit with the dynamic limit of proportionality (see Fig. 10) and considered that if hysteresis occurred in each stress cycle then fatigue fracture would eventually occur. This theory was shown to be approximately true for steels by Bairstow [23] and by later investigators [24]. Further work, however, showed that the method was not reliable, particularly for non-ferrous metals and its use was discontinued.

Many other attempts to determine the fatigue strength of a metal by a rapid method have depended on the change in some physical property caused by fluctuating stress. The methods have included measurements of the rise in temperature of the specimen [24] (which is, in effect, a measurement of the hysteresis) and changes in electrical resistance [25], magnetic permeability [26, 27], magnetic and eddy current losses [28], and thermal expansion [29]. It is likely that the changes in physical properties occurring during fatigue are caused by plastic deformation, so that these methods are liable to the same errors as the direct measurement of the deformation.

A different type of rapid method, first suggested by Prot [30], more closely resembles the normal fatigue testing method, but instead of operating at a constant range of stress, the stress range is increased at a certain constant rate until failure occurs. This ensures that each specimen factures and so yields a definite result. Prot assumed, firstly, that the ordinary $S$–$N$ curve, when plotted on a linear scale, is a hyperbola, which is asymptotic to the vertical axis and to the fatigue limit, and secondly, that the linear cumulative damage law holds. (See page 114.) From these assumptions, Prot showed that if the stress range applied to a specimen was increased at a constant rate, $a$ (expressed as the increase in alternating stress per cycle), then the stress at failure, $S_R$, would be given by the equation:

$$S_R = E + Ka^{0.5}, \qquad (5)$$

where $E$ is the fatigue limit and $K$ is a constant, dependent on the material. The tests are carried out at different values of $a$, and $S_R$ is plotted against $\sqrt{a}$. This should give a straight line relation and according to the above equation, the fatigue limit is equal to the intercept on the stress axis. In order to save time, the tests are not started at zero stress, but at an arbitrary stress range below which it is considered that no significant amount of damage would occur.

This method of testing has been described in some detail because it has aroused considerable interest and is sometimes used. A number of investigations have been made to determine the accuracy of the method and although good agreement with the normal testing method has sometimes been found [31, 32], the method has often proved unreliable [33–37]. It is sometimes found that the breaking stress $S_R$ is not related to $\sqrt{a}$, but to some other power of $a$ [33, 37]. Furthermore, it is doubtful whether any time is saved by the progressive loading tests and fatigue machines must be adapted before such tests can be performed. It has been claimed that the statistical efficiency of the Prot method is less than the probit or staircase method (see page 53), and that it cannot therefore, effect a saving in specimens [36].

The Prot method has been adapted and simplified by McKeown for use as a sorting test [38]. Usually, one specimen only is tested and $a$ is chosen so that failure does not occur in less than half a million cycles. If the breaking stress, $S_R$, is plotted against the fatigue strength determined

c

in the conventional way, it is found that all the results for one class of alloys fall close to a straight line or curve. The degree of correlation is quite good for lead alloys and for copper alloys (certainly better than the correlation between fatigue strength and tensile strength); for steels there is some degree of scatter and for aluminium alloys considerable scatter. McKeown attributed the poor correlation found for the aluminium alloys to their instability under fatigue stressing.

## Fatigue testing machines

It is probably true to say that the majority of fatigue investigations are carried out in rotating bending fatigue machines. In part, this is because these machines are reliable, cheap, and require little attention, but also because the type of stressing is the same as that applied to a great many components under service conditions. There are two important limitations to this method of testing, however; firstly it is restricted, virtually, to round specimens and secondly, the specimen can usually be subjected only to alternating stresses. Reversed bending machines are, therefore, more suitable for many applications, particularly for testing sheet and components and structures of complex shape. Direct stress fatigue machines are generally more complicated and more costly, but they are often preferred, because the addition of a static load can be easily arranged and because of the uniform stress distribution obtained. Furthermore, if the specimen is subjected to a constant load range, the stress is not affected by plastic deformation.

There are a great many different types of fatigue machine and the principle of operation of some of the most widely used will be described briefly. References to many others are quoted by Weibull [674] and in the A.S.T.M. Manual on Fatigue Testing [39] and another A.S.T.M. publication [40] includes a number of papers on large fatigue testing machines developed for testing large diameter shafts and other components. Brief specifications of some British and European machines are listed in Tables 1 and 2.

A common feature of almost all fatigue machines is a counter to record the number of stress cycles to which the specimen has been subjected and a device to stop the machine automatically when the specimen cracks or breaks.

### Direct Stress Machines

Direct stress or axial load fatigue machines can be driven mechanically, electromagnetically or hydraulically. The dynamic force in mechanically driven machines is usually obtained either with a motor driven crank or eccentric operating through a spring in series with the specimen or by means of rotating out-of-balance weights. Mechanical and electromagnetic

machines are often operated at, or close to, the resonant frequency in order
to reduce the power required, but large machines are usually operated
hydraulically at relatively low frequencies.

The N.P.L. slipping clutch fatigue machine is one of the simplest direct
stress machines available and the principle of operation is shown in Fig.
11 [41]. A direct alternating load on the testpiece T is obtained by the use
of a conventional crank and connecting rod driven by the motor D through
two pairs of compression springs $S_1 S_2$ compressed back to back within the
loading frame L. The mass M, fitted between the springs, is chosen so that
it resonates at the operating frequency, thus reducing the dynamic load in
the drive E. When starting the machine, the drive would have to transmit
the full load range but this is avoided by fitting a clutch C between the
drive and the mass. At low speeds the clutch is designed to slip, thus per-
mitting the motor speed to rise to the resonant frequency without transmitting large forces. When the resonant frequency is reached, the force
required to impart the oscillation is much less, and the clutch drives.
For the application of a static load to the testpiece, two further pairs of
compression springs $S_3$ are interposed between the loading frame and the

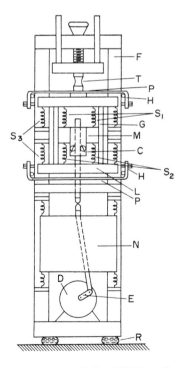

FIG. 11. General arrangement of the N.P.L. slipping clutch fatigue
machine.

TABLE 1. SPECIFICATIONS OF SOME

| Machine | Designation | Manufacturer | Drive |
|---|---|---|---|
| Slipping clutch (NPL) | | Samuel Gill, Coventry | Mechanical, resonant |
| Multiple unit (NPL) | | | Mechanical, non-resonant |
| Haigh | 30 cwt | Bruntons, Musselburgh, Scotland | Electromagnetic, non-resonant |
| Haigh | 6 ton | | Electromagnetic, non-resonant |
| Pulsator | | W. & T. Avery, Birmingham | |
| Vertical pulsator | PUV 0·6 PUV 2 PUV 6 PUV 20 | | |
| Horizontal pulsator | PPV 2 PPV 6 PPV 20 PPV 60 PB 3 PB 10 | Carl Schenck, Darmstadt, Germany | Mechanical, resonant |
| | PB 30 | | |
| Midget pulsator | PP 0·1 PP 0·3 | | |
| Vibrophore | 2 HFP 421 | | Electromagnetic, resonant |
| | 10 HFP 422 | Alfred J. Amsler, Schaffhouse, Switzerland | Electromagnetic, resonant |
| Alternating stress | 30WPZ BDA355 50WPZ BDA 401 100 WPZ BDA 404 UHW 6 | | |
| | UHS 20 UHS 40 UHS 60 | Losenhausenwerk, Dusseldorf, Germany | Hydraulic, non-resonant |
| | UHS 100 UHS 200 | | |

DIRECT STRESS FATIGUE MACHINES

| Load capacity—tons | | | Frequency c/min | |
|---|---|---|---|---|
| Alternating | Static | Maximum | | |
| 0·45 | 0·45 | 0·9 | 4000 | |
| | | 25 lb | 2820 | 24 testpieces can be tested simultaneously in pulsating tension |
| 0·75 | 0·75 | 1·5 | 6000 | |
| 3 | 3 | 6 | 3000 | |
| 10 | 10 | 20 | 2200 | |
| 0·3 | 0·36 | 0·6 | 1000–8000 | |
| 1 | 1·2 | 2 | 700–6000 | |
| 3 | 3·6 | 6 | 700–5000 | |
| 10 | 12 | 20 | 600–4000 | |
| 1 | 1 | 2 | 2600 | Also available with additional low speed (30 c/min) drive |
| 3 | 3 | 6 | 2400 | |
| 10 | 10 | 20 | 2200 | |
| 30 | 30 | 60 | 2000 | |
| 1 | 1·6 | 2·6 | 500–4500 | Load multipliers available up to 60 tons — with additional low speed (up to 100 c/min) drive and programme control unit |
| 3 | 5 | 8 | 400–3600 | |
| 10 | 16 | 26 | 350–2700 | do. up to 200 tons |
| 0·05 | 0·1 | 0·1 | 1450 max. | |
| 0·15 | 0·3 | 0·3 | 2900 max. | |
| 1 | 2 | 2 | 2100–14400 | 0·4 ton dynamometer also supplied |
| 5 | 10 | 10 | 3600–18000 | 2 ton dynamometer also supplied |
| 15 | 30 | 30 | 375–750 | Also available for pulsating fatigue tests only (Type PZ BDA) |
| 25 | 50 | 50 | 250–500 | |
| 50 | 100 | 100 | 250–500 | |
| 6 | — | 6 | 1000 1500 2000 3000 | |
| 10 | 20 | 20 | 333 | Also available with slow cycle unit and programme control unit |
| 20 | 40 | 40 | 500 | |
| 40 | 60 | 60 | 666 | |
| | | | 1000 | |
| 60 | 100 | 100 | | |
| 100 | 200 | 200 | 200–300 400–600 | |

TABLE 2. SPECIFICATIONS OF SOME BENDING, TORSION AND COMBINED STRESS FATIGUE MACHINES

| Type of machine | Manufacturer | Load capacity—lb.ft | | | Frequency c/min | |
|---|---|---|---|---|---|---|
| | | Alternating | Static | Maximum | | |
| Rotating bending | Macklow Smith, Putney, London | 50 | — | | Up to 6000 | Single or two point loading |
| Rotating cantilever | W. & T. Avery, Birmingham | 17 | — | | 3000 | Two testpieces can be tested simultaneously |
| Rotating cantilever | Alfred Amsler, Schaffhouse, Switzerland | 21 | — | | 1000, 2000 and 3000 | Two testpieces can be tested simultaneously |
| Rotating cantilever | Carl Schenck, Darmstadt, Germany | 20 | — | | 6000 and 12000 | |
| Rotating cantilever | Samuel Gill, Coventry | about 7 | — | | up to 8000 | Specially designed for high temperature testing |
| Rotating beam | Schenck | 27·5 | — | | 3000 | |
| Rotating beam | Schenck | 5500 | — | | 1000 and 1500 12500–17000 | |
| Rotating bending wire testing machine | Bruntons, Musselburgh, Scotland / Schenck | 11 | — | | 2000–6000 | |

| Type of test | Maker | | | | | Remarks |
|---|---|---|---|---|---|---|
| Reversed bending | Avery | 10 | 21 | 21 | 1420 | Alternative dynamometers supplied for maximum moments of 7 and 2 lb.ft. Special grips available for torsion or combined bending and torsion tests |
| Reversed bending | Bristol Siddeley Engines | about 150 | | — | 2000 | Adapted for high temperature testing, with provision for static tension or bending |
| Reversed bending, combined torsion and stress (NPL) | Bristol Siddeley Engines | about 150 | | | 2000 | Adapted for high temperature testing |
| Reversed bending and torsion | Amsler | 30 | 43·4 | 43·4 | 1500 | |
| Reversed bending and torsion | Amsler | 21·7 | 101 | 101 | 1500 and 3000 | |
| Reversed bending and torsion | | 50 | 580 | 580 | 1500 and 3000 | |
| Reversed bending and torsion | Schenck | 290 | | | 1500 and 3000 | |
| Torsion | | 2170 | | — | 1000–3000 | |
| Torsion | | 7233 | 14460 | 7233 | 1000–3000 | |
| Torsion | Amsler | 7233 | 21700 | 14460 | 1000–3000 | |
| Torsion | | 7233 | 14460 | 14460 | 1000–3000 | |
| Torsion | | 7233 | | | 1500–12000 | |

machine frame F. By correct choice of the stiffnesses of the two sets of springs in relation to the mass of the loading frame, the load range imposed on the testpiece is rendered virtually independent of its own stiffness. To ensure axial loading, the mass M is arranged to slide along guides G built into the frame L and the frame itself is supported on parallel flat strips P, stretched transversely across the main frame by lever fixings H. The top of the testpiece is held in a crosshead, which can be adjusted to accommodate testpieces of different lengths. A dynamic balancer N, mounted on springs from the main frame, reduces the vibration of the frame. The machine is driven by a variable speed d.c. motor at about 3000 cycles per min. A close speed control is not required, for provided the clutch is driving, the load on the testpiece is independent of the frequency and depends only on the throw of the crank.

The Schenck and Avery pulsator fatigue testing machines are mechanically driven by out-of-balance weights; Fig. 12 illustrates the general arrangement of the Avery machine. It consists of a heavy bed to which two helical

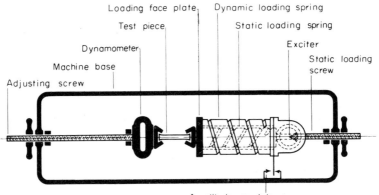

FIG. 12. General arrangement of Avery pulsator fatigue testing machine.
(*Courtesy, W. & T. Avery, Ltd.*)

springs are attached for static and dynamic loading. The springs are built concentrically, both being fixed at one end to the loading face-plate, which is supported on vertical struts with flexible joints. The inner spring is for applying the static load, and it is fitted with an adjusting screw at the opposite end to the face plate, which passes through a boss in the machine bed. The outer spring is for applying the alternating load and this is free to oscillate axially under the forces imposed by the exciter unit fitted at its end. The exciter unit consists of an out-of-balance rotor mounted on ball and roller bearings and it is driven through a flexible shaft by a d.c. motor fitted in the machine bed. The specimen is supported between the loading face-plate and a loop dynamometer which is carried on a bridge (not shown in Fig. 12) that traverses the sides of the bed. The bridge can be adjusted by a screw, passing through a boss in the bed, to suit the length of the specimen. The machine is designed to operate slightly below the resonant frequency of the oscillating system. Close speed control is required, therefore, and this is achieved by an electronic relay controlled by an amplitude regulator fitted to the machine. The dynamometer contains an illuminated slit and graticule and a measure of both the static and dynamic load can be obtained by means of a fitted microscope. In some of the larger Schenck machines of this type, a low speed hydraulic drive is incorporated and also a programme control unit by means of which a repeated sequence of eight different ranges of load can be applied automatically, each for a predetermined number of stress cycles [42].

Another mechanically driven machine is the Multiple Unit direct stress machine, also developed at N.P.L. This machine has been designed to test a number of small testpieces at once, up to a maximum of 24, in pulsating tension. The testpieces are equally spaced on a circle about the main axis of the machine with their axes vertical and their upper ends secured in a fixed head integral with the frame of the machine. Each of the heads carries a helical spring which is cyclically deflected by a wobble plate. The wobble plate does not rotate, but rocks on a universal mounting on the main axis. It is driven by a pair of fibre cams projecting from the upper face of a disc attached to the end of the driving motor shaft. By using springs of different stiffnesses a variety of load ranges can be obtained for any one setting of the wobble plate control.

One of the most successful of the early designs of direct stress machines is that due to Haigh; it is known as the Haigh machine and is still widely used in this country. It is a non-resonant machine, driven electromagnetically and the arrangement is shown in Fig. 13. The two electromagnets $M_1$ $M_2$ are supplied with alternating currents, $90°$ out of phase, from a motor alternator set. This produces an alternating force on the armature A, supported between the two magnets, which is transmitted to the lower end of the testpiece T. The upper end of the testpiece is held in the head H, which is bolted to the frame of the machine. The lower end of the armature is connected to the frame through springs S by which a static load can be applied to the testpiece. The stiffness of these springs is arranged so that the resonant frequency corresponds with the frequency of the load cycles, thus eliminating inertia forces which would affect the calibration of the machine. The dynamic load is measured by the voltage induced in secondary coils wound on the armature and the voltage reading is calibrated by comparison with the measured deflection of a weighbar mounted in the machine in place of the testpiece.

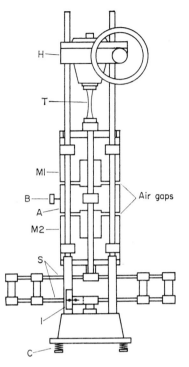

FIG. 13. General arrangement of the Haigh direct stress fatigue machine.
(*Courtesy, Bruntons, Ltd.*)

The Amsler high frequency Vibrophore is also driven electromagnetically, but unlike the Haigh machine, it operates at the resonant frequency of the vibrating parts. These consist of the main moving mass 1 (see Fig. 14) which vibrates on the specimen 3 and dynamometer 4 connected in series. The output from the impulse generator 13, fixed between the specimen and dynamometer, is amplified and fed-back to the driving magnet 14, thus ensuring a vibration at the resonant frequency. The frequency can be varied by altering the moving mass, or, to a smaller extent, by altering the testpiece stiffness. The deflection of the dynamometer is measured optically, a beam of light indicating directly on a scale both the static and dynamic loads. The load range is controlled automatically by means of a photo-electric regulating device actuated by the light beam of the dynamometer which governs the power input to the electrical drive. A pre-load spring 5 is incorporated to permit the application of a static load.

An advantage of using an electromagnetic drive operating at resonance is that high frequencies can be easily achieved. Frequencies up to 18,000 per min can be obtained in the Vibrophore, and Vidal and others [43] developed a small machine which operates on the same principle at 300,000 cycles per min. The same authors have subsequently developed another small machine [44] driven by piezoelectric excitation which operates at 5,500,000 cycles per min. A machine driven by a resonant magnetostriction transducer has been built by Neppiras [45] and this operates at about 1,000,000 cycles per min. At present, however, these machines are of academic interest only and have not been developed for normal routine fatigue investigations.

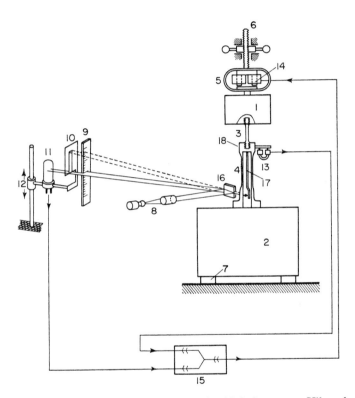

FIG. 14. Principle of operation of the Amsler high frequency Vibrophore fatigue testing machine. (*Courtesy, Alfred J. Amsler, Switzerland*)

| | |
|---|---|
| 1. Main moving mass | 10. Diaphragm |
| 2. Opposing mass | 11. Photoelectric cell |
| 3. Specimen | 12. Slides of photoelectric cell |
| 4. Dynamometer | 13. Impulse generator |
| 5. Pre-load spring | 14. Driving magnet |
| 6. Adjusting spindle | 15. Amplifier |
| 7. Vibration insulators | 16. Oscillating mirror |
| 8. Optical projector | 17. Comparison strip |
| 9. Dynamometer scale | 18. Specimen holder |

The principle of operation of a hydraulically operated Losenhausen fatigue machine is shown in Fig. 15. For fluctuating tensile tests the lower cylinder DU is shut off. The maximum tensile load is then obtained by adjustment of the hydraulic pump H1 and fluctuations in load below the maximum by switching in the pulsator R. To obtain alternating loads, the

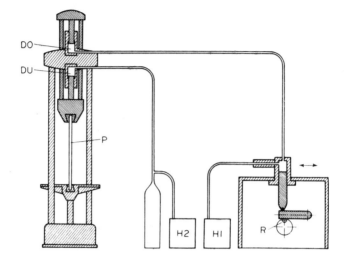

Fig. 15. Principle of operation of the Losenhausen UHS type fatigue machine. (*Courtesy, Losenhausenwerk, Germany*)

hydraulic pump H2 is switched on, producing a pressure in the lower cylinder DU acting in the opposite direction to the load in the upper cylinder DO. The lower piston is connected to a pressure vessel, which operates as an oil spring to compensate for the changing load in the upper piston. The static load is measured by means of a pendulum dynamometer and during fatigue tests the upper and lower load limits are shown on two differential spring type pressure gauges which are connected through the pulsator unit by means of a rotary valve connected to the working cylinders. A slow cycle unit and programme control unit can be incorporated in the machine.

*Rotating Bending Machines*

Rotating bending fatigue machines have been in use for about 100 years, from the time when Wöhler [46] built the first machine to investigate fatigue failure in railway axles. Since then a great many machines have been designed and built for testing specimens ranging from 0·05 in. to $9\frac{1}{2}$ in. diameter, and these are still often called Wöhler machines.

The rotating cantilever machine illustrated in Fig. 16a is the simplest type. One end of the specimen is held in a chuck by means of screws which are used to align the specimen and the load is applied through a bearing at the other end, either by weights or a spring. With this arrangement the bending moment increases linearly along the length of the specimen towards the chuck and failure occurs in the region where the transition radius meets the parallel portion of the specimen. To provide a constant range of stress along the specimen length, the section can be tapered, but alternatively, two-point or beam loading can be adopted, as illustrated in Fig. 16b and c. With two-point loading, one of the loads must be applied upwards. This can be achieved using spring loading or by dead-weight

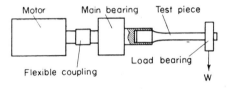

(a) Single point loading.

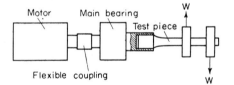

(b) Two point loading.

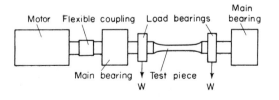

(c) Beam loading.

FIG. 16. Rotating bending fatigue machines

loading through a wire rope passing over a pulley. An alternative arrangement, used in the N.P.L. machine, consists of a single scale pan which is suspended from a hinged rectangular framework, supported on a pillar from the machine base. One vertical arm of the framework is split and the ends are connected, one to each load bearing, so that one is pulled upwards and the other downwards. One disadvantage of rotating bending machines is that a relatively long specimen is required. This has been avoided in the R. R. Moore rotating beam machine, which is commonly used in the United States, by hanging the load bearings on spindles and supporting the specimen between them.

A similar method has been adopted in the rotating cantilever machine designed for high temperature fatigue tests by Rolls-Royce, Ltd., Derby [47], and manufactured by Samuel Gill, Ltd. A short specimen, 2 in. long, is supported between two long collets; these project several inches from the ends of the furnace surrounding the specimen, so that the bearings do not become overheated. The machine is designed to operate at frequencies above the whirling speed of the collets–specimen assembly. One difficulty which arises in the use of rotating bending machines at high temperature is temperature measurement. The methods adopted are either to rely on a thermocouple held close to the specimen [47], or to tie a thermocouple to the specimen surface and to measure the e.m.f. through slip rings. Neither method is completely reliable, and this has prompted the use of machines in which the specimen is held stationary and the weight is rotated [39, 48]. For fatigue tests below room temperature, the specimen is usually cooled by immersing it in a liquid with a low boiling point. This presents difficulties in rotating bending tests, but these have been successfully overcome by mounting a machine vertically, immersing the specimen, collet and load bearing in a dewar flask containing the cooling liquid and then applying the load through a bell-crank lever pivoted above the dewar [49].

Rotating bending provides a convenient method for fatigue testing wire and this can be illustrated with reference to the Haigh–Robertson machine, manufactured by Bruntons (see Fig. 17). One end of the wire A is gripped in a chuck C, as in the headstock of a lathe and the other end B is arranged to run on a specially simple form of ball thrust-bearing that serves as a tailstock. This tailstock bearing is screwed forward to flex the wire, as shown, and the chuck C, together with the electric motor M that drives it, is arranged to swivel about a vertical axis on bearings A. The bending moment is greatest at mid-span so that failure occurs there and not in the grips. It should be noted that the wire does not whirl about the line AB, but rotates about its own curved axis of flexure.

The principal limitation of rotating bending machines is that the specimen can be subjected only to alternating stresses, although machines have been designed with provision for a static axial load [50, 51].

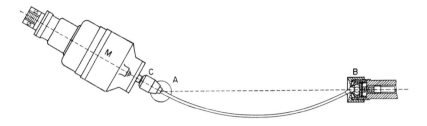

FIG. 17. Principle of action of the Haigh–Robertson fatigue testing machine for wire. (*Courtesy, Bruntons, Ltd.*)

## Reversed Bending Machines

A simple reversed bending machine is manufactured by Avery, and the principle of operation is shown in Fig. 18. The specimen is bolted at one end to a dynamometer and at the other end to a bending arm which is operated by a motor-driven double eccentric through a connecting rod; the bending arm oscillates about an axis passing through the mid-point of the specimen. As the dynamometer is considerably more flexible than the specimen, the machine operates approximately under a range of constant bending moment. The throw of the eccentric is adjusted to give the required bending moment which is determined from the deflection of a measuring arm. The arm is connected to the dynamometer and the deflections are measured by dial gauges. The driving motor is mounted on slide rails, so that it can be raised or lowered to apply an initial static

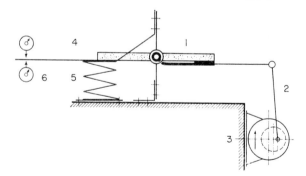

FIG. 18. Principle of operation of the Avery reversed bending fatigue machine. (*Courtesy, W. & T. Avery, Ltd.*)

1. Specimen
2. Driving motor with double eccentric
3. Adjustment of static initial load
4. Measuring arm
5. Dynamometer
6. Dial gauges

bending moment. Special grips are available to support round specimens at 90° or at 45° to the normal position, so that tests may be made either in torsion or under combined bending and torsion. Mechanically driven reversed bending machines have also been developed for testing a number of specimens simultaneously [52, 53], for use at high temperatures [54] and for testing electric cable [55].

A reversed bending fatigue machine in which bending or torsion or any combination of the two may be applied to the specimen was designed at the N.P.L. [56, 57], and developments of this machine are now manufactured by Bristol-Siddeley Engines and by Amsler. The arrangement of the N.P.L. machine is shown in **Fig. 19**. One end of the specimen S is

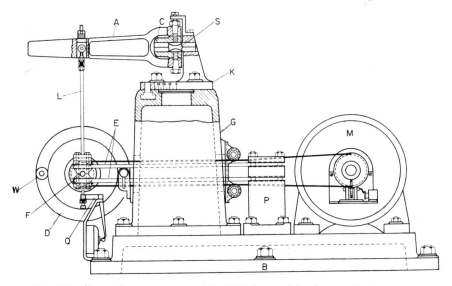

Fig. 19. General arrangement of the N.P.L. combined stress fatigue testing machine. (Gough Pollard and Clenshaw [56])

rigidly clamped in a movable bracket K bolted to the casting G which is attached to the baseplate B. The other end of the specimen is held in the collar C to which the arm A is pivoted about a vertical axis passing through the centre of the specimen. The disk D carrying the out-of-balance weights W is supported upon an axle and bracket housing F which is clamped to the ends of the springs E. The bracket is connected by links L to the centre of percussion of the arm A. The disk D is driven through a belt drive by the synchronous motor M, and the out-of-balance forces developed at the axle of the disk are transmitted as an alternating moment to the specimen through the arm A. The speed of the disk is adjusted, by varying the ratio of the pulley diameters, to the resonant frequency of all the moving parts vibrating on the outer ends of the springs E. By this means all inertia forces, other than those resulting from the out-of-balance weights, are eliminated. In the position shown in Fig. 19, cycles of reversed bending are imposed on the specimen. The bracket K and collar C can be rotated and clamped in any other position through a range of 90°, so that any combination of reversed bending and reversed torsion can be obtained.

A number of reversed bending fatigue machines have been developed which operate electromagnetically [39, 58, 59]. These are usually tuned to vibrate at the resonant frequency of the specimen assembly, and the main problem is to control the amplitude of vibration. The stress is usually calculated from measurement of the specimen deflection. By using a short stiff specimen without attached weights, it is possible to achieve very high frequencies; Wade and Grootenhuis [60], for example, reached a frequency of 230,000 cycles per min on an aluminium alloy specimen by this method. Very high frequencies can also be obtained in reversed bending machines driven pneumatically [61–63]. The method adopted is to blow air on to the specimen through a cavity whose volume can be varied so that its resonant frequency corresponds with that of the specimen.

*Fatigue Testing Components and Structures*

One of the problems of component testing is to reproduce service conditions as closely as possible, and in particular, to ensure that the failures produced in the fatigue tests are similar to those occurring in practice. Programme loading, that is, the application of load ranges of varying amplitude in the fatigue test, is one way to simulate service conditions more closely, and provision for this is available on some of the larger testing machines. It is not always possible to calculate the stress distribution in components undergoing fatigue tests and strain gauges may be required for this purpose. For some components special fatigue testing equipment is required, for example, for testing plain and roller bearings, gears or springs, and reference to this is made in Chapter IX.

For testing structures that are too large for conventional fatigue testing machines, the loading unit can be separated from its frame and used with a suitable test rig, so that instead of introducing the specimen into the machine, the machine is built round the specimen. With this method of testing, the structure is anchored to the floor and one or more oscillators are attached to it at suitable points. The methods adopted for driving the oscillators are similar to those used in fatigue machines; mechanical and hydraulic drives are the most widely used because electromagnetic oscillators do not generally provide sufficient power.

The most popular mechanical drive is obtained by rotating out-of-balance weights operating close to the resonant frequency [64–66]. This

D

provides a convenient means of carrying out fatigue tests on beams in bending [66], but it has also been used for torsional fatigue tests on shafts [67] and for direct stress tests [66]. The most difficult problem associated with this method is to maintain a constant range of load, because the load is very sensitive to change in frequency. The most effective way of achieving this is to control the frequency by means of a feed-back system from a vibration pick-up on the structure [67].

A mechanical drive using out-of-balance weights has also been used for fatigue testing aircraft structures, but it is considered suitable only for small exciting forces. For testing a large wing, for example, there are difficulties in attaching the heavy rotary exciter to the wing structure so as to avoid local damage and in providing a flexible drive to the rotating shaft, which may be subjected to large displacements [68]. Alternative methods used for aircraft structures are a spring and eccentric system, using the spring as a flexible connecting rod, or a fixed displacement system using a simple crank and connecting rod with a slipping clutch [69], as in the slipping clutch fatigue machine.

Hydraulic drives are used under non-resonant conditions and low frequencies are adopted in order to restrict dynamic effects from the motion of the structure. Amsler manufacture a pulsator and a range of hydraulic jacks for this purpose. The static load is measured with a pendulum dynamometer and the dynamic load with a manometer [70, 71]. One interesting application of hydraulic pressure is for testing aircraft pressure cabins [68]. Water is used instead of air because it is far less compressible, so that the energy to be dissipated, when failure occurs, is little more than the strain energy of the structure. It is, therefore, safer and, in addition, the failure is localized so that its origin can be easily traced and the test can be continued after repair. To balance the weight of water in the cabin, it is necessary to immerse it completely in water, for which special tanks are required.

### Fatigue specimens and their preparation

Both the shape and the finish of a fatigue specimen have an important effect on the fatigue strength and it is therefore necessary to take more care with the design and preparation of fatigue specimens than with specimens for other mechanical tests. In order to avoid failure occurring at the gripped ends of the fatigue specimen, the ends have to be made of larger section and it is important to provide a large transition radius between the ends and the test section to reduce the stress concentration.

Some typical fatigue specimens are illustrated in Fig. 20. The Wöhler fatigue specimen, Fig. 20a, can be used with either single or two-point loading. The specimen for a Haigh direct stress fatigue machine, Fig. 20b, is used for a range of test section diameters from 0·15 in. to 0·2 in. The length of the parallel portion is restricted to $\frac{1}{4}$ in. to prevent distortion or buckling of the specimen when it is loaded in compression. A working rule, developed from experience with direct stress fatigue machines is that the length of the parallel portion should not exceed $1\frac{1}{2}$ times the minimum diameter. The sheet fatigue specimen, Fig. 20c, is designed for pulsating

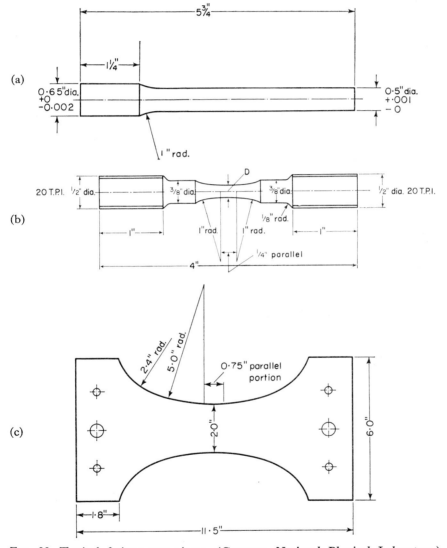

FIG. 20. Typical fatigue test pieces. (*Courtesy, National Physical Laboratory.*)
    (a) Testpiece for rotating cantilever fatigue machine
    (b) Testpiece for direct stress fatigue machine
    (c) Sheet testpiece for direct stress fatigue machine

tension tests; it is found that the width at the grips needs to be about three times the width of the test section if failure at the ends is to be prevented. The generous transition radii on all three specimens should be noted.

To determine the influence of stress concentrations on fatigue strength, tests may be made on notched specimens. There are no agreed standard notches and unfortunately every investigator seems to use a different notch, so that no one set of results can be compared with any other. The *Manual on Fatigue Testing* [39] lists five notches, which cover the range most common in engineering practice and the details of these are shown in Fig. 21. The values of the theoretical stress concentration factors (see page 131) were calculated by the methods given by Neuber [72].

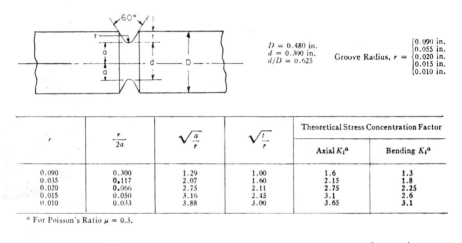

$D = 0.480$ in.
$d = 0.300$ in.
$d/D = 0.625$

Groove Radius, $r = \begin{cases} 0.090 \text{ in.} \\ 0.055 \text{ in.} \\ 0.020 \text{ in.} \\ 0.015 \text{ in.} \\ 0.010 \text{ in.} \end{cases}$

| $r$ | $\dfrac{r}{2a}$ | $\sqrt{\dfrac{a}{r}}$ | $\sqrt{\dfrac{t}{r}}$ | Theoretical Stress Concentration Factor | |
|---|---|---|---|---|---|
| | | | | Axial $K_t{}^a$ | Bending $K_t{}^a$ |
| 0.090 | 0.300 | 1.29 | 1.00 | 1.6 | 1.3 |
| 0.035 | 0.117 | 2.07 | 1.60 | 2.15 | 1.8 |
| 0.020 | 0.066 | 2.75 | 2.11 | 2.75 | 2.25 |
| 0.015 | 0.050 | 3.16 | 2.45 | 3.1 | 2.6 |
| 0.010 | 0.033 | 3.88 | 3.00 | 3.65 | 3.1 |

$^a$ For Poisson's Ratio $\mu = 0.3$.

$K_t = \dfrac{S_{max}}{S_n}$

$S_n = \dfrac{\text{Load}}{\text{Area}} = $ nominal stress

Stress concentration factor for axial loading.

FIG. 21. Notched fatigue testpieces. (*A.S.T.M. Manual on Fatigue* [39])

Care is required in the preparation of fatigue specimens to prevent cold working or overheating of the surface. Milling or turning is preferable to grinding, particularly for soft materials. When turning cylindrical specimens, the depth of cut should be gradually reduced, so that the last few cuts are only 0·001 to 0·002 in. Polishing is carried out in successive stages, starting with a fairly coarse emery cloth or paper and finishing with 000 or 0000. The purpose of polishing is to remove the circumferential scratches left by the machining and this is achieved most effectively by polishing diagonally or in a longitudinal direction. It is advisable to coat the specimen with vaseline after polishing until it is required for testing.

For further information of the preparation of fatigue specimens, reference should be made to an account of the methods used at the National Engineering Laboratory [73], or to the *Manual on Fatigue Testing* [39].

### Calibration of fatigue testing machines

There are no agreed standards of accuracy or methods of calibration for fatigue testing machines and, in this respect, fatigue testing methods fall short of static methods. This is unsatisfactory because the dynamic measurement of stress is more difficult than static measurement and errors are more likely to be made.

The most difficult problem is the calibration of direct stress fatigue machines. It is not usually satisfactory to determine the stress from a measure of the applied force, because it may be amplified by resonance or affected by the inertia of the moving parts. The method most often adopted is to use a weighbar or dynamometer to measure the applied stress. This is best fitted permanently in series with the testpiece, but it can be used in place of the testpiece as a means of calibrating an alternative method of measurement, such as a crank setting in a mechanically driven machine or a voltage in an electromagnetic machine. A weighbar consists of a member which is designed so that its deflection is wholly elastic when the maximum stress of the fatigue machine is applied. It may consist of a bar, a tube or a ring to which is attached some means of measuring its deflection while the fatigue machine is operating. Probably the most accurate method is to use wire resistance strain gauges to measure the strain in the weighbar; suitable circuits have been described by Billing [74] and by Roberts [75]. The method consists essentially of a Wheatstone bridge circuit; the strain gauges form one of the arms of the bridge, a decade box another arm and two equal constant resistances the remaining two arms. Using a cathode ray oscilloscope, the wave-form of the dynamic strain can be displayed when the fatigue machine is operating. By short circuiting the oscilloscope with a vibrator an interrupted trace is obtained, indicating no potential difference. This trace is superimposed on the tension and compression peak of the cycle in turn by adjustment of the decade box. The difference between the readings on the decade box when balanced with each peak is then proportional to the change in resistance of the strain gauges. The dynamic load can then be calculated using the result of a prior static calibration. The dynamic calibration method used at the National Engineering Laboratory, which is based on Billing's method has been described recently [76].

The advantage of the strain gauge method is that the response of the strain gauges is independent of frequency and an accuracy of $\pm 1\%$ of the maximum load range can be achieved. The disadvantage is the special equipment needed, including a power pack and high-gain amplifier. For this reason a mechanical or mechanical-optical weighbar may be preferred, particularly if a permanent installation is required. An accuracy of $\pm 1\%$ has been claimed for a proving ring modified for dynamic calibration [77]. For static calibration, the deflection of the proving ring is measured with a fitted micrometer. For dynamic calibration the micrometer is retained and is used in conjunction with a spring-loaded plunger having double electrical contacts for indicating purposes. In mechanical-optical systems the deflection of the weighbar is arranged to rotate a small mirror or mirrors and the movement is magnified by a suitable optical system. The simple rhomb and mirror system used for measuring deflections in static tensile tests is not suitable, because the static and dynamic calibrations may not be the same. Discrepancies probably arise because of the relative motion which occurs between the rhomb and its seating. This can be avoided by supporting the mirror on flexible cross springs or by using a spiral spring to transform an axial deflection into a rotation. A weighbar designed on this principle has shown good agreement with a strain gauge weighbar both statically and dynamically [78].

### The use of statistical methods in fatigue testing

If a number of similar fatigue specimens are tested at the same range of stress, considerable variation or scatter is found in the number of cycles to fracture. The extent of the scatter is dependent on a number of factors; it is generally greater on smooth polished specimens than on notched specimens or components, it is greater on high strength materials such as high tensile steels and age-hardened aluminium alloys than on soft materials like mild steel or copper, and it usually increases as the range of stress is decreased. In unfavourable circumstances the scatter can be very pronounced; for example, Sinclair and Dolan [79] carried out rotating bending fatigue tests at $\pm 30,000$ lb/in² on 57 polished specimens of the aluminium alloy 75S–T6, and the endurances ranged from 433,000 to 117,423,000. (This series of results is discussed in more detail later.)

It should be pointed out, however, that the scatter in stress range for a given endurance is much less than the scatter of endurance at a particular stress range. This is simply a result of the small slope of the $S–N$ curve and may be illustrated by reference to Figs. 6 and 7. Consequently, for applications where the stress range can be kept below the fatigue limit or long life fatigue strength, the problem of scatter is not a serious one and data obtained from $S–N$ curves consisting of 8 or 10 results, as described earlier, are usually adequate. It is when designing for a finite life, which is necessary when the stresses sometimes exceed the fatigue limit, that the problem of scatter must really be faced. This method of design is now being adopted for aircraft structures and to a certain extent for motor car components and it is in these circumstances that the application of statistical techniques has proved useful. There are a number of articles describing how statistics can be used to interpret fatigue results [80, 81, 674, 675].

The main purpose of fatigue testing is to obtain data which can be used as a guide for predicting the behaviour of materials in service. It is easiest to carry out tests on laboratory specimens, but it is not usually possible to assess service behaviour with sufficient accuracy from such tests, so that tests on components or structures are required. However, structural testing is expensive, so that the number of these tests is usually severely restricted. The problem is then to estimate the behaviour of a large number of service components from a small sample of test results. The adoption of statistical methods of testing and analysis provides a means of making the estimates quantitative and of assessing their reliability. A further use for statistics in fatigue testing is to determine, to some prescribed degree of confidence, whether the results of two series of tests are significantly different. This question may arise when assessing the influence of a heat treatment or manufacturing process on fatigue life.

*The Causes of Scatter*

Some of the scatter observed in fatigue test results must arise from variation in testing conditions and the testing procedure should, therefore, be closely controlled when making statistical investigations. This is particularly important because one cannot distinguish with certainty between the scatter from testing variations, and the scatter from variation in the material. Reproducible conditions are most easily obtained in rotating bending fatigue tests and this method of testing is often adopted for statistical experiments. A number of attempts have been made to determine the scatter introduced by experimental errors in this type of test. Ransom and Mehl [82] calculated that the scatter introduced by errors in the applied bending moment and measurement of the specimen diameter was small compared with the scatter they observed for the alloy steel SAE 4340; furthermore, no correlation was found between the endurance and the eccentricity of the specimen assembly. In an investigation of a 0·24% C steel, Clayton-Cave and others [83] found that the scatter was appreciably influenced by variation in the method of specimen preparation. When a high standard of specimen preparation was used, the results were significantly more variable if a batch of 12 machines were used than if all the tests were made in one machine. A more direct method of distinguishing between the effects of experimental error and metallurgical factors was adopted by McClintock [84, 85], by comparing the scatter in endurance with the positions on the specimens at which fracture occurred. The stress in the specimens varied along their length, so that variations in the position of fracture could be attributed directly to inherent variation in the material. He found that the scatter in endurance was more than could be accounted for entirely by the material variation and, again, an improvement in the method of specimen preparation was required before a satisfactory correlation was achieved.

It appears from the results of these experiments that materials do show an inherent scatter in their resistance to fatigue and that the variation is not entirely due to variations in testing procedure. This would be expected, of course, from the imhomogeneous nature of metals, but the contribution of the various metallurgical factors to scatter is not clearly established. For steels, it might be expected that scatter would be influenced by the inclusion content, but the evidence is somewhat conflicting (see page 64). Scatter might also arise from variations in grain size, alloy composition or heat treatment. Ineson and others [86], for example, found a variation of about 5% in the fatigue limit between the top and bottom of an ingot of steel of about 60–65 tons/in² tensile strength, and this they attributed to local variations in composition and heat-treatment.

A further source of scatter, which may well be more important in practice, is that arising from sample to sample rather than from one specimen to another within a single sample. Variations during manufacture are bound to occur with the result that the fatigue strength of an alloy to one material specification may vary widely. G. Forrest [87], for example, has quoted the variation found in normal production in the rotating bending fatigue strength of extruded aluminium alloys. For ruling sections up to 2 inches the fatigue strength at $10^8$ cycles of the alloy HE 15 WP (DTD 364) varied from $\pm 9$ to $\pm 12$ tons/in² and the alloy to specifications DTD 683 and 363 from $\pm 9\frac{1}{2}$ to $\pm 13$ tons/in². Comparable data are not available for steels or other non-ferrous alloys, but no doubt similar variations occur in these materials.

*Analysis of Fatigue Data*

In the application of statistics to fatigue, the data to be analysed usually consist of the endurances of a sample of specimens tested at a constant stress range. The distribution of endurances can be represented graphically by means of a histogram. This is a diagram showing the number of values falling within successive intervals and is illustrated in Fig. 22 for the 57 results quoted by Sinclair and Dolan [79]. For a whole population of specimens the histogram can be replaced by a smooth curve, and this is known as a frequency distribution curve. For statistical analysis the shape of this curve must be assumed—and, of course, the reliability of the analysis will be dependent on the accuracy with which the chosen curve represents the actual population distribution. It is found that the frequency

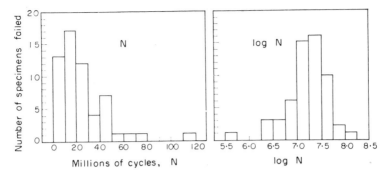

FIG. 22. Histograms showing fatigue-life distribution for 57 specimens of 75S–T6 aluminium alloy tested at 30,000 p.s.i. (Sinclair and Dolan [79])

distribution of fatigue endurances $N$ does not usually fit the "Normal" or "Gaussian" curve, but that a fairly close approximation can often be obtained if the data are transformed to log $N$. This is known as a log-normal distribution and much of the statistical analysis of fatigue data has been carried out on this basis.

The Normal distribution is defined by the equation:

$$y = \frac{1}{\sigma \sqrt{(2\pi)}} \exp \left\{ - \frac{(x - \bar{X}_P)^2}{2\sigma^2} \right\} \qquad (6)$$

where $\int_{x_1}^{x_2} y \, dx$ is the relative frequency of occurrence of values of $x$ between $x_1$ and $x_2$, $\sigma$ is the standard deviation and $\bar{X}_P$ is the arithmetic mean of all the values. The relation between $y$ and $x$ is symmetrical about the mean value $\bar{X}_P$ and approaches the $x$ axis asymptotically on both sides of the mean.

The distribution is completely defined by the arithmetic mean $\bar{X}_P$ and the standard deviation $\sigma$, so that if these values were known for a complete population it would be possible to determine the probability of survival to any particular value. In practice, however, data from a limited sample only are available, so that $\bar{X}_P$ and $\sigma$ are not known precisely.

The arithmetic mean and standard deviation for the sample, $\bar{x}$ and $s$ respectively, can be calculated from the following equations:

$$\bar{x} = \sum \frac{x}{n} \qquad (7)$$

$$s = \left( \frac{\Sigma(x - \bar{x})^2}{(n - 1)} \right)^{\frac{1}{2}} \qquad (8)$$

where $n$ is the number of values in the sample, but these represent only point estimates of $X_P$ and $\sigma$. It is possible to estimate the latter but not with complete certainty, so that the values can only be quoted within certain limits, with a certain measure of confidence [80, 81]. Similarly, the probability of survival to a particular value may be estimated, but again, only with a certain measure of confidence. Thus, it may be said, with a confidence level of $\gamma$, that at least $p\%$ of the population is greater than $\bar{x} - ks$, where $\bar{x}$ and $s$ are values computed for the sample by means of equations (7) and (8). $k$ is a function of $p$, $\gamma$ and $n$, where $n$ is the sample size; computed values are quoted in the A.S.T.M. statistical guide [80] and some of these are reproduced in Table 3. (It is also possible to deal with a sample of results, which includes specimens that have not failed, by using the standard methods for deducing normal distribution parameters from incomplete data [88].)

From the values in Table 3 it is possible to estimate, from a sample of results, the endurance or safe life which may be expected for the population with varying degrees of confidence. This is illustrated in Table 4, using a sample of six results quoted in the Royal Aeronautical Society Data Sheets [81], which are closely approximated to a log-normal distribution. The values of $\bar{x}$ and $s$ are calculated from equations (7) and (8) and the safe life is given by $(\bar{x} - ks)$ using the appropriate value of $k$ from Table 3. Table 4 illustrates the way in which the safe life depends on the percentage of survivals $p$, and degree of confidence $\gamma$ required. For many applications in practice, and particularly in aircraft there are some components for which the safe life must be based on a much higher proportion than $90\%$ survivals. Consequently, a lower safe life must be accepted, and this is also illustrated by the results in Table 4. On the basis of the six results, the safe life with $95\%$ confidence for $90\%$ survivals (or $10\%$ failures) is 238,000; if only $1\%$ failures are acceptable, the safe life falls to 112,000 and for 1 failure in 1000, to 63,700, that is less than one-tenth of the mean endurance of the sample. The value can be increased to some extent by increasing the sample size, but this is uneconomic for full-scale components, and the number tested under the same conditions is usually limited in practice to between 5 and 10.

One of the main difficulties of estimating safe life for a low probability of failure is the uncertainty of the application of the frequency distribution. To determine the endurance producing one failure in 1000 requires at least 1000 tests which is clearly impracticable. It is convenient to present experimental results by plotting the probability of failure against log $N$, on log-probability paper, for this is so arranged that the log-normal distribution is represented by a straight line. The results of Sinclair and Dolan on plain specimens of the aluminium alloy 75S are plotted in this way in Fig. 23. The lines drawn through the experimental points represent the log-normal curves having the same means and the same standard deviations

TABLE 3. VALUES OF $k$ FOR NORMAL DISTRIBUTION—[80]

$n$ = Sample size   $p$ = % Survival   $\gamma$ = Confidence level

| $p$ / $n$ | $\gamma = 0.50$ | | | | $\gamma = 0.90$ | | | | $\gamma = 0.95$ | | | |
|---|---|---|---|---|---|---|---|---|---|---|---|---|
| | 90 | 95 | 99 | 99.9 | 90 | 95 | 99 | 99.9 | 90 | 95 | 99 | 99.9 |
| 3 | 1·498 | 1·939 | 2·765 | 3·688 | 4·258 | 5·310 | 7·340 | 9·651 | 6·158 | 7·655 | 10·552 | 13·857 |
| 4 | 1·419 | 1·830 | 2·601 | 3·464 | 3·187 | 3·957 | 5·437 | 7·128 | 4·163 | 5·145 | 7·042 | 9·215 |
| 5 | 1·382 | 1·780 | 2·526 | 3·362 | 2·742 | 3·400 | 4·666 | 6·112 | 3·407 | 4·202 | 5·741 | 7·501 |
| 6 | 1·360 | 1·750 | 2·483 | 3·304 | 2·494 | 3·091 | 4·242 | 5·556 | 3·006 | 3·707 | 5·062 | 6·612 |
| 8 | 1·337 | 1·719 | 2·436 | 3·239 | 2·219 | 2·755 | 3·783 | 4·955 | 2·582 | 3·188 | 4·353 | 5·686 |
| 10 | 1·324 | 1·702 | 2·411 | 3·205 | 2·065 | 2·568 | 3·532 | 4·629 | 2·355 | 2·911 | 3·981 | 5·203 |
| 12 | 1·316 | 1·691 | 2·395 | 3·183 | 1·966 | 2·448 | 3·371 | 4·420 | 2·210 | 2·736 | 3·747 | 4·900 |
| 15 | 1·308 | 1·680 | 2·379 | 3·163 | 1·866 | 2·329 | 3·212 | 4·215 | 2·068 | 2·566 | 3·520 | 4·607 |
| 20 | 1·301 | 1·671 | 2·366 | 3·143 | 1·765 | 2·208 | 3·052 | 4·009 | 1·926 | 2·396 | 3·295 | 4·319 |

TABLE 4. ESTIMATE OF "SAFE LIFE" FROM SAMPLE OF 6 SPECIMENS ASSUMING LOG-NORMAL DISTRIBUTION

| SPECIMEN | 1 | 2 | 3 | 4 | 5 | 6 |
|---|---|---|---|---|---|---|
| ENDURANCE $N$ | 420,000 | 579,000 | 640,000 | 800,000 | 900,000 | 1,200,000 |
| LOG $N$ | 5·623 | 5·763 | 5·806 | 5·903 | 5·954 | 6·079 |

The results are closely approximated to a log-normal distribution. Mean value of log $N$, $x = 5·855$ and standard deviation $s = 0·159$ (ref. 81).

"SAFE LIFE" IN THOUSANDS OF CYCLES

| $n$ \ $p$ | $\gamma = 0·50$ | | | | $\gamma = 0·90$ | | | | $\gamma = 0·95$ | | | |
|---|---|---|---|---|---|---|---|---|---|---|---|---|
| | 90 | 95 | 99 | 99·9 | 90 | 95 | 99 | 99·9 | 90 | 95 | 99 | 99·9 |
| 6 | 436 | 378 | 288 | 211 | 288 | 231 | 152 | 93·7 | 238 | 184 | 112 | 63·7 |

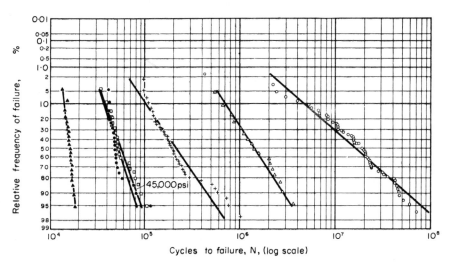

FIG. 23. Logarithmic-Normal probability diagram showing individual
fatigue lifetimes obtained at different stresses. (Sinclair and Dolan [79])

▲ 62,500 lb/in²    □ 45,000 lb/in²    △ 35,000 lb/in²
● 50,000 lb/in²    + 40,000 lb/in²    ○ 30,000 lb/in²

as calculated from the corresponding experimental data. At first sight the
experimental results appear to fit the log-normal distribution quite closely,
but if the lines are extrapolated to a probability of failure of 0·001%, they
indicate that failure is more likely to occur at ±40,000 than at ±45,000
or ±50,000 lb/in².

The problem has been nicely illustrated by Cox [89] in relation to the
results at ±30,000 lb/in² (see Fig. 23). He showed that these results can
be fitted to a curve representing an equal chance of failure in each and
every cycle, just as well as to the straight line representing the log-normal
distribution. (It should be noted that the lowest endurance obtained, about
433,000 cycles, lies so far from this line that it appears to belong to the
series of results at a higher stress.) However, this series of results is not
typical, for general experience has shown that the relations obtained on
log-probability diagrams, such as those shown in Fig. 23, usually deviate
gradually from straight lines by curving upwards at low probabilities of
failure.

A number of alternative frequency distribution curves have been suggested in attempts to obtain closer correlation with the experimental data.
The best known of these are Weibull's method [90], and the "extreme
value" method proposed by Freudenthal and Gumbel [91]. Weibull
suggested an empirical relation defined by three parameters, and by this
means it is usually possible to fit the relation to experimental results more

closely than with the log-normal distribution, which is dependent on only two parameters. The extreme value distribution was developed from a statistical theory of fatigue, and it is claimed for this reason to be preferable to other distributions.

The log-normal distribution is most convenient for determining whether two or more series of results are from the same population or whether they are significantly different. The problem, in effect, is to determine with what probability the difference between two series of results would occur if they were from the same population. If the differences would be expected to occur by chance once in every 100 times, the two series are said to differ with a 99% level of significance. The distinction between "significant" and "not significant" in this respect is arbitrary, but is conventionally drawn at 95%. If a difference is found to be not significant, it may mean either that there is no real difference, or that a difference may exist but the results are too few or too scattered to reveal it.

Considering two series of results, the first problem is to determine whether the standard deviations are significantly different or not. This depends on the variance ratio, defined by the equation:

$$F = s_1^2/s_2^2 \qquad (s_1 > s_2) \tag{9}$$

where $s_1$ and $s_2$ are the standard deviations of the two samples, and on the degrees of freedom $\gamma_1 = (n_1 - 1)$ and $\gamma_2 = (n_2 - 1)$, where $n_1$ and $n_2$ are the sample sizes. The value of $F$ at the 95% significance level can be obtained from Fig. 24, for various values of $\gamma_1$ and $\gamma_2$. (Curves or tables for other significance levels are available elsewhere [80, 81].) If this value is less than that determined from the standard deviations of the samples, then the difference is significant; if not, the difference is not significant, and a further test should be made to determine whether the difference between the mean values of the two samples is significant or not. This is achieved by means of Student's "$t$" test, where $t$ is given by the equation:

$$t = \frac{\bar{x}_1 - \bar{x}_2}{s\sqrt{(1/n_1 + 1/n_2)}}, \tag{10}$$

where $\bar{x}_1$ and $\bar{x}_2$ are the means of the two samples and $s^2$ is the common variance, given by the equation:

$$s^2 = \frac{(n_1 - 1)s_1^2 + (n_2 - 1)s_2^2}{n_1 + n_2 - 2} \tag{11}$$

The level of significance may then be obtained from Fig. 25 for the appropriate values of $t$ and the degrees of freedom $\gamma = (n_1 + n_2 - 2)$.

In engineering components the fatigue life is often affected by a number of different factors with the result that populations of fatigue data are very likely to be mixed. In these circumstances, a statistical treatment may be

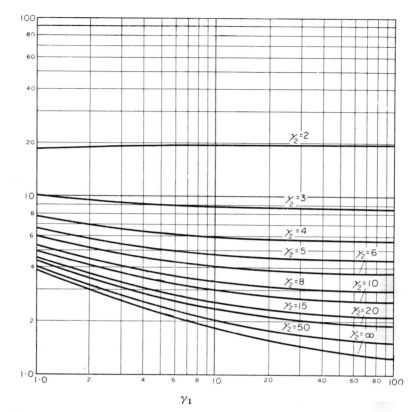

FIG. 24. Values of the variance ratio $F$ at the 95% significance level.
(Royal Aero Soc. Data Sheets [81])

helpful in distinguishing the factors and discovering the causes of premature failure or wide scatter. This has been demonstrated by Cox [89] from data obtained on small screws.

### Test Procedures

Owing to the scatter between the individual results of fatigue tests, the stress–endurance relation cannot be represented completely by a single curve, but must be considered as a series of curves, each representing a definite probability of failure $P$. Sinclair and Dolan derived such a series of curves from their data on aluminium alloys and the result is shown in Fig. 26.

Several test procedures have been derived for determining the fatigue limit or fatigue strength for a particular endurance, on a statistical basis. In the "Probit" method one or more groups of specimens are tested for a fixed number of cycles at several ranges of stress close to the appropriate

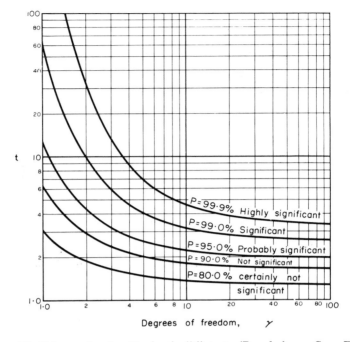

FIG. 25. Values of $t$ for Student's "$t$" test. (Royal Aero. Soc. Data Sheets [81])

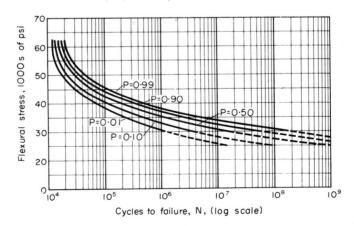

FIG. 26. $P$–$S$–$N$ diagram derived from data for small unnotched specimens of 75 S–T aluminium alloy. (Sinclair and Dolan [79])

fatigue strength. The results may then be represented by plotting the proportion of specimens that survive the required endurance against the stress range. Experience has shown that the results of such tests tend to be on a straight line if plotted on probability paper [80]. The results may be obtained more economically by adopting the Staircase method, although the time required may be longer as the specimens must be tested one at a time. The first specimen is tested at a stress range equal to the estimated value of the fatigue strength. If it survives the required endurance, the second specimen is tested at a stress range one increment higher, but if it fails, the second specimen is tested at a stress range one increment lower than the first. This procedure is repeated with further specimens until sufficient results have been obtained.

## CHAPTER III

# FATIGUE STRENGTH OF METALS

In this chapter it is intended to consider alternating fatigue strengths determined either in bending or direct stress on plain unnotched specimens at air temperature. Data obtained under these conditions can be used as a guide for the selection of materials for use in service, although it will not usually be possible to apply the results directly to design problems without making allowance for such factors as combined static and alternating loads, the surface condition and stress concentrations.

The alternating fatigue strengths for a selection of engineering materials are included in Tables 82–84, pages 360–381. When comparing the values of fatigue strength for different materials, the following points should be taken into consideration. There is often considerable variation between different samples of material to one specification, so that in comparing two materials, a difference of 10% or even 20% between the quoted values of fatigue strength may not be significant. Fatigue strengths determined in direct stress may be up to 25% lower than those determined in bending. Bending fatigue strengths are dependent on the size of the fatigue specimen, decreasing with increase in the size (see page 135). The fatigue strength must always be related to the number of cycles to fracture $N$, unless the material shows a distinct fatigue limit.

Where the data were available, other mechanical properties are quoted in the tables, so that a comparison may be made between these and the fatigue strength. It is found that fatigue strength is approximately related to tensile strength and this is shown for the alloys of a number of metals in Figs. 28, 35, 38, 40 and 43. The accuracy with which the fatigue strength can be estimated from the tensile strength can be gauged by the scatter in the points about the mean line or curve in the figures. The ratio of fatigue strength to tensile strength is known as the endurance ratio. A relation might be expected between fatigue strength and elastic limit or yield stress, since it is generally believed that fatigue failures usually result from plastic deformation, but the ratio of fatigue strength to yield strength varies widely, even for similar materials.

## Fatigue strength of iron and steel

It has already been mentioned that one of the characteristics of the

56

fatigue behaviour of steels is that the $S$–$N$ curve usually shows a distinct fatigue limit. This is most marked in plain carbon steels and usually occurs at a value of $N$ between $10^5$ and $10^7$. For these materials it is, therefore, possible to determine the fatigue limit by continuing fatigue tests only to $10^7$ cycles and this procedure is usually adopted. With alloy steels, on the other hand, the fatigue limit is less distinct and it may be necessary to continue fatigue tests to longer endurances. From the results of fatigue tests on a large number of alloy steels, Frith [92, 93] has concluded that to determine the fatigue limit it is necessary to continue the tests to $20 \times 10^6$ cycles for steels of 60 tons/in² tensile strength, to $40 \times 10^6$ cycles for steels of 80 tons/in² tensile strength and to 100 to $300 \times 10^6$ cycles for steels of 110 tons/in² tensile strength. It is doubtful whether steels of the highest strength show a fatigue limit at all, but the $S$–$N$ curves tend to flatten out at long endurances, and if fatigue tests are continued to the number of cycles recommended by Frith, the value of the fatigue strength obtained is adequate for most practical purposes. Some typical $S$–$N$ curves, mostly from Frith's results, are shown in Fig. 27. The carbon steel shows a distinct fatigue limit; no fractures occurred after $2 \cdot 3 \times 10^6$ cycles, although five tests were continued for $10^8$ cycles. By contrast, for the steel of 110 tons/in² tensile strength, eight specimens fractured after endurances of more than $10^7$ cycles, including three which had endured more than $10^8$ cycles. Another feature illustrated in Fig. 27, is the increase in the scatter of the results, which occurs as the tensile strength is increased. Many more

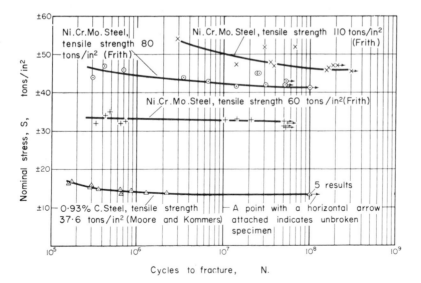

FIG. 27. $S$–$N$ curves for steels. (Frith [92], Moore and Kommers [94])

tests would be required to determine accurately the fatigue strength of the high-strength steels than of the carbon steel.

The relation between the fatigue strength of steels (determined in rotating bending on polished specimens) and the tensile strength is shown in Fig. 28. Up to a tensile strength of about 80 tons/in², the endurance ratio has an average value quite close to a half. About 180 of the results plotted in Fig. 28 are for steels with a tensile strength below 80 tons/in²; of these over 70% have an endurance ratio between 0·4 and 0·55 and over 95% between 0·35 and 0·6. The tensile strength of steels is very closely related to the hardness and it therefore follows that a relation exists between hardness and the fatigue limit, similar to that between the tensile strength and the fatigue limit. The ratio of tensile strength to Brinell Hardness Number is equal to approximately 0·22 for steels, when the tensile strength is measured in tons/in².

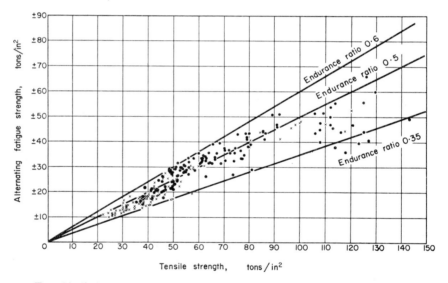

FIG. 28. Relation between rotating bending fatigue strength and tensile strength of wrought steels, based on fatigue limit or failure in 10⁷ to 10⁸ cycles. All results are based on specimens tested in the longitudinal direction.

× carbon steels ● alloy steels

For steels with tensile strengths above 80 tons/in², the endurance ratios are more variable and, often, no further increase in fatigue strength is achieved by increasing the tensile strength above 100 tons/in². The wide variation in fatigue strength and the low values of endurance ratio of high-strength steels is a cause of some concern. It is generally attributed to the stress-raising effect of inclusions and other inhomogeneities in the structure and to the presence of internal stresses that are not relieved by the low tempering temperatures adopted to achieve high strength.

It must be emphasized that the relation between fatigue limit and tensile strength which has been discussed and the results which are shown in Fig. 28 all relate to fatigue limits determined in rotating bending on small polished specimens, and that the presence of stress concentrations or corrosive conditions can reduce the fatigue strength to very low values. This is illustrated in Fig. 29 by a diagram originally due to Bullens [95],

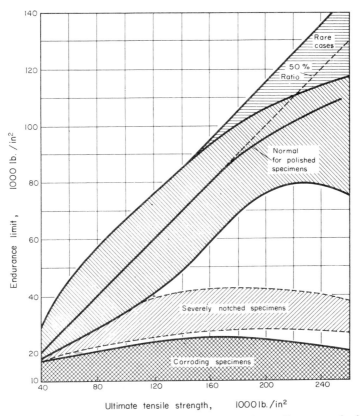

FIG. 29. Relation between fatigue strength and tensile strength for polished, notched and corroding specimens of steels. (Bullens [95])

which has been reproduced many times. It shows that the highest strength steels are more sensitive to notches and corrosion than those of medium strength, so that the material with the highest fatigue limit on polished specimens is not necessarily the one which will be the most resistant to fatigue fracture in service. The results in this figure are for steels only, but non-ferrous metals behave in a similar manner.

*Effect of Chemical Composition*

As the fatigue strength of steels is fairly closely related to the tensile strength, it follows that any factor which increases the tensile strength (such as heat-treatment or the addition of an alloying element) will, in general, result in an increase in fatigue strength. Considering, firstly, the influence of composition, additions of carbon, manganese, nickel, chromium, molybdenum, vanadium, copper, boron and phosphorus each increase the fatigue strength approximately in proportion to their influence on the tensile strength and hardness.

The fatigue limit of plain carbon steels increases considerably with the carbon content, although there is some evidence that the endurance ratio falls slightly. Cazaud [96] has investigated the influence of the nickel content in steels and concluded that a reduction from $3\frac{1}{2}\%$ to $1\%$ does not adversely affect the fatigue strength for either plain or notched specimens. An improvement of the fatigue strength and endurance ratio of nickel and nickel–chromium steels can be achieved by the addition of molybdenum, provided that advantage is taken of the ability of such steels to withstand higher tempering temperatures without softening appreciably.

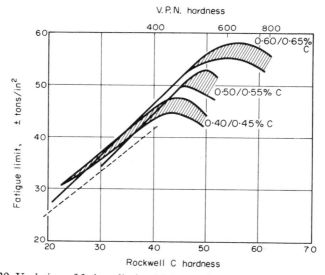

FIG. 30. Variation of fatigue limit with increasing hardness. (Garwood and others [97])
— — — — Fatigue ratio 0·5.

The maximum fatigue strength that can be achieved with alloy steels is increased by increasing the carbon content, see Fig. 30 [97]. This may be because with increasing carbon content, high strength can be obtained with a higher tempering temperature and this allows a greater relief of the internal stresses introduced by quenching. It may be noted that the highest value for the fatigue strength recorded by Frith [92], 51 tons/in$^2$ at $10^8$ cycles was for a 1% carbon, 1½% chromium steel, heat treated to 831 D.P.N. and that a value of 58 tons/in$^2$ at $10^8$ cycles has been obtained on a similar steel which had been vacuum-melted [98]. Russell and Walker [99] investigated the fatigue strength of a tool steel containing 0·75% carbon, 18% tungsten, 4% chromium and 1% vanadium, because it is possible with this steel to achieve high strength with a high tempering temperature. The results were disappointing, however, and it was suggested that residual stresses might not be relieved by a high tempering temperature in this material and that massive carbides might be an additional source of weakness [100].

The results of some recent American work have shown that the fatigue strength of high tensile steel can be increased by the addition of copper [666]. The tests were based on only $10^5$ cycles, but a fatigue strength as high as 200,000 lb/in$^2$ (89 tons/in$^2$) was claimed for an induction-melted alloy containing 0·45% carbon, 0·83% chromium, 0·68% molybdenum, 0·17% vanadium and 1·3% copper, after tempering at 400°F (204°C).

The phosphorus content of steels is usually kept to a minimum to prevent embrittlement, but it is claimed [101] that a high phosphorus content in low-alloy steels improves the fatigue strength of both plain and notched specimens to a greater extent than the tensile strength. Sulphur is usually considered detrimental to fatigue strength because it produces non-metallic inclusions, but its presence is only likely to be serious in high-strength steels. It is well established that in mild steel, the presence of sulphur in quantities up to 0·1% has no effect on the fatigue limit [102]. The addition of lead to steels to improve machinability may reduce the fatigue strength slightly, the reduction becoming greater with increase in tensile strength [103, 104]. For example, Woolman and Jaques [104] found that the addition of 0·15 to 0·2% lead reduced the fatigue strength by about 20% for a steel of 115 tons/in$^2$ tensile strength, 5–10% for a steel of 75 tons/in$^2$ tensile strength and had no significant effect on steels below 55 tons/in$^2$ tensile strength.

Austenitic stainless steels with high nickel and chromium contents show a distinct fatigue limit and an endurance ratio which is similar to that of other steels of the same tensile strength. They possess two important attributes, a high resistance to corrosion fatigue and very low fatigue notch sensitivity. In addition, they are resistant to higher temperatures and are used in place of ferritic steels at temperatures above 500–600°C.

## The Influence of Heat-Treatment and Microstructure

In general, the effect of composition on fatigue strength is less important than the heat treatment and microstructure. The fatigue strength is usually increased by any heat treatment that increases the tensile strength, but for a given tensile strength it is dependent to some extent on the micro-structure [105].

A structure consisting wholly of ferrite often has a fatigue limit greater than half its tensile strength, but the strength is low. For steels treated to higher strengths, the best fatigue properties are obtained with tempered martensite. For example, Dolan and Yen [106] compared the fatigue strengths of a martensitic type of structure, produced by rapid quenching, with one consisting mainly of ferrite and pearlite, produced by a slow quench. Tests were made on a carbon steel and two alloy steels, which were all tempered to about the same tensile strength. The endurance ratios for the tempered martensite were consistently above those for the mixed structure, by 5–9% for unnotched specimens and 11–44% for notched specimens.

It has been suggested that the lower fatigue resistance of mixed structures generally, may be attributed to "metallurgical notches" which might be coarse pearlite, free ferrite, segregation of the alloying elements or austen-ite retained during quenching. Some attempts have been made recently to determine the effect of these factors quantitatively. Borik, Chapman and Jominy [107] determined the fatigue strength of a number of alloy steels, heat treated to the same hardness, but with different amounts of tempered martensite in the structure. The fatigue strength was reduced by about 10% by the presence of 20% non-martensitic structure, but there was little further reduction as the martensite content was further reduced. A similar method has been used by Frankel, Bennett and Pennington [108] to deter-mine the effect of retained austenite. The presence of about 10% of retained austenite reduced the fatigue strength (at $10^5$ cycles) by 10–15%, and greater quantities had little further effect.

Tempering a quenched steel at a low temperature may result in an increase in fatigue strength without any decrease in tensile strength. As the tempering temperature is raised, however, both the tensile strength and fatigue strength are reduced, although the endurance ratio is usually increased. The influence of grain size on the fatigue strength of steels is only of minor importance. Fine-grained materials usually show a higher fatigue strength than coarse-grained, but this is offset to some extent by their greater sensitivity to notches.

### Effect of Inclusions

The influence of inclusions on the fatigue strength of steel depends prim-arily on their size and shape, on their resistance to deformation, on their orientation to the stress and on the strength of the steel. The reduction in fatigue strength is thought to arise from the stress concentration intro-duced by the inclusion or by the cavity containing the inclusion. Elongated inclusions or cavities have little effect if they lie parallel to the direction of the stress, but may seriously reduce the fatigue strength if they lie perpendicular to it. The presence of inclusions may therefore result in considerable directionality of the fatigue properties; they will usually be elongated in the direction of rolling and will therefore have little effect on the longitudinal fatigue strength, but may appreciably reduce the transverse or torsional fatigue strengths.

The fatigue strengths of soft steels are little affected by the presence of inclusions; additions of lead and sulphur, for example, do not markedly reduce their fatigue strength. Teed [109] has pointed out that wrought iron has as much as $2\frac{1}{2}\%$ of siliceous material, in the form of threads running in the direction of rolling, yet the transverse fatigue strength is equal to the longitudinal fatigue strength and the endurance ratio in the transverse direction is generally slightly higher than in the longitudinal direction. In his investigation of rolled alloy steels, Frith [92] found that the inclusions present appeared to have no significant effect on the fatigue strength of steels treated to 60 tons/in² tensile strength. When treated to 80 tons/in² tensile strength, the transverse fatigue strength was slightly affected, while at 110 tons/in² tensile strength, both the longitudinal and transverse fatigue strengths were considerably reduced. (See Table 82, page 364). The effects were most marked in basic electric-arc steels owing to the presence of undeformed spherical silicate inclusions. When these were avoided by manufacturing the steel in a basic-lined electric-arc furnace using a siliceous slag, the fatigue strength (for a steel treated to 750 D.P.N.) was increased by about 25% to the value obtained for open-hearth steels.

Ransom and Mehl [110] have shown that the presence of inclusions in the nickel–chrome–molybdenum steel SAE 4340, has a greater effect on the transverse fatigue strength than on the longitudinal fatigue strength. They found that the transverse fatigue strength was related to the ductility in a transverse tensile test, low values of each resulting from the presence of fragmented stringer-type inclusions. On a forging from a heat of vacuum melted steel, which was essentially free from inclusions, the transverse fatigue strength was increased by 50% to a value almost equal to the longitudinal fatigue strength [111]. Stewart and Williams [112] investigated the effect of inclusions by means of bending and torsion fatigue tests. On relatively soft steels (of about 40 tons/in² tensile strength), they found that the presence of longitudinal inclusions had no influence on the longitudinal bending fatigue strength, but reduced the torsional fatigue strength by 20 to 25%. This resulted in unusually low values of the ratio of the torsional-to-bending fatigue strengths.

The importance of the size of inclusions has been demonstrated by Cummings, Stulen and Schulte [113] from the results of many fatigue tests on the low alloy steels SAE 4340 and 4350, heat-treated to tensile strengths between 60 and 135 tons/in². The inclusions were spheroidal and ranged in size up to 0·003 in. diameter. At low ranges of stress, fatigue fractures propagated from a single inclusion greater than 0·001 in. diameter, and the endurance at a given stress range was inversely proportional to the inclusion size. No simple relation between inclusion size and endurance was obtained at high stress ranges because fractures then resulted from more than one crack.

The influence of inclusions on the fatigue strength of a number of steels heat treated to a tensile strength of about 125 tons/in² has been investigated by Atkinson [662]. He concluded that the size of inclusions alone does not offer a basis for comparison of the several different types of inclusion which normally occur together in steel, but that the number and shape of the inclusions must also be considered. He has therefore introduced a "Fairey inclusion count", which takes account of these factors, and he showed that this could be correlated with the fatigue strength.

Epremian and Mehl [114] investigated the relation between metallurgical factors and the statistical variation of fatigue properties. Their results from tests on SAE 4340 steel and Armco iron indicated that the scatter in fatigue endurance and in the fatigue limit was much more dependent on the inclusion content than on the composition or heat treatment. It might, therefore, be expected that vacuum melted steel would show less scatter in fatigue, but although vacuum melting may increase the fatigue strength appreciably, it does not appear to reduce the scatter [98, 115]. Styri [115] attributed scatter to local weak areas in the structure and, in addition to inclusions, there might be local segregation, free ferrite, retained austenite and internal stress.

The influence of the manufacturing process on fatigue strength has been investigated recently by Fisher and Sheehan [661] for the alloy steel SAE 4340, heat treated to tensile strengths between 115 and 140 tons/in². The results demonstrated clearly that the presence of large inclusions was detrimental, although a close correlation between inclusion size and fatigue strength was not obtained. Good results were obtained with vacuum melting, but the highest fatigue strength was achieved by air induction melting, deoxidizing firstly with carbon and finally with aluminium. After oil quenching from 1550°F (843°C) and tempering at 400°F (204°C) the bending fatigue strength was 66 tons/in², based on 50% survivals at $10^7$ cycles. The authors thought that this might be the highest fatigue strength yet achieved for any metal, though it may be challenged by copper-bearing steels (see page 61).

*Directionality*

Many comparisons have been made between the longitudinal and transverse fatigue strengths of steels and these show that the difference between the two varies considerably even for steels of about the same strength. It is clear that the presence of inclusions has an important bearing on the directionality of fatigue strength. The other important factor is the preferred orientation of the grains introduced by working. The directionality may, therefore, on both counts, be expected to increase as the reduction in diameter from ingot to bar is increased and this has been demonstrated by Frith [92]. His results on steels treated to 110 tons/in$^2$ tensile strength showed a reduction in fatigue strength in the transverse direction of 21 to 36% for steels reduced 86% from ingot to bar and 41% for a steel reduced 95%. It is also found that the directionality is greater near the surface of a forging than at the centre where the material is less severely worked [116]. Frith [92] has quoted the results of other investigators, which show that in general, the reduction in fatigue strength in the transverse direction increases with the strength of the steel. The average and maximum values of the reductions observed, including his own and some more recent results [110, 111, 116, 117, 118], are shown in the following table:

TABLE 5. REDUCTIONS IN THE FATIGUE STRENGTH OF STEEL IN THE TRANSVERSE DIRECTION

| Fatigue strength in longitudinal direction tons/in$^2$ | Average reduction in fatigue strength in transverse direction | Number of values averaged | Maximum reduction quoted |
|---|---|---|---|
| Up to 20 | 15% | 15 | 26% |
| 20 to 30 | 17% | 16 | 31% |
| 30 to 40 | 20% | 23 | 45% |
| Over 40 | 29% | 13 | 41% |

*The Fatigue Strength of Steel Wire and the Effect of Cold Work*

The fatigue properties of patented steel wire have been investigated comprehensively by Gill and Goodacre [119]. They showed that the fatigue strength was markedly dependent on the condition of the surface. If no special care was taken to remove the decarburized surface layer, the fatigue strength was practically independent of the carbon content and in this condition the fatigue strength was reduced if the reduction by drawing was increased above 75% (see Fig. 31). When the decarburized layer was removed before drawing, on the other hand, the fatigue strength was improved, up to the maximum reductions investigated, by increasing either the carbon content or the percent reduction (Fig. 32). The improvement in fatigue strength was generally accompanied by some reduction in endurance ratio, however (Fig. 33). This behaviour is typical for steel cold

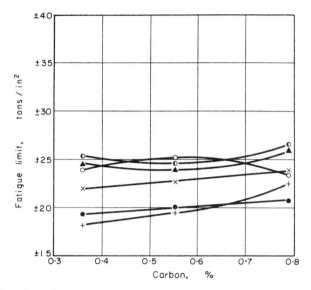

FIG. 31. Effect of carbon content on the rotating bending fatigue limit of wires drawn from decarburized lead-cooled patented rod. (Gill and Goodacre [119]).

Reduction:  ▲  85%      ◐  80%        ○  75%
                ×  50%      +  25%
                     ●  Patented condition.

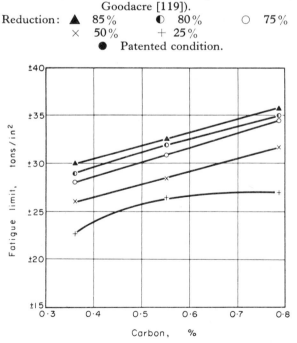

FIG. 32. Effect of carbon content on the rotating bending fatigue limit of wires drawn from lead-cooled patented rods free from decarburization. (Gill and Goodacre [119]). (See Fig. 31 for symbols.)

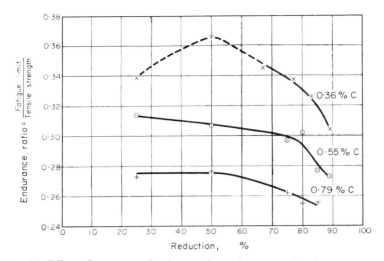

FIG. 33. Effect of percent reduction on the endurance ratio of wires drawn from lead-cooled patented rods free from decarburization. (Gill and Goodacre [119])

worked either by drawing or by rolling—the fatigue strength is improved but not usually to the same extent as the tensile strength [116, 120, 121]. Similar results have been obtained on carbon steel wire by Shelton and Swanger [122] and by Godfrey [123]. In further tests Gill and Goodacre showed that the fatigue strength of patented steel wire could be improved by as much as 20% by tempering at 150 or 200°C.

### Brittle Fracture and Fatigue

In some circumstances steels are liable to break in a brittle manner by a process which does not involve repeated application of stress and is quite distinct from fatigue. Such brittle fractures present a serious practical problem because they often lead to catastrophic failure. They are most likely to occur on large size components or structures as a result of shock loading, particularly if the temperature is low [656].

The classical theory of brittle fracture is that there is a brittle fracture stress at which the metal will break in a brittle manner, either by cleavage through the grains or along the grain boundaries. Provided the yield stress of a metal is below the brittle fracture stress, then it will break in a ductile manner, as illustrated in Fig. 34a, but if the brittle fracture stress is below the yield stress, then brittle fracture will occur as illustrated in Fig. 34b. This is a simplified view of the problem which is consistent with the observed behaviour. It does not explain the mechanism governing brittle fracture, which is not yet fully understood [124].

Susceptibility to brittle fracture is increased by a decrease in temperature and by an increase in strain rate, because these conditions raise the yield stress more than the brittle fracture stress. The presence of a notch also increases the likelihood of brittle fracture because the triaxial stresses produced under load in the vicinity of a notch reduces the ratio of shear stress to normal stress. Impact tests, such as the Izod and Charpy, in which notched specimens are broken by impact loading, are designed to induce brittle fracture. By carrying out impact tests at different temperatures, the transition from brittle to ductile fracture can be determined and this gives a measure of the liability of a metal to brittle fracture.

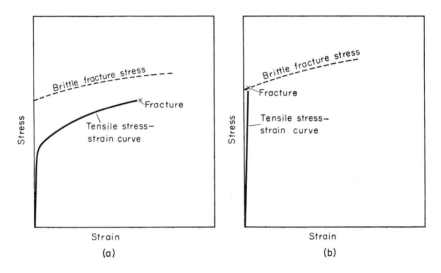

Fig. 34. Brittle fracture stress and tensile stress–strain curves (a) for a ductile material; (b) for a brittle material.

As fatigue fractures occur with little overall deformation it might be expected that steels susceptible to brittle fracture would show reduced fatigue strengths. In fact, attempts to establish a correlation have shown that this is not generally so. This is illustrated, for example, by a comparison of two steels, each with a tensile strength between 60 and 65 tons/in², one practically phosphorus free and in the quenched and tempered condition, giving an impact transition temperature of −88°C and the other, a similar steel, but with 0·06% phosphorus and heat treated to give an impact transition temperature of +130°C [125]. Fatigue tests were carried out at air temperature on both steels with plain specimens and with notched specimens ($K_t = 3.4$) and the results showed no significant difference between the two steels. A similar result was obtained from tests on a 1% chromium steel, both at air temperature and at −37°C [126]. It is possible that a difference between the fatigue strengths of the embrittled and non-embrittled steels in these experiments would have been found at lower temperatures. From the available data of the fatigue strength of steels at low temperatures, however, it would seem that the fatigue strength is not adversely affected by brittleness unless the temperature is very low. A decrease in both the tensile and fatigue strength of iron and zinc was observed by McCammon and Rosenberg [127], but only when the temperature was reduced below $-183\,^{\circ}$C.

Another aspect of the interrelation of brittle fracture and fatigue is the possibility that the application of fluctuating stresses may increase the susceptibility to brittle fracture. There is some evidence to show that there is not much effect, provided there are no fatigue cracks [128], but once a crack has formed, resistance to brittle fracture will be much reduced.

### Failure by Static Fatigue

Steels with a tensile strength above 80 tons/in² are liable to fail after a period of time under the application of a static load. This behaviour is known as delayed fracture or static fatigue, but the process is quite distinct from fatigue resulting from varying stress. The effect is particularly marked in steels which have been electroplated and it is therefore thought to result from hydrogen embrittlement [129, 670].

### Cast Steel

The fatigue strength of cast steel is usually lower than that of wrought steel of the same tensile strength, but cast steel is often less notch sensitive and a comparison of the notched fatigue strengths may show little difference between the two. This is illustrated by a comparison of the fatigue properties of comparable cast and wrought steel made by Evans, Ebert and Briggs [130]. A summary of their results is contained in Table 6.

TABLE 6. A COMPARISON OF THE ENDURANCE RATIOS OF COMPARABLE
CAST AND WROUGHT STEELS [130]

|  | Wrought steel | Cast steel |
|---|---|---|
| Carbon steels, unnotched | 0·48 | 0·40 |
| Low alloy steels, unnotched | 0·55–0·60 | 0·42–0·50 |
| Carbon and low alloy steels, notched | 0·27–0·32 | 0·27–0·32 |

The authors point out that in the as-cast condition the fatigue strength may be further reduced by a poor surface finish and decarburization, but is unlikely to be significantly influenced by directionality.

*Cast Iron*

The fatigue behaviour of cast iron is, in some ways, similar to that of steel. It usually shows a distinct fatigue limit and, as for steel, the ratio of the fatigue limit to the tensile strength is approximately equal to a half, for low and moderate strengths, and falls to lower values at high strength. Cast iron differs from steel and other metals, however, by its relative insensitivity to notches under fluctuating stresses. This behaviour is attributed to the graphite flakes which act as stress raisers, so that the addition of a mechanical notch has less effect than in other materials. In nodular cast irons the internal stress raisers are less severe with the result that the unnotched fatigue strength is higher, but the material is more sensitive to notches (see page 154). The fatigue behaviour of cast iron has been reviewed by Morrogh [131] and Angus [676].

Most of the data available on the fatigue of cast iron are for flake-graphite material; there are some data for nodular cast irons and relatively little for malleable cast irons. The bending fatigue limit of a number of cast irons is plotted against the tensile strength in Fig. 35. It can be seen from this figure that the fatigue strengths of nodular cast irons are usually higher than flake-graphite irons of the same tensile strength.

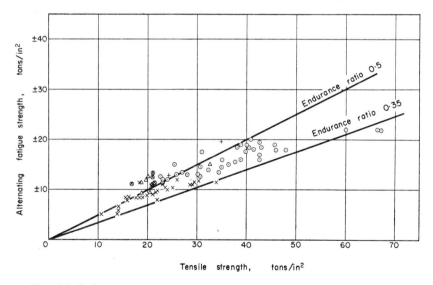

Fig. 35. Relation between rotating bending fatigue strength and tensile strength of iron, based on fatigue limit or failure in $10^7$ cycles.

×—Flake-Graphite Cast Iron
⊙—Nodular Cast Iron
+—Malleable Cast Iron
△—Ingot Iron
⊗—Wrought Iron

The tensile and fatigue strengths of cast iron can be improved by heat treatment. Normalizing usually produces a fine pearlitic structure which is better than a partially ferritic structure sometimes found in as-cast material. An increase in fatigue strength of nodular cast iron has been obtained by normalizing material with a pearlitic structure in the as-cast condition, although there was no improvement in the notched fatigue strength [132]. Tensile strengths up to 100 tons/in² can be obtained on nodular iron by hardening and tempering; such treatments increase the fatigue strength, but reduce the endurance ratio and increase the notch sensitivity [133].

## Fatigue strength of non-ferrous metals
### Aluminium Alloys

Because of the importance of aluminium alloys in aircraft, their fatigue behaviour has received considerable attention. The information available has been reviewed by G. Forrest [87] and by Templin [134] and a large amount of data has been collected by Grover, Gordon and Jackson [135].

Aluminium alloys can be divided into two groups, low and medium strength alloys which depend for their strength primarily on the alloying elements in solution and high strength alloys which are specially heat-treated to develop high strength by precipitation—that is, age-hardening. The first group show good fatigue properties in relation to their tensile strengths. The $S–N$ curves for these materials tend to become horizontal at long endurances and aluminium–magnesium alloys may show a distinct fatigue limit.

The age-hardened alloys, on the other hand, show $S–N$ curves which continue to slope downwards to very long endurances and their fatigue strengths are low in relation to their tensile strengths. The differences in shape of the $S–N$ curves for various types of aluminium alloy are illustrated in Fig. 36. There is usually more scatter in the results for the higher strength alloys, although this is not well marked for the results shown. Oberg [137] has shown that the $S–N$ curve for an aluminium–zinc–magnesium alloy does eventually become flatter and his results are shown in Fig. 37; three specimens which remained unbroken after endurances of about $7 \times 10^9$ cycles were retested at a higher stress range. The number of cycles to failure at the higher stress range for each of the three specimens was greater than for specimens not previously stressed. It would appear, in view of these results, that it is sufficiently accurate for most practical purposes to regard a fatigue strength based on failure in $10^8$ cycles for these alloys as equivalent to a fatigue limit.

The relation between fatigue strength ($10^8$ cycles) and tensile strength is shown in Fig. 38. It can be seen that the endurance ratios for the low-strength wrought alloys are comparable with those of low-strength steels

F

(Fig. 28), but that there is little increase in fatigue strength with increase in tensile strength above 20 tons/in². The lower strength aluminium–copper alloys (such as L.65 (DTD 364) and the American alloy 24S) have fatigue strengths comparable with the aluminium–zinc–magnesium alloys [138]. It has been suggested that the disappointing fatigue properties and

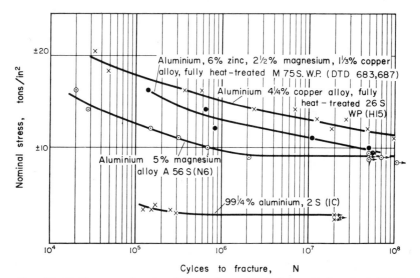

Fig. 36. *S–N* curves for aluminium alloys. (Aluminium Labs., Ltd. [136])

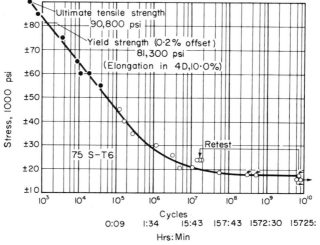

Fig. 37. *S–N* curve for aluminium alloy 75 S–T6. (T. T. Oberg [137])

    ●   Fracture, 90 cycles/min.

    ○   Fracture, 10,600 cycles/min.

    ○→ Specimen unbroken.

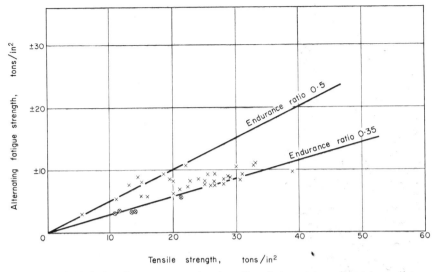

FIG. 38. Relation between rotating bending fatigue strength and tensile
strength of aluminium alloys, based on $10^8$ cycles.
× Wrought alloys.  ⊗ Cast alloys.

the continuously falling *S–N* curves of the age-hardened alloys are caused
by overageing, accelerated by the action of fluctuating stresses and there is
some evidence to support this argument [139–141].

The fatigue strength of aluminium alloys is influenced to some extent
by manufacturing processes. One factor affecting the fatigue behaviour is
the structure of the cast ingot or billet and there is a tendency for the
fatigue strength to decrease with increase in size of the ingot. Some results
quoted by G. Forrest [87] for aluminium–zinc–magnesium alloys, show
that the fatigue strength of specimens cut from ruling sections of over 4
inches are about 15% lower than those from ruling sections of under 2
inches. In general, the fatigue strengths of extrusions are higher than those
of forgings of similar composition. The influence of grain size is uncertain
but there is some evidence that a fine grain size results in a higher fatigue
strength than a coarse grain size [87]. Recent work on an aluminium–
zinc–magnesium alloy has shown that the size and number of intermetallic
particles affects the fatigue strength in a manner similar to that of inclusions in high tensile steels [668].

Waisman and others [142] have investigated the influence of flaws in
rolled plate of the aluminium–zinc–magnesium alloy 7075 in the fully
heat treated condition by means of fluctuating tension fatigue tests on
$\frac{1}{2}$ in. diameter specimens. The presence of large disc-shaped flaws 0·1
to 0·2 in. long had little effect on the fatigue strength of specimens cut in
the direction of rolling, but reduced the transverse fatigue strength by

about 20%, and by 30–40% if the flaws were at the surface. Such behaviour is exceptional, however, for it is well established that the fatigue strength of aluminium alloys is generally little affected by directionality [143]. G. Forrest [87] has stated that he has not found a difference between longitudinal and transverse values of more than 10%.

The fatigue strength of low and medium strength aluminium alloys can be increased by cold work, as is shown for three alloys in Fig. 39. No improvement is obtained by cold working the age-hardened alloys.

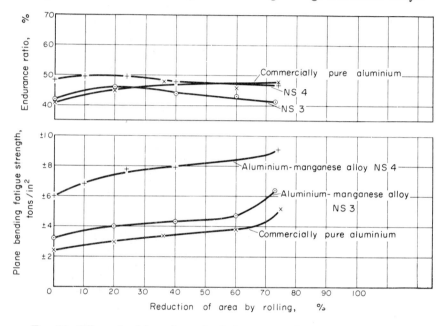

FIG. 39. Effect of cold work on the fatigue strength and endurance ratio of non-heat-treatable aluminium alloys. (G. Forrest [87])

The fatigue behaviour of cast aluminium alloys has been investigated fully by Templin and his co-workers [144]. Sand-cast and plaster-cast alloys show comparable fatigue properties; for unnotched specimens, permanent-mould cast alloys are slightly superior although there is considerable overlapping of results. For small specimens with sharp notches there is no significant difference between the fatigue strengths of the three types of casting, but die-cast alloys show superior fatigue properties, both notched and unnotched, and are comparable with wrought alloys. A comparison of cast and wrought alloys is shown by the relation between fatigue strength and tensile strength in Fig. 38.

Aluminium alloy sheet is widely used and there is a considerable amount of data available on its fatigue behaviour [135]. A comparison is made in

Table 7 of the fatigue strength of sheet with that of extruded bar of similar material. The table includes some results for alclad sheet, that is alloy sheet coated with a thin layer of pure aluminium to improve its corrosion resistance. The fatigue strength of unclad sheet is usually somewhat below that of bar material and cladding reduces the fatigue strength further. The axial fatigue strength of sheet is usually lower than the bending fatigue strength and there is a marked dependence on the width of the sheet tested; this is discussed further on page 141.

## Magnesium Alloys

Magnesium alloys are widely used, particularly as castings, because of their low density, and there is considerable information available on their fatigue behaviour [135, 145, 146]. The stress–endurance curve for magnesium alloys does not usually show a distinct fatigue limit, but the slope of the curve is usually less steep than for high strength aluminium alloys. The fatigue strength of wrought magnesium–aluminium alloys can be as high as 10 tons/in² on a basis of $10^8$ cycles, and their endurance ratio is usually between 0·35 and 0·5. Magnesium–manganese alloys have lower fatigue strengths and lower endurance ratios, but are less susceptible to corrosion and stress-corrosion than magnesium–aluminium alloys.

As for other metals, it is usually found that if the strength of magnesium alloys is increased by alloy additions, such as aluminium, which form solid solutions, then the fatigue strength is increased approximately in proportion to the increase in tensile strength. If, on the other hand, the increase in strength is achieved by precipitation hardening, or to a lesser extent, by cold work, the fatigue strength at short endurances may be improved but the improvement tends to disappear at long endurances. The fatigue strength of magnesium alloys may be affected by the structure and the presence of internal stresses in the cast billet and there is a decrease in fatigue strength with an increase in section size.

The fatigue behaviour of sand-cast magnesium alloys has been thoroughly investigated by Frith [146], both at air temperature and at high temperatures. The alloys he tested ranged from 9 to 17 tons/in² tensile strength at air temperature and the rotating bending fatigue strengths ($10^8$ cycles) from 3 to 6 tons/in², but there was no correlation at all between the fatigue strength and the tensile strength.

There is a considerable amount of fatigue data for magnesium alloy sheet and in Table 8 a comparison is made between the endurance ratio of sheet and extruded bar.

## Copper Alloys

The relation between fatigue strength and tensile strength is more variable for copper alloys than for most other metals, as may be seen from

TABLE 7. ALTERNATING FATIGUE STRENGTH OF ALUMINIUM ALLOY SHEET

| Material | Condition | Rotating bending fatigue strength of extrusion (10⁷ cycles) tons/in² | Width of sheet fatigue specimens | Type of fatigue stress for sheet specimens | Fatigue strength of sheet (10⁷ cycles) tons/in² | Tensile strength of sheet tons/in² | Fatigue strength of sheet ÷ Fatigue strength of extrusion | Reference |
|---|---|---|---|---|---|---|---|---|
| 2 S; 99¼% Al | Annealed 0·048 in. thick | | [Tapered — maximum width approx. ½ in | B | 2·3 | 5·5 | | Aluminium Laboratories [136] |
| | Quarter hard 0·048 in. thick | | | | 2·7 | 6·5 | | |
| | Half hard 0·048 in. thick | | | | 3·3 | 7·5 | | |
| | Fully hard 0·048 in. thick | | | | 5·3 | 10 | | |
| 26 S; 4¼% Cu, ¾% Si; ¾% Mn, ½% Mg, | Solution-treated 0·048 in. thick | 12 | Approx. ½ in. | | 8·5 | 29 | 0·71 | |
| | Solution-treated, Alclad 0·048 in. thick | | | | 6 | 27 | 0·50 | |
| | Fully heat-treated 0·048 in. thick | 13 | | | 9·5 | 32 | 0·73 | |
| | Fully heat-treated, Alclad 0·048 in. thick | | | | 6 | 29 | 0·46 | |
| 54 S; 3½% Mg, ⅓% Mn, | Annealed 0·080 in thick | | Approx. ¾ in. | | 6·8 | 15 | | |
| | Quarter hard 0·080 in. thick | | | | 8 | 19 | | |
| A 56 S; 5% Mg, ⅓% Mn, | Annealed 0·080 in. thick | | Approx. ¾ in. | | 7·6 | 18·5 | | |

| Material | Condition | | Thickness | | 9 | 23·5 | | Reference |
|---|---|---|---|---|---|---|---|---|
| 65 S; 1% Mg, ½% Si, ¼% Cu, ¼% Cr, | Quarter hard 0·080 in. thick | 9 | | | | | | Grover, Gordon and Jackson [135] |
| | Solution-treated 0·048 in. thick | | Approx. ½ in. | | 6·4 | 14 | 0·71 | |
| | Fully heat-treated 0·048 in. thick | 9·5 | | | 6·6 | 21 | 0·69 | |
| M 75 S; 6% Zn, 2½%Mg, 1⅓%Cu, ¼% Mn, ⅛% Cr, | Fully heat-treated, Alclad 0·080 in. thick | 10·5 | Approx. ¾ in. | | 6 | 35 | 0·57 | |
| 75 S–T6 (Al–Zn–Mg) | Fully heat-treated 0·032 in. thick | 13·4* | 0·25 in. | Ax | 10·3 | 38 | 0·77 | |
| | | | 0·5 in. | | 7·8 | 38 | 0·58 | |
| | | | 1·0 in. | | 8·5 | 38 | 0·63 | |
| | | | 2·0 in. | | 6·9 | 38 | 0·52 | |
| | 0·064 in. thick, Alclad | | | B | 9·6 | 36·6 | 0·72 | |
| | 0·064 in. thick, Alclad | | | | 6·4* | 33·9* | 0·48 | |
| | 0·066 in. thick, Alclad | | | | 6·6 | 34·8 | 0·49 | |
| | 0·066 in. thick, Alclad, transverse | | | | 6·6 | 36·2 | 0·49 | |

* Average of two results.
B = Reversed bending.
Ax = Axial stress.

TABLE 8. ALTERNATING FATIGUE STRENGTHS OF MAGNESIUM ALLOY SHEET
(From data collected by Grover, Gordon and Jackson [135])
Fatigue data for extrusions from rotating bending tests and on sheet from reversed bending tests

| Material | Condition | Fatigue specimen size (in.) | Fatigue strength ($10^8$ cycles) (tons/in²) | Tensile strength (tons/in²) | Endurance ratio | Endurance ratio of sheet ÷ Endurance ratio of extrusion |
|---|---|---|---|---|---|---|
| Mg 3% Al, 1% Zn alloy AZ 31 | As extruded | 0·3d | 7·8* | 17·7* | 0·44 | |
| | 0·02 in. sheet, A | 0·5 wide | 6·9 | 16·5 | 0·42 | 0·95 |
| | 0·02 in. sheet, half hard | 0·5 wide | 7·8 | 19·2 | 0·41 | 0·93 |
| | 0·064 in. sheet, A | 0·65 wide | 6·0 | 16·5 | 0·36 | 0·82 |
| | 0·064 in. sheet, half hard | 0·65 wide | 6·7 | 19·2 | 0·35 | 0·79 |
| Mg 6% Al, 1% Zn alloy AZ 61 | As extruded | 0·3d | 8·9 | 20·1 | 0·44 | |
| | 0·02 in. sheet, A | 0·5 wide | 6·2 | 19·2 | 0·32 | 0·73 |
| | 0·02 in. sheet, half hard | 0·5 wide | 8·0 | 21·0 | 0·38 | 0·86 |
| | 0·064 in. sheet, A | 1·0 wide | 6·2 | 19·2 | 0·32 | 0·73 |
| | 0·064 in. sheet, half hard | 1·0 wide | 6·7 | 21·0 | 0·32 | 0·73 |
| Mg 1% Mn alloy M 1 | As extruded | 0·3d | 4·7 | 17·0 | 0·28 | |
| | 0·02 in. sheet, A | 1·0 wide | 4·5 | 14·7 | 0·31 | 1·11 |
| | 0·02 in. sheet, half hard | 0·5 wide | 4·7 | 16·5 | 0·28 | 1 |
| | 0·064 in. sheet, A | 1·0 wide | 3·3 | 14·7 | 0·22 | 0·78 |
| | 0·064 in. sheet, half hard | 1·0 wide | 4·7 | 16·5 | 0·28 | 1 |

Average = 0·87

* Average of 2 results.
A = Annealed.

Fig. 40. The *S–N* curves do not usually show a fatigue limit and the fatigue results plotted in Fig. 40 are for failure in $10^8$ cycles. The fatigue strength is influenced by a number of factors, particularly by the alloy composition, the grain size and the degree of working.

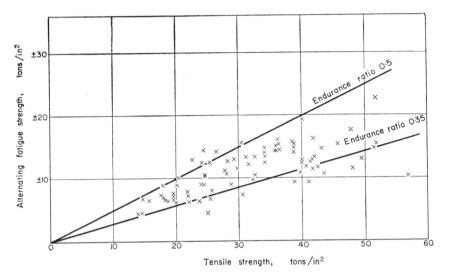

FIG. 40. Relation between rotating bending fatigue strength and tensile strength of wrought copper alloys.

Pure copper has a fatigue strength of only about 6 tons/in²; this is increased by solid-solution-hardening as in copper–zinc and copper–tin alloys, but the highest fatigue strengths are obtained in age-hardening alloys such as copper–beryllium, although little improvement in fatigue strength is obtained by increasing the tensile strength above 30 tons/in².

The influence of grain size on the fatigue strength of copper alloys may be appreciable as shown by the results given in Fig. 41. Comparatively little initial working increases the fatigue strength of copper alloys rapidly, while further working produces less effect and may even reduce it; the relation between fatigue strength and the reduction of area by cold work is shown in Fig. 42 for a number of alloys.

Copper alloys are often used as strip, sheet or wire and the fatigue properties in these conditions have been widely investigated in the United States [135, 147, 152–154]. In Table 9 a comparison is made of the endurance ratio of sheet with that of copper rod of the same composition. It may be noted that the fatigue strength of the leaded brass sheet, quoted in the table, is higher in the transverse direction than in the longitudinal direction; this behaviour is often found in copper alloy sheet [147].

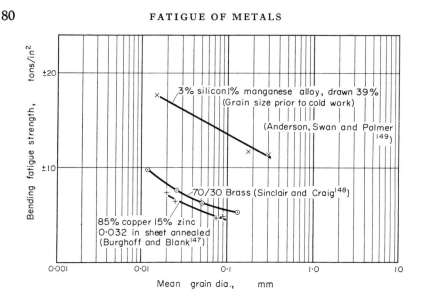

FIG. 41. Effect of grain size on the fatigue strength of copper alloys,
based on $10^8$ cycles.

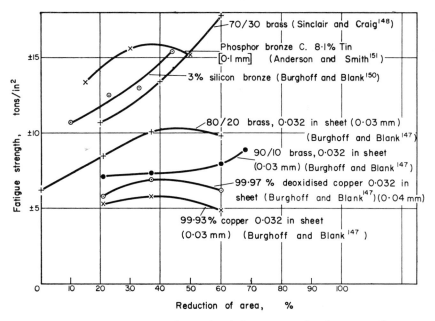

FIG. 42. Effect of cold work on the fatigue strength of copper alloys,
based on $10^8$ cycles.

Figures in brackets give grain size before reduction.
Sheet tested in plane bending; other material in rotating bending.

TABLE 9. ALTERNATING FATIGUE STRENGTHS OF COPPER ALLOY SHEET
(From data collected by Grover, Gordon and Jackson [135])

Fatigue data on rod from rotating bending tests and on sheet from reversed bending tests.

| Material | Condition | Ready to finish grain size (mm) | Fatigue specimen size (in.) | Fatigue strength ($10^8$ cycles) (tons/in$^2$) | Tensile strength (tons/in$^2$) | Endurance ratio | Endurance ratio of sheet ÷ Endurance ratio of rod |
|---|---|---|---|---|---|---|---|
| 99·95% Cu | ½ in. rod drawn 36% | 0·040 | 0·3d | 8·0 | 21·8 | 0·37 | |
| | 0·020 in. sheet drawn 21% | | | 6·0 | 19·8 | 0·30 | 0·81 |
| | 0·020 in. sheet drawn 50% | | | 6·0 | 23·5 | 0·26 | 0·70 |
| Phosphor bronze A 4% Sn | ½ in. rod, hard, drawn 30% | 0·090 | 0·3d | 13·4 | 31·1 | 0·43 | |
| | 0·02 in. sheet, half hard | | | 11·6 | 35·2 | 0·33 | 0·77 |
| Phosphor bronze C 8% Sn | ½ in. rod, hard, drawn 30% | 0·100 | 0·3d | 15·6 | 36·1 | 0·43 | |
| | 0·02 in. sheet, half hard | | | 9·8 | 39·3 | 0·25 | 0·58 |
| High leaded brass 62% Cu 2·8% Pb 64% Cu 2·0% Pb | 0·75 in. rod | | 0·4d | 8·0 | 26·9 | 0·30 | |
| | 0·032 in. sheet, A | 0·035 | | 6·7 | 21·9 | 0·31 | 1·03 |
| | 0·032 in. sheet drawn 21% | 0·035 | | 7·1 | 28·8 | 0·25 | 0·83 |
| | 0·032 in. sheet drawn 21%, transverse | 0·035 | | 8·5 | 34·1 | 0·25 | 0·83 |
| 85/15 brass | 0·5 in. rod drawn 4% | 0·025 | 0·3d | 9·3 | 20·0 | 0·46 | |
| | 0·032 in. sheet, A | Annealed 0·025 | | 6·5 | 18·7 | 0·35 | 0·76 |

Average = 0·79

A = Annealed.

Some fatigue data obtained on copper wire by Burghoff and Blank [152] are shown in Table 10. Unlike some of the results shown in Fig. 42 the fatigue strength of each alloy tested increased with the amount of drawing, although this was always accompanied by a decrease in the endurance

TABLE 10. ROTATING BENDING FATIGUE STRENGTHS OF
COPPER ALLOY WIRE (0·072 in. dia.)
(Data from Burghoff and Blank [152]).

| Material | Temper (% reduction) | Fatigue strength ($10^8$ cycles) (tons/in²) | Tensile strength (tons/in²) | Endurance ratio |
|---|---|---|---|---|
| 91·2% Cu 8·8% Zn | 84 | 10·3 | 32·4 | 0·32 |
| | 60 | 9·4 | 27·2 | 0·35 |
| 80·06% Cu 19·94% Zn | 84 | 11·8 | 48·2 | 0·25 |
| | 60 | 10·3 | 39·7 | 0·26 |
| 69·32% Cu 30·65% Zn | 84 | 9·8 | 53·6 | 0·18 |
| | 60 | 8·7 | 44·0 | 0·20 |
| 62·62% Cu 37·38% Zn | 84 | 9·8 | 52·7 | 0·19 |
| | 60 | 8·5 | 41·5 | 0·20 |
| 98·79% Cu 1·20% Sn | 84 | 14·3 | 32·1 | 0·45 |
| | 60 | 12·7 | 29·5 | 0·43 |
| 79·90% Cu 0·79% Sn 19·30% Zn | 84 | 15·4 | 55·8 | 0·28 |
| | 60 | 12·7 | 46·4 | 0·27 |
| 97·12% Cu 1·39% Si 1·45% Zn | 84 | 12·5 | 41·7 | 0·30 |
| | 60 | 10·9 | 32·6 | 0·34 |
| 79·53% Cu 20·02% Ni 0·46% Mn | 88 | 15·2 | 37·6 | 0·40 |
| 98·59% Cu 1·13% Ni 0·21% P | 98 | 17·9 | 51·8 | 0·35 |
| | 94 | 17·4 | 48·6 | 0·36 |
| | 75 | 15·0 | 40·6 | 0·37 |

ratio. The fatigue strengths are generally lower than those found in copper rod, which may be attributed to the surface imperfections of the wire, which was subjected only to a straightening operation after drawing.

*Nickel Alloys*

The endurance ratio of nickel and nickel alloys, based on rotating bending fatigue results at $10^8$ cycles (they do not show a distinct fatigue limit) usually lie between 0·35 and 0·5, with slightly lower values when treated to high tensile strengths. They are often used for sheet or wire and a comparison of the fatigue strengths of sheet and rod is made in Table 11 and some fatigue data for wire are given in Table 12. The behaviour is similar to that of copper alloys. Nickel base alloys containing chromium are widely used at high temperatures and their fatigue properties are discussed in Chapter VIII.

*Titanium Alloys*

The fatigue strengths of titanium alloys, relative to their tensile strengths, are as good as, or better than, steels, many showing an endurance ratio above a half. (See Fig. 43.) The *S–N* curve for most of the alloys tend to become horizontal at long endurances and some show a distinct fatigue limit. Titanium alloys are particularly susceptible to hydrogen embrittlement [156] but the presence of hydrogen does not adversely affect the fatigue strength either for plain or notched specimens [157]. Some alloys maintain considerable strength up to 400 or 500°C and all show good resistance to corrosion and corrosion fatigue.

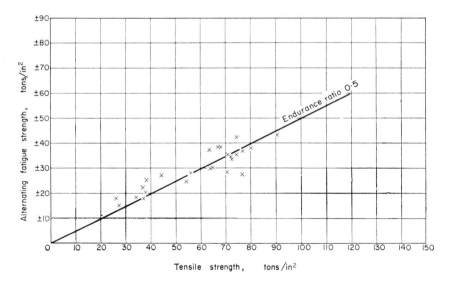

FIG. 43. Relation between rotating bending fatigue strength and tensile strength of titanium alloys, based on $10^7$ or $2 \times 10^7$ cycles.

TABLE 11. ALTERNATING FATIGUE STRENGTHS OF NICKEL ALLOY SHEET
(From data collected by Grover, Gordon and Jackson [135])

Fatigue data on rod from rotating bending tests and on sheet from reversed bending tests on specimens 0·23 in. wide

| Material | Condition | Fatigue strength (10⁸ cycles) (tons/in²) | Tensile strength (tons/in²) | Endurance Ratio | Endurance ratio of sheet ÷ Endurance ratio of rod |
|---|---|---|---|---|---|
| 98·9% commercial nickel | 0·02 in. sheet, A | 10·2 | 32·1 | 0·32 | — |
| | 0·02 in. sheet, A, transverse | 10·1 | | | |
| | 0·02 in. sheet, rolled 37% reduction | 17·9 | 50·6 | 0·35 | — |
| | 0·02 in. sheet, rolled 37%, transverse | 18·3 | | | |
| | 0·02 in. sheet, rolled 60% reduction | 18·3 | 54·2 | 0·34 | — |

| | | | | |
|---|---|---|---|---|
| **Monel (67% Ni 30% Cu)** | | | | |
| ½ in. to 1 in. rod, A | 13·8–16·1 | 35–38 | 0·41 (Av.) | 0·73 |
| 0·02 in. sheet, A | 9·8 | 32·9 | 0·30 | |
| ½ in. to 1 in. rod, cold drawn, stress relieved | 17·6–21·2 | 41–50 | 0·43 (Av.) | 0·65 |
| 0·02 in. sheet, rolled 44% reduction | 14·5 | 51·7 | 0·28 | |
| 0·02 in. sheet, rolled 56% reduction | 14·0 | 54·8 | 0·26 | 0·60 |
| **K. Monel (3% Al)** | | | | |
| ½ in. to 1 in. rod, A | 15·2–18·6 | 39–40 | 0·43 (Av.) | 0·67 |
| 0·02 in. sheet, A | 11·6 | 39·4 | 0·29 | |
| ½ in. to 1 in. rod, hot rolled, age-hardened | 20·1–23·6 | 61–77 | 0·32 (Av.) | 0·75 |
| 0·02 in. sheet, heat treated | 16·5 | 68·3 | 0·24 | |
| | | | | Average = 0·68 |

A = Annealed.

*Lead Alloys*

The fatigue behaviour of lead and lead alloys at room temperature is similar to that of other metals at higher temperatures. Recrystallization may occur under cyclic stressing and fatigue cracks always follow the grain boundaries. The fatigue strength is dependent on the frequency of the stress cycle, as it is for other metals at high temperatures (see page 251) and also on the corrosive effect of the atmosphere (see page 227); the *S–N* curve does not show a fatigue limit. The fatigue strength of commercially pure lead is very low—about 400 lb/in²—but this can be increased appreciably by the addition of alloying elements. Fine-grained material, in general, shows a higher fatigue strength than coarse-grained, although the effect may be masked by recrystallization and grain growth during test. Some results obtained by Hopkin and Thwaites [158] illustrating the effect of grain size on some lead alloys are shown in Fig. 44.

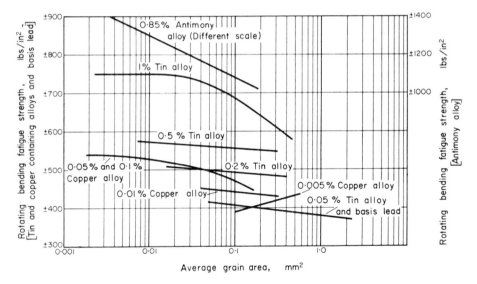

FIG. 44. Effect of grain size on the fatigue strength of lead alloys, based on $20 \times 10^6$ cycles at 3,000 cycles/min. (Hopkin and Thwaites [158].)

*Other Metals*

There is a limited amount of information on a number of other metals. Pure cast tin shows a rotating bending fatigue strength of 380 lb/in² for an endurance of $10^8$ cycles and shows intercrystalline fatigue fractures [159]. Molybdenum appears to show a fatigue limit at about $10^7$ cycles and values of the endurance ratio as high as 0·8 have been reported [160]. Some data for gold, silver, cadmium and zinc are included in Table 83.

TABLE 12. ROTATING BENDING FATIGUE STRENGTHS OF NICKEL ALLOY WIRE
Data from Kenyon [155].

0·0375 in. diameter wire, drawn 75% reduction.

| Material | Fatigue strength ($10^8$ cycles) (tons/in$^2$) | Tensile strength (tons/in$^2$) | Endurance ratio |
|---|---|---|---|
| 99·46% Nickel | 22·1 | 64·4 | 0·34 |
| Monel, 66% Ni 31% Cu | 20·7 | 62·5 | 0·33 |
| Inconel, 79·6% Cu 13·3% Cr 6·4% Fe | 22·5 | 92·4 | 0·24 |
| K Monel, 66% Ni 29% Cu 3% Al, stress equalized | 21·6 | 72·3 | 0·30 |
| K Monel, age-hardened | 19·9 | 89·3 | 0·22 |
| 55% Fe—36% Ni—7% Cr | 20·3 | 67·4 | 0·30 |
| 77% Ni—13% Cr—6·6% Fe | 21·9 | 89·7 | 0·24 |
| Z Nickel, 98·45% Ni | 19·0 | 103 | 0·18 |

## The resistance of metals to fatigue failure from a small number of stress reversals

There are some applications such as pressure vessels, the landing gear of aircraft, and the working parts of guns, where the total life may involve only some hundreds or thousands of stress cycles. In these circumstances a material can usually withstand stresses appreciably above its fatigue limit or long life fatigue strength so that a knowledge of the fatigue behaviour of materials at low endurances is required if economic design is to be achieved.

At the high stresses which materials can withstand for low endurances, there is often considerable plastic deformation during each stress cycle. This has led to the use of the term "progressive fracture" to describe failure resulting from a small number of stress reversals and it may be that the mechanism of failure under these conditions is different from fatigue failure at long endurances. Certainly the appearance of fractured surfaces supports this; fractures resulting from endurances up to several thousand stress reversals often resemble static tensile fractures and are quite distinct from typical fatigue fractures [161, 162].

G

As a result of the occurrence of considerable plastic deformation during fatigue at low endurances, the stress is not directly proportional to the strain; it is therefore necessary to draw a distinction between resistance to alternating stress and resistance to alternating strain, and in practice it is often resistance to alternating strain which is more important. This is because in engineering parts, fatigue failures almost always propagate from regions of stress concentration and if a part is subjected to a fluctuating load, the material in the region of a stress concentration will be constrained by the surrounding elastic material to a given strain range.

Considering firstly, the resistance of materials to alternating stress, the static tensile strength gives a point on the $S$–$N$ curve at a $\frac{1}{4}$ cycle and one needs to know how this is connected with the conventional $S$–$N$ curve, which is usually known only for endurances greater than $10^4$ or $10^5$ cycles. Conventional fatigue testing methods are unsuitable for investigating the range from 1 to 10,000 cycles because the frequency of the stress cycle is too high. Fortunately the influence of frequency on the fatigue strength of most metals is small (at least at room temperature), so that the low cycle range can be investigated at low frequencies and the results correlated satisfactorily with those obtained at longer endurances at higher frequencies.

In order to summarize the information available of the fatigue strength of metals at low endurances, the ratio of the fatigue strength for failure in a given number of cycles to the tensile strength is plotted against the endurance in Fig. 45. Results obtained in fluctuating tension tests are discussed in Chapter IV (see page 102). To avoid confusion, only limits within which the results lie have been plotted. Different limits are shown for axial stress, rotating bending and reversed bending and these include data collected for a wide variety of steels by Weisman and Kaplan [161] and for steels, aluminium alloys and magnesium alloys from the results of other investigators [163–168]. The axial stress fatigue strength for a low number of cycles can be estimated approximately by extrapolating the $S$-log $N$ curve backwards from $10^4$ or $10^5$ cycles by means of a straight line to the tensile strength at $\frac{1}{4}$ cycle; this usually gives a conservative estimate of the fatigue strength.

The values of the stress for the rotating and the reversed bending results are calculated from the elastic bending law, neglecting the influence of plastic deformation on the stress distribution. At low endurances this is the most important reason for the difference between results in bending and direct stress and it accounts for values of the bending fatigue strength appearing to be higher than the tensile strength.

Considering the wide variety of materials for which results are included in Fig. 45 the spread of the results is surprisingly small; evidently the fatigue strength of metals at low endurances is quite closely related to the

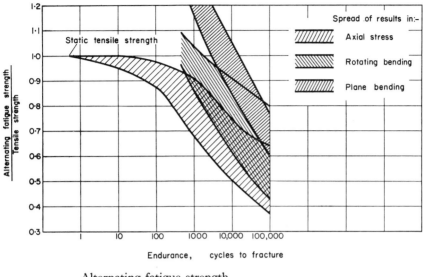

FIG. 45. $\dfrac{\text{Alternating fatigue strength}}{\text{Tensile strength}}$ for metals at low endurances.

tensile strength. In contrast to this behaviour, the resistance of materials to alternating strain at low endurances is not related to the tensile strength. This has been demonstrated by Low [169], who showed that within the range 10 to $10^4$ cycles, the fatigue life in reversed bending for widely differing ductile materials depended, within quite close limits, on the range of strain only. For steels, Kooistra [170] found that for endurances less than about 5000 cycles the resistance to alternating strain correlated best with the ductility of the steel, as indicated by the elongation in a static tensile test; for endurances between about 5000 and 20,000 cycles the resistance was almost independent of the tensile properties, while above 20,000 cycles the resistance was more closely proportional to tensile strength. All the results quoted by Low and by Kooistra lie within the narrow limits shown in Fig. 46. These results include a number of steels and aluminium alloys, copper, brass and phosphor-bronze all tested by Low, a carbon steel tested by Kommers [169], and steels ranging from 25 to 87 tons/in$^2$ tensile strength quoted by Kooistra.

It should be noted that the limits shown in Fig. 46 were determined from tests on ductile materials and they may not apply to brittle materials like cast iron. For ductile materials, however, the range of materials falling within the band of Fig. 46 is very wide and the result is, therefore, of considerable practical significance. For example, the results indicate that for applications involving up to $10^4$ cycles of strain, little or nothing may be gained by the use of a material of high tensile strength.

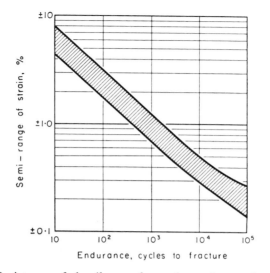

Fɪɢ. 46. Resistance of ductile metals to alternating strain at low endurances.

Coffin [171] has investigated the relation between the number of cycles
to fracture $N$ and the range of cyclic *plastic* strain $\Delta \epsilon_p$ and has shown that
the experimental results quoted by Low [169] and Kooistra [170] and other
results, obey closely the empirical equation:

$$N^{\frac{1}{2}} \Delta \epsilon_p = \text{constant.} \qquad (12)$$

In addition, he found that for $N = \frac{1}{4}$ cycle, the value of the strain range
predicted by this equation was generally in good agreement with the true
strain at fracture measured in a static tensile test.

This implies that the resistance of a material to alternating plastic strain
is dependent on its ductility. The resistance of a material to alternating
elastic strain, on the other hand, is dependent primarily on its strength.
The resistance to total alternating strain thus depends primarily on ductility
at high stresses when plastic strain predominates and primarily on strength
at low stresses when elastic strain predominates.

The influence of a superimposed static strain has little effect on the
range of strain which a material can withstand at low endurances. This
is because the plastic deformation redistributes the stresses so that the
initial static stress is reduced to a low value after a few stress cycles. On
the other hand, the presence of a notch can reduce the range of strain
appreciably and in the absence of experimental evidence it would be wise
to allow a reduction equal to the stress concentration factor, unless the
notch is very small.

## The resistance of metals to repeated impact

The single blow impact test in which a notched specimen is fractured by a blow from a falling tup or pendulum is one of the most widely used methods of mechanical testing. It is useful as a quality control test and to assess the resistance of a material to fracture from shock loading. Engineering parts in service, however, may be subjected to repeated shock loading, so that the behaviour of materials under conditions of repeated impact may also be important.

Repeated impact tests are usually carried out by subjecting a notched specimen to repeated blows of constant energy. For short endurances, up to 10 or 20 blows, the total energy required to produce failure may be approximately constant and independent of the number of blows, indicating that the material is able to absorb a certain limiting amount of energy. Consequently, if the energy per blow is plotted against the endurance, the curve obtained falls steeply at first, but at longer endurances the curve becomes much flatter and resembles a normal fatigue *S–N* curve quite closely. This is illustrated by some results, plotted in Fig. 47. The tests were made on specimens of the Charpy V-notch type, 0·394 in. square, 2·165 in. long containing a 45° notch 0·079 in. deep on one side. The

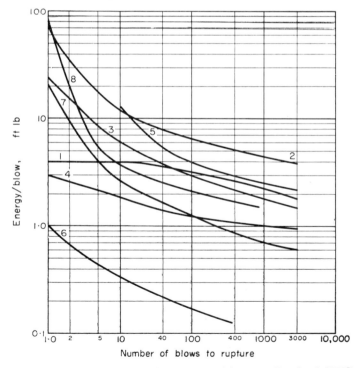

FIG. 47. Behaviour of metals to repeated impact. (Layland [172])
Details of the materials tested are quoted in Table 13.

specimen was supported as a simple beam with the notch on the tension side and was subjected to about eight blows per minute.

The resistance of a material to fracture from one blow, depends primarily on its notch-impact ductility, while the resistance to a large number of blows—say a million or more—depends primarily on its fatigue strength. Between these two extremes the influence of ductility decreases and that of fatigue strength increases with increase in the number of blows required to cause fracture. From the results of repeated impact tests on steels it would appear that the influence of ductility predominates up to about 100 or 1000 blows [173–175]. In other words, for resistance to less than 100–1000 blows, a low strength ductile material is likely to be more resistant than a less ductile material of higher strength, but for a greater number of blows the stronger material is likely to be more resistant. As would be expected, this behaviour is similar to that observed in materials subjected to alternating strain.

TABLE 13. MATERIALS TESTED FOR RESISTANCE TO REPEATED IMPACT [172]

| Material | Condition | Yield stress (tons/in²) | Tensile strength (tons/in²) | Reduction in area % |
|---|---|---|---|---|
| 1. AISI B1111 steel screw stock (0·13% C max.) | Cold drawn | 34·6 | 37·2 | 59 |
| 2. AISI 4140 alloy steel (0·8–1·1% Cr, 0·15–0·25% Mo) | Quenched and tempered | 56 | 60 | 60 |
| 3. AISI 8620 alloy steel (0·4–0·7% Ni, 0·4–0·6% Cr, 0·15–0·25% Mo) | Hot rolled | 29·0 | 50 | 60 |
| 4. As above | Carburized $\frac{1}{32}$ in. and hardened | — | — | — |
| 5. AISI 303 stainless steel (17–19% Cr, 8–10% Ni) | Cold drawn and annealed | 18 | 40 | 50 |
| 6. ASTM Grade 20 grey cast iron | As cast | — | 10·0 | — |
| 7. ASTM Grade 60–45–10 Nodular cast iron | Annealed | 22 | 30 | 18 |
| 8. Aluminium-silicon bronze | Cold drawn | 36·9 | 44·5 | 71 |

## CHAPTER IV

# THE INFLUENCE OF STRESS CONDITIONS ON FATIGUE STRENGTH

In Chapter III, in comparing the fatigue strengths of different materials, only results determined under simple alternating stresses on plain polished specimens were considered. In this chapter, the influence of the more complex stress conditions often occurring in practice will be discussed. These include the effect of a mean stress superimposed on an alternating stress, combined shear and tensile stresses, stress cycles of varying amplitude and the frequency of the stress cycle.

## The influence of mean stress

By far the greatest proportion of fatigue data available have been determined from alternating stress tests, that is with the mean stress of the cycle equal to zero. This is largely a matter of convenience because fatigue data are most easily obtained from rotating bending machines which do not permit the application of a mean stress. In practice, however, many components and structures are subjected to stresses which fluctuate between different values of tension and compression. The most important condition to be considered is the influence of a static tensile stress superimposed on an alternating tension–compression stress, but even for this condition, there are relatively few data. A number of empirical relations have therefore been put forward which enable an estimate to be made of the fluctuating fatigue strength if the alternating fatigue strength and the tensile strength of the material are known.

*Empirical Relations for Predicting Fatigue Strength under Fluctuating Stresses*

The fatigue strength of a material under fluctuating stresses, that is with a static stress superimposed on the alternating stress, can be represented on a diagram in which the alternating stress $S_a$ is plotted against the static or mean stress $S_m$, as in Fig. 48. This is sometimes known as an $R$–$M$ diagram, where $R$ is the range of stress, equal to twice the alternating stress. The alternating fatigue limit or the alternating stress for a given endurance is plotted on the ordinate and the static tensile strength on the abscissa. The curve joining the two points represents the contour of the combinations of static and alternating stress giving the same endurance.

To determine this curve experimentally a number of $S$–$N$ curves are required, each for a constant value of $S_m$, $S_a$, or $R$ (equal to $S_{min}/S_{max}$). The two straight lines and the curve shown in Fig. 48 represent the three most widely used empirical relations. The straight line joining the alternating fatigue strength to the tensile strength is the modified Goodman law. Goodman's original law included the assumption that the alternating fatigue limit was equal to one-third of the tensile strength and this has since been modified to the relation shown, using the alternating fatigue strength determined experimentally. The original law is not now used and the

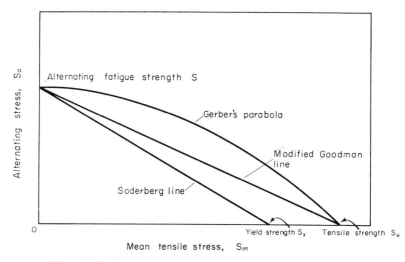

FIG. 48. Fatigue strength—static strength or $R$–$M$ diagram.

modified law is often referred to simply as the Goodman law. Gerber found that the early experimental results of Wohler fitted closely to a parabolic relation and this is now known as Gerber's parabola. The third relation, known as Soderberg's law is given by a straight line from the alternating fatigue strength to the static yield strength. For many purposes it is essential that the yield stress should not be exceeded and this relation is intended to fulfil the conditions that neither fatigue failure nor yielding shall occur. The relationships may be written mathematically as follows:

$$\text{Modified Goodman Law,} \quad S_a = S\left(1 - \frac{S_m}{S_u}\right), \tag{13}$$

$$\text{Gerber's Law,} \quad S_a = S\left(1 - \left(\frac{S_m}{S_u}\right)^2\right), \tag{14}$$

$$\text{Soderberg's Law,} \quad S_a = S\left(1 - \frac{S_m}{S_y}\right), \tag{15}$$

where $S_a$ is the alternating stress associated with a mean stress $S_m$, $S$ is the alternating fatigue strength, $S_u$ the tensile strength and $S_y$ the yield strength.

An alternative method, which is sometimes used to present fluctuating stress fatigue data is shown in Fig. 49. In this diagram the limits of the fluctuating stress for a given endurance are plotted against the mean stress; the modified Goodman law and the Gerber parabola are shown.

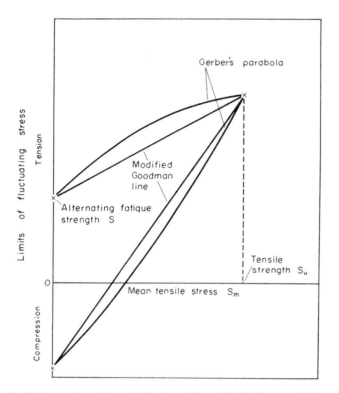

FIG. 49. Fatigue strength—static strength or $R$–$M$ diagram (alternative method of plotting).

*The Effect of a Mean Tensile Stress on the Fatigue Strength of Ductile Metals*

Some results of experiments which have been made to determine the influence of a static tensile stress on the axial fatigue strength are summarized in Tables 14, 15 and 16 for steels, aluminium alloys and other non-ferrous metals respectively. In order to compare the behaviour of different alloys on one diagram, the ratio of the alternating stress to the alternating fatigue strength is plotted against the ratio of mean stress to

TABLE 14. EFFECT OF MEAN TENSILE STRESS ON THE AXIAL FATIGUE STRENGTH OF STEEL

| Material | Tensile strength tons/in² | Endurance | Alternating fatigue strength tons/in² | Fluctuating fatigue strength tons/in² | Symbol in Fig. 50 | Source | Ref. |
|---|---|---|---|---|---|---|---|
| Ni Cr Mo steel | 56 | $10^7$ | 31 | $10\pm29$, $20\pm27$, $30\pm22$ | I | O'Connor and Morrison | 176 |
| Ni Cr Mo steel SAE 4340<br>SAE 2330<br>SAE 8630 | 87<br>70·5<br>54·5<br>65<br>47·5 | $10^7$ | 29·5<br>31<br>29·5<br>30<br>24 | 21·5±21·5<br>26±26<br>20·5±20·5<br>23·5±23·5<br>21±21 | K<br>L<br>M<br>N<br>O | Oberg and Ward | 167 |
| Ni steel | 45·5<br>50<br>55 | $10^7$ | 16<br>17·5<br>19·5 | 6±14<br>7±16·5<br>2±19·5 | Q | Moore and Jasper | 135 |
| Cr Mo steel | 49 | $10^7$ | 22 | 22±16·5 | H | Hempel and Krug | 135 |
| Ni Cr Mo steel SAE 4340 | 70·5 | $1·5 \times 10^7$ | 31 | 25·5±25·5, 53·5±11 | J | Trapp and Schwartz | 177 |
| Mild steel | 25·2 | $10^6$ | 13 | 12·8±8·7, 9·9±10·7, 5±12·2 | A | Haigh | 24 |
| Mild steel | 26·5 | $10^7$ | 12·3 | 20±6·8, 16·1±9·9, 9·6±10·3, 5·9±10·9, 2·8±11·8 | B | Gough and Wood | 178 |
| St 52 0·17% C 1·4% Mn<br>0·44% C 1·7% Mn<br>0·64% C<br>4·2% Ni 0·96% Cr<br>3·5% Ni 0·77% Cr | 35·5<br>56<br>51<br>43<br>57 | $2 \times 10^6$ | 19·5<br>25·5<br>19·5<br>23·5<br>30 | 4±18·5, 8±16<br>4±24, 7·5±23·5, 17±21<br>7·5±17<br>9±21·5<br>22±26, 11·5±27 | C<br>D<br>E<br>F<br>G | Pomp and Hempel | 179 |
| 4% Cr 8% Ni 7% Mn<br>Austenitic:<br>cold worked 10%<br>cold worked 20%<br>cold worked 30% | 56·5<br>61·5<br>68 | $10^7$ | 22·5<br>25·5<br>25·5 | 20±20<br>21·5±21·5<br>22±22 | P | Cina | 121 |

tensile strength in Figs. 50, 51 and 52. The results for steels, shown in Fig. 50, mostly lie between the Goodman line and the Gerber parabola. The spread in the results does not appear to be related to the type of steel nor to any mechanical property. For most of the results shown, the maximum stress of the cycle is below the yield stress. If the yield stress is exceeded, there may be considerable permanent deformation, but the results where this occurred are all above the Goodman line. Gough and Wood [178], showed that for mild steel, the permanent deformation occurring during a fatigue test was no more than that caused by one application of the maximum stress of the cycle, provided that the fatigue limit was not exceeded. On the other hand, more recent Japanese work [186] has shown that much more deformation may result from repeated stressing, even below the fatigue limit. Moreover, for some steels, fatigue stressing produced deformation at stresses considerably below the static yield stress—in other words, yielding can occur below the Soderberg line.

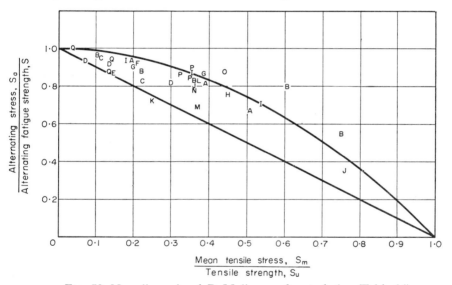

FIG. 50. Non-dimensional *R–M* diagram for steels (see Table 14).

The behaviour of aluminium alloys is shown in Fig. 51 and of other non-ferrous metals in Fig. 52. A number of medium strength aluminium alloys give values below the Goodman line. These alloys show a high ratio of alternating fatigue strength to tensile strength, but a very low ratio of yield to tensile strength, so that even for low mean stresses the maximum stress of the cycle is above the yield stress; it is possible that, in contrast to steel, yielding accounts for the marked effect of mean stress in these alloys. All the results for high strength age-hardened aluminium alloys

TABLE 15. EFFECT OF MEAN TENSILE STRESS ON THE AXIAL FATIGUE STRENGTH OF ALUMINIUM ALLOYS

| Material | Tensile strength tons/in² | Endurance | Alternating fatigue strength tons/in² | Fluctuating fatigue strength tons/in² | Symbol in Fig. 51 | Source | Ref. |
|---|---|---|---|---|---|---|---|
| Al-2% Mg, BS1470 annealed | 13·1 | 5 × 10⁷ | 6·8 | 3±5·0 | A | Woodward, Gunn and Forrest | 180 |
| Al-2% Mg, BS1470 cold rolled | 15·8 | 10⁷ | 7·3 | 4±6·3, 8±5·3 | B | | |
| Al-2% Mg, BS1477 hot rolled | 13·3 | 5 × 10⁷ | 8·0 | 3·5±5·8, 7±5·3 | C | | |
| Al-4% Mg, BS1477 hot rolled | 20·2 | 5 × 10⁷ | 10·0 | 5±7·3, 15±4·1 | D | | |
| Al-5% Mg, BS1476 as extruded | 18·3 | 5 × 10⁷ | 8·0 | 4·5±5·4 | E | | |
| Al-5% Mg, BS1476 as extruded | 17·8 | 5 × 10⁷ | 9·3 | 4·5±5·0 | F | | |
| Al-1% Si, BS1476 fully heat treated | 20·0 | 5 × 10⁷ | 6·2 | 5±5·6, 15±3·3 | G | | |
| Al-1% Mg-0·6% Si BS1476 fully heat treated | 23·8 | 5 × 10⁷ | 7·8 | 5·75±6·5, 11±5·8, 17·5±4·5 | H | | |
| Al-4% Cu, BS1476 solution treated | 35·1 | 5 × 10⁷ | 11·3 | 5±10·5, 10±9, 15±7·7, 20±5·5 | I | | — |

| Material | | | | | | Author | Ref. |
|---|---|---|---|---|---|---|---|
| Al-4% Cu, BS1476 fully heat treated | 35·4 | $5 \times 10^7$ | 11·5 | 5±10·8, 10±9·5, 15±10, 20±8·5, 25±5·1 | J | | |
| Al-4% Cu, BS1476 (9.6 in. diam extrusion) | 35·0 | $5 \times 10^7$ | 10·9 | 7·5±9·2, 15±8, 20±7 | K | | |
| | 32·0 | $5 \times 10^7$ | 10·9 | 8·75±7·8 | L | | |
| Al-Zn-Mg, DTD 363A fully heat treated | 42·6 | $5 \times 10^7$ | 13 | 10·7±10·8 | M | | |
| Al-Zn-Mg, DTD 363A (8×4 in. extrusion) | 39·6 | $10^7$ | 8·5 | 9·75±5·3 | N | | |
| Al-Cu 2014-T6 | 31·2 | $5 \times 10^8$ | 6·7 | 4·5±6·7, 8·9±6·7, 13·4±6·2, 17·9±5·8, 22·4±4·9 | O | Howell and Miller | 181 |
| Al-Cu 2024-T4 | 30·3 | | 7·6 | 4·5±7·6, 8·9±7·1, 13·4±6·7, 17·9±5·3, 22·4±4·0 | P | | |
| Al-Cu 6061-T6 | 20·1 | | 5·3 | 4·5±4·9, 8·9±4·5, 13·4±3·6 | Q | | |
| Al-Zn-Mg 7075-T6 | 36·6 | | 8·9 | 4·5±8·5, 8·9±7·6, 13·4±6·7, 17·9±6·2, 22·4±5·3, 26·8±4·5 | R | | |
| Al-Cu 14S-T6 | 31 | $5 \times 10^8$ | 6·7 | 2·2±6·7, 4·5±6·2, 6·7±6·2, 8·9±5·8, 11±5·8 | S | Howell and Stickley | 135 |
| Al-Mg 52S-H36 | 17·5 | $5 \times 10^8$ | 6·7 | 2·2±6·7, 4·5±6·7, 6·7±6·2, 8·9±5·8 | T | | |
| Al-Zn-Mg 75S-T6 | 36·5 | $5 \times 10^8$ | 8·5 | 2·2±8·0, 4·5±7·6, 6·7±7·1, 8·9±6·7 | U | | |
| Al-Cu 24S-T4 | 33 | $10^7$ | 11·5 | 4·5±10, 9·5±8·5, 15·5±6, 25±3·7 | V | de Money and Lazan | 182 |

TABLE 16. EFFECT OF MEAN TENSILE STRESS ON THE AXIAL FATIGUE STRENGTH OF NON-FERROUS ALLOYS (EXCLUDING ALUMINIUM)

| Material | Tensile strength tons/in² | Endurance | Alternating fatigue strength tons/in² | Fluctuating fatigue strength tons/in² | Symbol in Fig. 52 | Source | Ref. |
|---|---|---|---|---|---|---|---|
| Mg ZK 60<br>Mg AZ 80 | 21·5<br>24 | $10^7$ | 8·5<br>10·3 | 7·1±7·1<br>7·2±7·2 | D<br>E | Oberg and Trapp | 166 |
| Ti–Al–V alloy | 60·5<br>68<br>76 | $10^7$ | 32·5<br>34<br>38 | 15±26, 31±19<br>19·5±32, 35·5±20<br>20·5±35, 38·5±21·5 | G<br>H<br>I | Anon. | 183 |
| Naval brass | 28·7 | $10^6$ | 12·0 | 4±10·5, 6·2±9·6, 7·7±8·7 | A | Haigh | 24 |
| Mg, 8½% Al ½% Zn A9v<br>Mg, 8% Al ¼% Zn AZ855 | 14·8<br>21·7 | | 3·5<br>6·6 | 2·6±2·6<br>5·4±5·4 | B<br>C | Beck | 145 |
| 40% Co 20% Ni 20% Cr Alloy S–816 | 68·5 | $2 \times 10^7$ | 25 | 11·5±23, 23±15·5, 40·5±10 | J | Vitovec and Lazan | 184 |
| 20% Cr 20% Ni 20% Co iron alloy N–155 | 53 | $10^8$ | 21 | 9·5±19, 33·5±11 | K | Anon. | 185 |

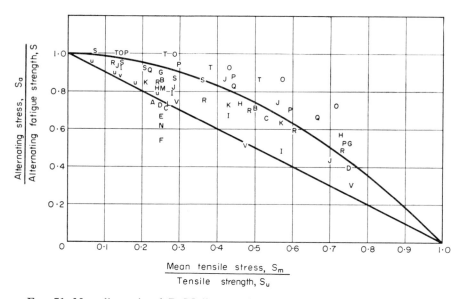

FIG. 51. Non-dimensional *R–M* diagram for aluminium alloys (see Table 15).

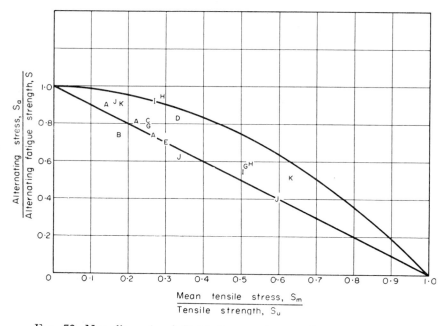

FIG. 52. Non-dimensional *R–M* diagram for non-ferrous metals (excluding aluminium alloys) (see Table 16).

are above or very close to the Goodman line except one. The exception is for a large extrusion of the aluminium–zinc–magnesium alloy, DTD 363A, and this low value may be caused by micro-constituents acting as inherent stress raisers [180] (see page 163).

Summarizing all the results for ductile metals shown in Figs. 50–52, 90% lie above the Goodman line and two-thirds between the Goodman line and the Gerber parabola. Although not 100% safe, the Goodman line can therefore be recommended as a useful working rule in design, when the fluctuating stress fatigue data are not available. All the results considered were obtained from tests on plain unnotched specimens and these conclusions do not necessarily apply to engineering parts containing stress raisers. The influence of mean stress on fatigue strength in the presence of stress concentrations is discussed in Chapter V.

The experimental results discussed so far relate to axial stress conditions, but similar results are obtained in bending. In general, the reduction in the range of stress with increasing static stress may be less in bending than in axial stress, firstly because the section is not reduced in bending if yielding occurs and secondly because the static stress in bending may be relaxed by plastic deformation. However, these effects are probably only important if the yield stress is exceeded, for experimental results in bending, as in axial stress, fall mostly between the Goodman line and the Gerber parabola. Only a limited amount of information is available on fluctuating fatigue strengths at low endurances, but both for steels [161] and for aluminium alloys [181] most of these results also lie between the Goodman line and the Gerber parabola.

The influence of mean stress is particularly important for sheet material, because sheet is normally stressed only in tension and some data are shown in Fig. 53. Details of the materials tested and the testing conditions are given in the following table:

TABLE 17. INFORMATION RELATING TO RESULTS IN FIG. 53
(Axial load tests. All results based on $10^7$ cycles.)

| Material | Specimen dimensions | | Reference |
|---|---|---|---|
| | width in. | thickness in. | |
| SAE 4130 Cr–Mo steel | 1 | 0·075 | 187 |
| 24S–T3 Al–Cu alloy | 1 | 0·09 | 187 |
| 75S–T6 Al–Zn–Mg alloy | 1 | 0·09 | 187 |
| AZ31A-H24 Mg, 3% Al, 1% Zn alloy, half hard | 1 | 0·064 | 135 |
| AZ61A-H24 Mg, 6% Al, 1% Zn alloy, half hard | 0·5 | 0·064 | 135 |
| M1A-H24 Mg, 1% Mn alloy, half hard | 0·5 | 0·064 | 135 |

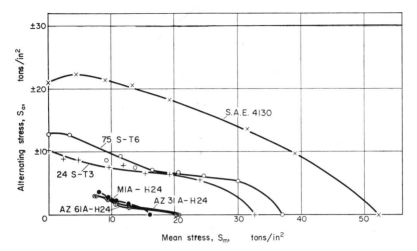

FIG. 53. $R$–$M$ diagram for sheet material.

All of the results for the steel sheet lie above the Goodman line and most of those for the aluminium alloys. For the magnesium alloys no tests were made in alternating stress, so that the Goodman line cannot be drawn. However, if it is assumed that the alternating fatigue strength is equal to one-third of the tensile strength, all the results for the magnesium–aluminium alloys lie below the Goodman line. Tests were also made on sheet specimens of the three magnesium alloys in the annealed conditions and these also gave results below the Goodman line.

### The Effect of a Mean Compressive Stress on Ductile Metals

While the addition of a static tensile stress reduces the range of stress which a material can withstand, the addition of a static compressive stress usually increases it. The experimental evidence is not always reliable, because of the difficulties of applying a true axial compressive load to fatigue specimens. A collection of data by Sines [188], however, including only those results where special precautions were taken to ensure axiality of loading, shows the effect clearly. These results, together with more recent British data, are shown in Fig. 54. The ratio of alternating stress to the alternating fatigue strength is plotted against the ratio of the mean stress to the yield stress. The behaviour is particularly significant with regard to the effect of residual stresses on fatigue strength.

### The Effect of Mean Shear Stress on Ductile Metals

In contrast with the effect of tensile and compressive mean stresses, a mean shear stress superimposed on an alternating shear stress usually has very little effect on the fatigue strength provided that the maximum stress

H

in the cycle does not exceed the yield stress. This is apparent from Fig. 55, a diagram due to Smith [189], showing a large number of experimental results for both ferrous and non-ferrous metals. More recent tests have shown a small reduction in fatigue strength with increasing mean shear stress for nickel–chrome–molybdenum steel [56, 190], and for the aluminium alloy 75S–T6 [135]. It is also found that a mean shear stress has little effect on bending fatigue strength, but a mean tensile stress reduces the alternating shear fatigue strength and a mean compressive stress increases it [56, 188].

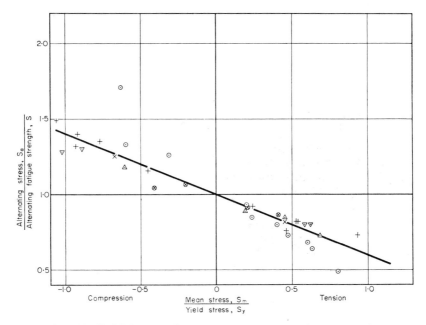

Fig. 54. *R–M* diagram for static tension and static compression.

○  Woodward, Gunn and Forrest, Aluminium Alloys to BS1476 [180].
⊗  O'Connor and Morrison Ni.Cr.Mo. Steel [176].
+  Nishihara and Sakurai, C. Steels            ⎫
△  Nishihara and Kojima, Duralumin            ⎬  From G. Sines [188]
▽  Ros and Eichinger, Mild Steel               ⎪
×  Newmark *et al.* Aluminium Alloy 24S–T     ⎭

*The Effect of Mean Stress on Cast Iron*

The data so far considered relate only to ductile metals and the behaviour of cast iron is quite different because the graphite flakes act as stress raisers. A mean tensile stress usually reduces the fatigue strength to a greater extent than predicted by the Goodman line and unlike ductile

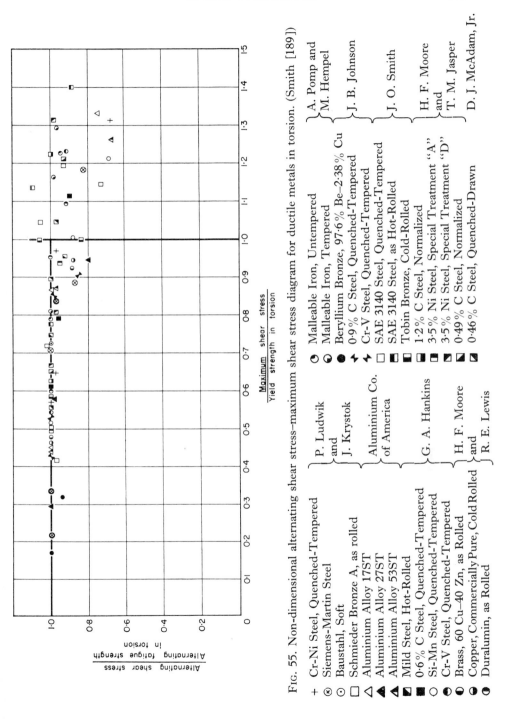

Fig. 55. Non-dimensional alternating shear stress–maximum shear stress diagram for ductile metals in torsion. (Smith [189])

+ Cr-Ni Steel, Quenched-Tempered } P. Ludwik and J. Krystok
⊗ Siemens-Martin Steel
⊙ Baustahl, Soft
□ Schmieder Bronze A, as rolled
◁ Aluminium Alloy 17ST } Aluminium Co. of America
◀ Aluminium Alloy 27ST
◀ Aluminium Alloy 53ST
■ Mild Steel, Hot-Rolled
○ 0·6% C Steel, Quenched-Tempered } G. A. Hankins
◐ Si-Mn Steel, Quenched-Tempered
◑ Cr-V Steel, Quenched-Tempered
○ Brass, 60 Cu–40 Zn, as Rolled } H. F. Moore and R. E. Lewis
● Copper, Commercially Pure, Cold Rolled
● Duralumin, as Rolled

○ Malleable Iron, Untempered } A. Pomp and M. Hempel
◐ Malleable Iron, Tempered
● Beryllium Bronze, 97·6% Be–2·38% Cu } J. B. Johnson
✦ 0·9% C Steel, Quenched-Tempered
✦ Cr-V Steel, Quenched-Tempered
□ SAE 3140 Steel, Quenched-Tempered } J. O. Smith
■ SAE 3140 Steel, as Hot-Rolled
◧ Tobin Bronze, Cold-Rolled
◨ 1·2% C Steel, Normalized
◪ 3·5% Ni Steel, Special Treatment "A" } H. F. Moore and T. M. Jasper
◪ 3·5% Ni Steel, Special Treatment "D"
◪ 0·49% C Steel, Normalized
◪ 0·46% C Steel, Quenched-Drawn } D. J. McAdam, Jr.

metals, static torsion produces a similar effect on the fatigue strength in
torsion. Some experimental results are shown in Fig. 56 where the ratio
of alternating stress to the alternating fatigue strength for both torsion
and axial stress results are plotted against the ratio of the mean tensile
stress to the tensile strength. Most of the results for grey cast iron lie
below the Goodman line, but above the following empirical relation suggested by Smith [189]:

$$S_a = S \frac{\left(1 - \dfrac{S_m}{S_u}\right)}{\left(1 + \dfrac{S_m}{S_u}\right)} \tag{16}$$

The results for malleable cast iron, however, lie above the Goodman line
and one would expect nodular cast iron to behave like malleable cast iron
in this respect.

The fatigue strength of cast iron can be greatly increased by a static
compressive stress. Morrogh [131], reviewing the comprehensive data of
Pomp and Hempel [191], points out that the ratios of fatigue strengths in
pulsating compression to pulsating tension for all types of grey iron average
3·3. The average value of this ratio for malleable cast irons is 1·5, which is
similar to that for ductile metals.

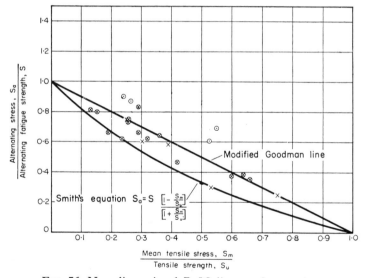

FIG. 56. Non-dimensional *R–M* diagram for cast iron.

×   Grey cast iron in axial stress (from various sources, Smith [189])
⊗   Grey cast iron in torsion (based on the maximum principal stress
which is equal to the maximum shear stress) (from various sources,
Smith [189]).
○   Malleable cast iron in axial stress (Pomp and Hempel [191])

## The resistance of materials to fatigue under complex stress

Many engineering parts are subjected to complex fluctuating stresses, for example, combined bending and torsion in crankshafts and triaxial stresses in tubes subjected to internal or external pressure. It is sometimes necessary, therefore, in design, to predict fatigue strengths under complex stress and this must often be attempted from a knowledge only of the uniaxial fatigue strength.

### Criteria Governing Failure under Complex Stress

Many attempts have been made to determine a criterion governing fatigue failure under complex stress. A similar problem arises with regard to elastic failure under complex static stress and the hypotheses put forward to determine the criteria governing static failure have been applied to fatigue. Among the more important of these are:
1. Maximum principal stress
2. Maximum shear stress
3. Maximum shear strain energy (von Mises)
4. Maximum principal strain

If $p_1$, $p_2$, $p_3$ are the amplitudes of the alternating principal stresses, where $p_1 \geqslant p_2 \geqslant p_3$ and $S$ is the alternating uniaxial fatigue strength, the above criteria can be written as follows:

1. *Maximum Principal Stress Criterion*

$$p_1 = S \tag{17}$$

2. *Maximum Shear Stress Criterion*

$$p_1 - p_3 = S \tag{18}$$

3. *Shear Strain Energy* (von Mises)

$$(p_1 - p_2)^2 + (p_2 - p_3)^2 + (p_3 - p_1)^2 = S^2 \tag{19}$$

4. *Maximum Principal Strain*

$$p_1 - \sigma(p_2 + p_3) = S \tag{20}$$

where $\sigma$ is Poisson's ratio.

As fatigue failures usually propagate from the surface, where one principal stress is zero, it is usually sufficient to consider biaxial stresses only. The relation between the two principal stresses for the first three of the above criteria under biaxial stress conditions is shown in Fig. 57. The experimental results plotted in this diagram are discussed later. When the two principal stresses are of the same sign (in phase), as they are, for example, in a tube subjected to fluctuating pressure, the criteria of maximum principal stress and maximum shear stress give the same relation (Fig. 57a); when the two principal stresses are of opposite sign (out of

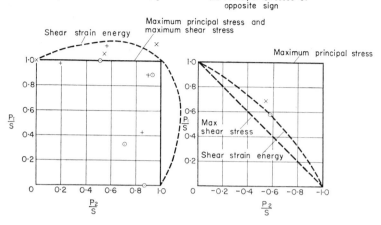

FIG. 57. Biaxial stress relations for fatigue under combined stresses.

*Experimental Results*

$\times$ $\begin{cases} \text{Majors and others [192],} \\ \text{Mild Steel SAE 1020} \end{cases}$

$+$ $\begin{cases} \text{Morikawa and Van Griffis [194],} \\ \text{Mild Steel SAE 1020 ($10^6$ cycles)} \end{cases}$

$\odot$ $\begin{cases} \text{Bundy and Marin [193],} \\ \text{Aluminium Alloy 14S–T4 ($10^6$ cycles)} \end{cases}$

phase), as they are in alternating torsion, all the criteria give different relations (Fig. 57b). To compare fatigue strengths in torsion and bending is therefore a convenient method for determining the suitability of the various criteria and this is the method which has most often been used.

*Comparison of Fatigue Strengths in Bending and Torsion*

The predicted value of the ratio of torsion fatigue strength $t$ to bending fatigue strength $b$ for each criterion is as follows:

TABLE 18

Predicted ratio of $\dfrac{\text{Fatigue strength in torsion } t}{\text{Fatigue strength in bending } b}$

| | | |
|---|---|---|
| 1. | Maximum principal stress | 1 |
| 2. | Maximum shear stress | 0·5 |
| 3. | Shear strain energy | 0·577 |
| 4. | Maximum principal strain | $\left(\dfrac{1}{1+\sigma}\right)$ |

Poisson's ratio is usually between 0·25 and 0·35 for metals, which gives a predicted value between 0·74 and 0·8 for the maximum principal strain criterion.

A number of investigators have determined fatigue strengths both in bending and in torsion and the values they obtained for each are compared in Figs. 58 and 59; lines representing the criteria are plotted for comparison with the experimental results. It is clear from these results that the ratio $t/b$ varies quite widely for different materials, so that no one criterion is adequate to describe the general behaviour.

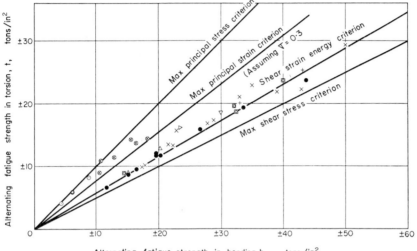

FIG. 58. Comparison of fatigue strengths in bending and torsion for cast iron and steel.

● Steels, Ludwik [195]
✕ Steels, Gough, Pollard and Clenshaw [56]
+ Steels, Frith [196]
△ Steels, Nishihara and Kawamoto [197]
▽ Steels, Findley [211]
▷ Steels, Williams [135]
⊡ Steels, Morrison, Crossland and Parry [118]
⊙ Cast Irons, Ludwik [195]
⊗ Cast Irons, Gough, Pollard and Clenshaw [56, 199]
⊛ Cast Irons, Nishihara and Kawamoto [200]

The ratio bears no relation to the tensile strength of the metal, but the results fall into two distinct groups, the value of $t/b$ being considerably higher for cast metals than for ductile metals. This, again, results from the presence of internal notches in the cast metals (see page 112). The results are summarized in the following table:

TABLE 19

| Material | Range of ratio $t/b$ | No. of results considered | Average value $t/b$ |
|---|---|---|---|
| Wrought steels | 0·52–0·69 | 31 | 0·60 |
| Wrought aluminium alloys | 0·43–0·74 | 13 | 0·55 |
| Wrought copper and copper alloys | 0·41–0·67 | 7 | 0·56 |
| Wrought magnesium alloys | 0·49–0·60 | 2 | 0·54 |
| Titanium | 0·37–0·57 | 3 | 0·48 |
| Cast iron | 0·79–1·01 | 9 | 0·90 |
| Cast aluminium and magnesium alloys | 0·71–0·91 | 5 | 0·85 |

In the absence of experimental data, the fatigue strength in torsion may be predicted approximately from the average values of $t/b$ quoted in the table. For the non-ferrous metals, the number of cycles $N$ on which the fatigue determinations were based are given in Fig. 59. For steels the ratio $t/b$ is not usually much affected by the value of $N$ chosen for the comparison, but for aluminium alloys the ratio decreases as $N$ increases. For example, the average values of $t/b$ for five aluminium alloys (quoted by Grover, Gordon and Jackson [135]) are as follows:

TABLE 20

| $N$ | $10^5$ | $10^6$ | $10^7$ | $10^8$ | $5 \times 10^8$ |
|---|---|---|---|---|---|
| $t/b$ | 0·67 | 0·66 | 0·64 | 0·58 | 0·56 |

There are not sufficient data available to show whether other non-ferrous metals behave in this way.

*Fatigue Strengths under Combined Bending and Torsion*

As the experimental values of $t/b$ vary so widely from one material to another none of the criteria can be relied upon for the prediction of fatigue strengths under other combined stress conditions. This was appreciated by Gough, who derived two empirical equations, based on the experimental value of the ratio $t/b$ for this purpose [57].

On a polar diagram of $b$ plotted against $t$, the criteria of maximum shear stress and shear strain energy are represented by quadrants of ellipses and Gough proposed the empirical ellipse quadrant given by the equation:

$$\frac{S_b^2}{b^2} + \frac{S_t^2}{t^2} = 1, \tag{21}$$

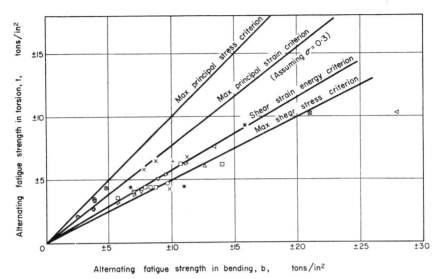

Fɪɢ. 59. Comparison of fatigue strengths in bending and torsion for
non-ferrous metals.

▢ Aluminium Alloy ⎫
⊠ Titanium ⎬ Morrison, Crossland and Parry (10⁷ cycles) [118]
× Aluminium Alloys, Matthaes (10⁷ cycles) [201]
+ Aluminium Alloy, Nishihara and Kawamoto (10⁷ cycles) [200]
△ Aluminium Alloy, Sauer and Lemmon (10⁷ cycles) [202]
▽ Aluminium Alloys, Ludwik (10⁷ cycles) [195]
○ Magnesium Alloy, Mathaes (10⁷ cycles) [201]
◪ Magnesium Alloy Ludwik (10⁷ cycles) [195]
▷ Copper Alloys, Ludwik (10⁷ cycles) [195]
□ Aluminium Alloys, Alcoa (5 × 10⁸ cycles) [135]
◁ Titanium, Williams (10⁷ cycles) [135]
✱ Copper Alloys, Moore (10⁸ cycles) [135]
⊗ Cast Aluminium Alloy, Matthaes (10⁶ cycles) [201]
⊙ Cast Magnesium Alloy, Matthaes (10⁶ cycles) [201]
⊘ Cast Aluminium Alloys, Ludwik (10⁷ cycles) [195]

where $S_b$ is the semi-range of direct stress due to bending and $S_t$ is the
semi-range of shear stress due to torsion at the fatigue strength of the
combination. This equation fitted closely experimental results in combined
bending and torsion obtained by Gough [56, 57, 203] for solid and hollow
specimens of twelve ductile steels.

It was found, however, that the experimental results for cast iron did
not fit the ellipse quadrant. The ratio $t/b$ for cast iron usually lies between
the values predicted by the criteria of maximum principal stress and maximum principal strain. These criteria are represented on the polar diagram
by arcs and not quadrants, and Gough found that experimental results in

combined bending and torsion for cast iron were in close agreement with an empirical ellipse arc given by the equation:

$$\frac{S_t^2}{t^2} + \frac{S_b^2}{b^2}\left(\frac{b}{t} - 1\right) + \frac{S_b}{b}\left(2 - \frac{b}{t}\right) = 1 \qquad (22)$$

Cox [204] has shown by mathematical analysis that a material containing randomly oriented holes should obey the ellipse arc equation and that the ratio of $t/b$ should lie between $\frac{3}{4}$ and 1 depending on the shape of the holes. The behaviour of cast iron is thus consistent with the theory that the graphite flakes behave as holes. The same result is obtained on the basis of either the maximum principal stress criterion or the maximum shear stress criterion, because the maximum stress occurs at the edges of the holes, where the other two principal stresses are zero. It is most likely, in fact, that failure of cast iron depends on the maximum principal tensile stress, because its compressive strength is about five times its tensile strength.

In further experiments on a ductile steel, Gough [56] showed that if static bending or torsional stresses were superimposed on dynamic stresses, the experimental results were still in good agreement with the ellipse quadrant. Experiments on seven ductile steels, however, using sharply notched specimens, gave results in quite close agreement with the ellipse arc and not with the ellipse quadrant. Further tests on the same seven steels using specimens with a transverse hole (hole diameter one tenth of the specimen diameter), gave results which also fitted the ellipse arc [205] and were in good agreement with Cox's analysis [206]. The average values of the fatigue strength reduction factor, $K_f$, for the seven steels were as follows:

TABLE 21. RANGE OF $K_f$ FOR SEVEN DUCTILE STEELS

|  | Alternating bending | Alternating torsion |
|---|---|---|
| V-notch [56] | 1·47–2·43   (Av. 1·92) | 1·18–1·78   (Av. 1·47) |
| Transverse hole [205] | 2·19–2·42   (Av. 2·31) | 1·62–2·24   (Av. 1·93) |

In practice, for example in crankshafts, the alternating torsion and bending stresses may be out of phase. The influence of phase difference has been investigated by Nishihara and Kawamoto [200] for two steels, a cast iron and an aluminium alloy. The combined stress fatigue strengths with the torsion and bending out of phase were never less than the in phase fatigue strengths. The maximum differences, which occurred at a phase difference of 90°, were about 10% for the steels, 30% for the cast iron, while there was no difference for the aluminium alloy.

## Fatigue Strengths under Biaxial and Triaxial Tension Stresses

A number of attempts have been made to determine the conditions governing fatigue failure in thin tubes subjected to fluctuating internal pressure and axial load and the results are compared with the fracture criteria in Fig. 57. Most of the data were obtained under conditions of pulsating internal pressure and pulsating axial tension, so that the principal stresses were both tensile (Fig. 57a). The data do not conform closely to any of the failure criteria and this can be attributed partly to the anistropy of the material tested, the fatigue strength in the circumferential direction being less than in the axial direction. The two results obtained with combined internal pressure and axial compressive stress show clearly that failure is dependent primarily on the maximum shear stress or shear strain energy and not the maximum principal stress. (Fig. 57b.) Tests on thick cylinders have also shown that the fatigue strength depends primarily on the shear stress and the triaxial stress apparently has little effect [118]. These results are summarized in Chapter IX (see page 311).

## Correlation of Failure Criteria with Fatigue Behaviour

For ductile metals the closest correlation with the experimental value of the ratio of fatigue strengths in torsion to fatigue strengths in bending $(t/b)$ is given by the shear strain energy or von Mises criterion (cf. Tables 18 and 19). This criterion is equivalent to the average shear stress on different planes and in different directions for all the crystals in the metal and also to the condition that slip shall occur in all the crystals. Peterson [207] has pointed out that since failure by fatigue is a local phenomenon, it is unlikely to depend on slip occurring throughout the metal, so that the approximate agreement between the criterion and the experimental data may be fortuitous. If slip in one grain were sufficient to propagate a fatigue crack, then dependence on the maximum shear stress criterion would be expected. It seems likely that slip may be required in more than one, though not in all grains, and this could account for values of $t/b$ greater than 0·5, but not greater than 0·577.

The ratio may also be affected by anisotropy, that is by a difference in fatigue strength in different directions in the metal, because the planes of maximum shear stress in torsion are at 45° to those in bending. This is likely to reduce the ratio $t/b$, but there is some evidence to show that the effect is generally quite small [198]. Another factor which could account for an increase in the ratio of $t/b$ is the influence of the normal stress on the plane of maximum shear stress. It has been well established that this has no effect on elastic failure under static loading conditions; however, the fact that a static tensile stress decreases fatigue strength, while a static compressive stress increases it, suggests that the normal stress on the shear plane may be important in fatigue. A criterion of fatigue failure on this basis was first put forward by Stanfield [208] in the form:

$$S_t + \mu p = S, \tag{23}$$

where $S_t$ is the alternating shear stress, $p$ is the alternating normal stress on the same plane and $\mu$ is a constant. Stanfield compared this criterion with the results of Gough and Pollard, and Stulen and Cummings [209] and Findley [210, 211] have compared it with more recent data. Unfortunately the value of $\mu$ must be determined empirically and, in fact, if $\mu$ is calculated from experimental values of the bending and torsion fatigue strengths, the criterion becomes identical with Gough's ellipse arc (Equation 22). This does not conform very closely with the result of tests in combined bending and torsion, nor with the results of pulsating internal pressure tests.

It must therefore be concluded that there is at present no criterion which can satisfactorily account for fatigue failure under complex stress conditions. In the absence of a fundamental criterion, Gough's empirical relations can be recommended for the determination of fatigue strengths under combined bending and torsion.

## The effect of fluctuations in stress amplitude and cumulative damage

Fatigue tests are normally carried out using a constant stress amplitude for each test piece, because this is easy to do experimentally and because it gives a straightforward method of presenting the data. However, this seldom represents the loading conditions to which engineering parts are subjected in service, where fluctuating loads may vary widely in amplitude often in a random manner. The problem therefore arises of predicting the fatigue life under varying stress amplitude from the results of conventional fatigue tests.

### The Linear Damage Law

The simplest basis on which to predict the fatigue life under varying stresses from an $S$–$N$ curve is by means of the linear damage law. This is a hypothesis first suggested by Palmgren [212] and restated by Miner [213] and is sometimes known as Miner's law. The assumption is made that the application of $n_1$ cycles at a stress range $S_1$ for which the average number of cycles to failure is $N_1$, causes an amount of fatigue damage $n_1/N_1$ and that failure will occur when

$$\sum \frac{n}{N} = 1 \tag{24}$$

$n/N$ is called the cycle ratio.

Many experiments have been carried out to determine the effect of fluctuations in stress amplitude on fatigue life and the results have usually been compared with the linear damage law; recent reviews of these experiments on cumulative damage have been written by Roylance [214] and by Schijve and Jacobs [215].

## Two-Step Tests

The simplest of these experiments are those which are confined to only two stress levels. These may be two-step tests in which a certain number of stress cycles are applied to the test piece at one stress range and the test continued to fracture at a second stress range. Alternatively, the stress may be changed from one stress range to the other at regular intervals and such tests are known as block, or interval, tests. These tests do not resemble service conditions, but may serve a useful purpose for assessing the linear damage law and indicating its limitations.

The results of two-step tests carried out by Kommers [216] on a mild steel are shown in Fig. 60. The right-hand curve is the original S–N curve,

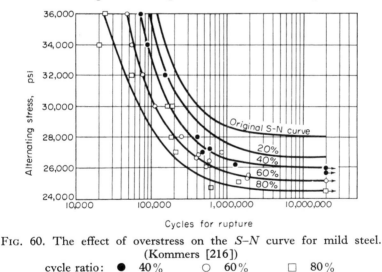

Cycles for rupture

FIG. 60. The effect of overstress on the S–N curve for mild steel.
(Kommers [216])
cycle ratio: ● 40% ○ 60% □ 80%

while those to the left were obtained after subjecting the test pieces to a given proportion of their fatigue life at a stress above the fatigue limit, a process known as overstressing. S–N curves are shown after cycle ratios of 0·2, 0·4, 0·6 and 0·8, at ±36,000 lb/in². It is clear from the results that the initial stressing has reduced both the fatigue limit and the subsequent fatigue life at stresses above the fatigue limit. Kommers carried out a great many tests of this kind on iron and steel and some of his results are summarized in Table 22. The results showed that a slight overstress does not markedly reduce the fatigue limit, even if continued for a large proportion of the normal life, but this is not true for a high overstress. A similar result was obtained by Bennett [217] for an alloy steel.

Many earlier investigators carried out tests of this type to determine how much overstress could be applied to a material without reducing its fatigue limit. From such tests they determined a "damage line", plotted on an S–N diagram, giving the number of cycles required, at a given stress range, to damage the material; the result of these experiments are summarized in the Battelle handbook [218]. For most materials damage occurs at a low cycle ratio, particularly at high stresses (cf. Table 22).

A great many experiments have been carried out more recently using two-step tests to assess the linear damage law and the results of some of these are summarized in Table 23 for steels and in Table 24 for aluminium alloys. The cumulative cycle ratio is equal to $\Sigma(n/N)$ and has a value of 1 if the linear damage law is obeyed. The values quoted in the tables are mostly an average of a number of tests; where several pre-stress cycle ratios were investigated, the range of these average values is shown. It has not been possible to include all the relevant information of the testing conditions, which may be obtained by reference to the original reports, but the data given enable some tentative conclusions to be drawn of the general behaviour.

For steels, the cumulative cycle ratio is usually greater than one when the

TABLE 22. DAMAGE DUE TO OVERSTRESS (Kommers [231])
PERCENTAGE DECREASE IN FATIGUE LIMIT

| Material | 10% Overstress* | | | 20% Overstress | | | 30% Overstress | | |
|---|---|---|---|---|---|---|---|---|---|
| | Cycle ratio: | | | Cycle ratio: | | | Cycle ratio: | | |
| | 20% | 50% | 80% | 20% | 50% | 80% | 20% | 50% | 80% |
| 0·27% C steel | 3 | 9 | 15 | 4 | 15 | 22 | 7 | 18 | 30 |
| 0·48% C steel | 10 | 20 | 26 | 13 | 20 | 28 | 20 | 24 | >45 |
| 0·62 % C steel | 5 | 10 | 13 | 11 | 18 | 25 | 13 | 20 | 27 |
| Cast iron | 1 | 2 | 3 | 8 | 8 | 9 | 11 | 14 | 18 |
| Annealed ingot iron | 1 | 3 | 5 | 2 | 7 | 12 | — | — | — |
| Cold-drawn ingot iron | 8 | 9 | 10 | 8 | 14 | 19 | 10 | 17 | — |

* % overstress is the percentage by which the pre-stress exceeds the fatigue limit.

TABLE 23. CUMULATIVE CYCLE RATIOS DETERMINED FROM TWO-STEP FATIGUE TESTS ON STEELS

| Material | Type of loading ø | Approximate endurance in constant amplitude tests millions of cycles | | Total no. of results obtained | No. of tests made for each result | Cumulative cycle ratio $\sum \frac{n}{N}$ | | | Ref. |
|---|---|---|---|---|---|---|---|---|---|
| | | High stress | Low stress | | | H–L* | L–H | Interval tests | |
| | | | | *Plain testpieces* | | | | | |
| Mild steel SAE 1020 (0.2% C) | R.B. | 0·32 | 0·50 | 4 | 1–3 | | 1·71–2·35 | | 216 |
| | | 0·22 | 0·50 | 4 | 1–3 | | 1·68–1·85 | | |
| | | 0·17 | 0·50 | 4 | 1–3 | | 1·23–1·96 | | |
| | | 0·14 | 0·50 | 4 | 1–3 | | 0·85–1·27 | | |
| | | 0·14 | 0·32 | 4 | 1–3 | | 1·28–1·69 | | |
| Mild steel | R.B. | 0·2 | 1·0 | 23 | 1 | | 0·84–1·40 | | 219 |
| Mild steel | R.B. | 0·3 | 0·9 | 12 | 6–8 | 0·75–1·1 | 1·05–1·25 | | 214 |
| A–7 structural steel (0·15–0·26% C) | R.B. | 0·12 | 1·0 | 6 | 2–4 | 0·80–0·90 | 1·3–2·0 | 0·95–1·1 | 220 |
| Ni Cr Mo steel SAE 4340 | R.B. | 0·05 | 0·45 | 2 | 5 | 0·91 | 1·24 | | 220 |
| Ni Cr Mo steel SAE 4340 | R.B. | 0·035 | 0·25 | 14 | 2–10 | 0·90–1·17 | 1·46–1·56 | 0·93–1·63 | 221 |
| | R.B. | 0·01 | 0·2 | 2 | 6–10 | 0·73 | 1·14 | | |
| Ni Cr Mo steel SAE 4340 quenched and tempered spheroidized | R.B. | 0·039 | 0·056 | 3 | 20 | 0·91–1·01 | | | 222 |
| | | 0·098 | 0·159 | 3 | 20 | 0·81–0·93 | | | |
| Cr Mo steel SAE 4130 sheet | Ax Fluct. | 0·06 | 0·5 | 6 | 3 | 0·65–0·85 | 1·1–1·25 | | 187 |
| Armco iron | R.B. | 0·2 | 1·7 | 2 | 12 | 1·0 | 0·65 | | 223 |
| | | | | *Notched testpieces* | | | | | |
| Cr Mo steel SAE X4130 | R.B. | 0·26 | 0·96 | 5 | 7–11 | 0·72–0·95 | 0·85–1·42 | | 217 |
| | | 0·093 | 0·26 | 5 | 7–11 | 0·83–1·00 | 0·93–1·13 | | |
| | | 0·044 | 0·093 | 5 | 7–11 | | | | |
| A–7 structural steel (0·15–0·26% C) | Fluct. Tension | 0·08 | 0·2 | 18 | 1–10 | 0·7–1·7 | 0·86–1·9 | 0·77–1·18 | 220 |

ø R.B. = Rotating bending and Ax = Axial stress.
* High stress, followed by low stress.

TABLE 24. CUMULATIVE CYCLE RATIOS DETERMINED FROM TWO-STEP FATIGUE TESTS ON ALUMINIUM ALLOYS

| Material | Type of loading | Approximate endurance in constant amplitude tests in millions of cycles | | Total no. of results obtained | No. of tests made for each result | Cumulative cycle ratio $\sum \dfrac{n}{N}$ | | Interval tests | Ref. |
|---|---|---|---|---|---|---|---|---|---|
| | | High stress | Low stress | | | H–L | L–H | | |
| *Plain testpieces* | | | | | | | | | |
| L 65 (Al Cu) | R.B. | 0·105 | 0·95 | 4 | 5 | 0·5–0·9 | 1·11–1·29 | 0·8–1·1 | 224 |
| DTD 683 (Al–Zn) | R.B. | 0·05 | 0·5 | 13 | 15–39 | 0·14–0·77 | 1·25–1·35 | 0·3–1·1 | 225 |
| | | 0·05 | 10 | 15 | 9–20 | | 1·25–1·63 | 0·5–1·8 | |
| | | 0·5 | 10 | 12 | 15–23 | | 1·15–1·55 | | |
| 75S–T (Al–Zn) | R.B. | | | 13 | 2–7 | 0·43–0·78 | | 0·67–2·73 | 215 and 226 |
| | | | | 21 | 1–4 | | | 0·63–8·33 | |
| 75S–T6 | R.B. | From 0·05 up to 16 | | 9 | 20 | 0·56–1·0 | 1·0–2·27 | 0·47–3·44 | 227 |
| 75S–T | R.B. | From 0·2 up to 26 | | 30 | 1 | | | | 219 and 228 |
| 76S–T61 (Al–Zn) | R.B. | 0·01 | 5 | 2 | 6 and 10 | 0·63 | 1·45 | 0·72 | 229 |
| 24S–T3 sheet | Ax. Alt. | 0·05 | 1·95 | 2 | 4 and 18 | 1·10 | | 0·87–0·94 | 229 |
| 75S–T6 sheet | Ax. Alt. | From 0·015 up to 1·65 | | 15 | 4–94 | 1·01–1·44 | 0·71–1·04 | 1·02 | 229 |
| 24S–T3 sheet | Ax. | 0·030 | 0·46 | 2 | 4 and 24 | 1·04 | 0·74 | 1·03 | 229 |
| 75S–T6 sheet | Fluct. | 0·033 | 0·34 | 3 | 4–16 | 1·05 | | | 229 |
| 24S–T sheet | Ax. | 0·036 | 0·16 | 10 | 1–7 | 0·97–>22·8 | 1·01–2·04 | | 187 |
| 75S–T sheet | Fluct. | 0·018 | 0·066 | 10 | 2–4 | 1·09–>14·8 | 1·14–1·44 | | 187 |
| 24S–T Alclad sheet | Fluct. tension | 0·10 | 1·0 | 10 | 10 | 1·37–2·36 | 0·75–0·85 | 1·01–1·05 | 230 |
| | | From 0·048 up to 3·0 | | 14 | 1 | 0·80–1·30 | 0·75–1·49 | | 213 |
| *Notched testpieces* | | | | | | | | | |
| 24S–T Alclad sheet | Fluct. tension | 0·10 | 1·0 | 11 | 10 | 1·67–>6·5 | 1·10–1·27 | 1·77–1·81 | 230 |
| *Components* | | | | | | | | | |
| Riveted joint 24S–T Alclad | Fluct. tension | 0·10 | 1·0 | 27 | 5–10 | 0·81–1·34 | 0·84–1·24 | 1·08–1·96 | 215 |
| | | 0·19 | 2·1 | 2 | 9 | 5·87 | 0·86 | | 215 |

low stress is applied first, while it is usually less than one when the high stress is applied first. For aluminium alloys the behaviour is much less consistent; the results available in rotating bending on plain specimens show the same trend as steel, but the results in fluctuating tension do not, nor do the results for notched specimens. In general, the results of the interval tests are closer to a cumulative cycle ratio of one.

### The Effect of Understressing, Coaxing and Rest Periods

The effect of the load sequence on the fatigue life of steel is much more marked if alternating stresses, both above and below the fatigue limit, are applied. It has already been mentioned that overstressing may cause a reduction in the fatigue limit. Conversely, understressing, that is the application of stress cycles below the fatigue limit, may increase it.

It has always been a common practice in fatigue testing to retest the unbroken specimens which have been originally tested below the fatigue limit. It was soon found that if these specimens were retested at a stress range above the fatigue limit, they usually gave longer endurances and a higher fatigue limit than those not previously tested. For example, Kommers [231] showed that 20 million cycles at a stress range just below the fatigue limit increased the fatigue limit of Armco iron by 23%. It was discovered later that even greater increases in fatigue strength could be achieved if the stress range was increased in small increments at intervals of several million cycles, a process now known as coaxing. For example, Gough [24], quotes an increase in fatigue strength for mild steel of nearly 30%, achieved by stressing below the fatigue limit for 250 million cycles and then increasing the stress range by $\pm 0.2$ tons per $in^2$ at intervals of 10 to 18 million cycles. (From the results of early investigations, cast iron appeared to be the most susceptible material to understressing and coaxing, for Kommers [231] obtained an increase in fatigue strength of over 30% by understressing and Moore, Lyon and Inglis [232], an increase of over 40% by coaxing. Recent results, however, have shown little or no increase in fatigue strength by understressing for various types of cast iron [233, 234]; the reason for this discrepancy is not known.)

It is also found that the fatigue strength of iron and carbon steels can be increased if rest periods are introduced at intervals during a fatigue test. For example, Bollenrath and Cornelius [235] showed that the endurance of a soft iron was increased more than 100 times by rest periods of 23 hours at intervals of one seventh of the original endurance. The increase in fatigue strength increases with the rest time and the effect can be considerably accelerated by increase in temperature during the rest periods. Rest periods, on the other hand, have no significant effect on the fatigue endurance of alloy steels and non-ferrous metals.

It was thought originally that the effects of understressing and coaxing

I

resulted from work-hardening, but it has since been shown by Sinclair [236] that a significant increase in fatigue strength occurs only in those metals whose strength can be increased by strain ageing. It therefore seems probable that these effects and the beneficial effects of rest periods can be attributed to strain ageing [237] (see page 344).

### The Effect of Residual Stress on Cumulative Damage

If the results for plain specimens are compared with those for notched specimens in Tables 23 and 24 it will be seen that in general, the results for notched specimens vary more widely from the linear damage law. Values of the cumulative cycle ratio considerably greater than one have been obtained for notched specimens, particularly in fluctuating tension tests. The reason for this behaviour is that the application of a high stress may cause yielding at the root of the notch, with the result that a residual stress is set up. If tensile yielding occurs, the resultant residual stress is compressive and this increases the resistance of the material to further application of tensile stress.

Under these circumstances the static application of a high load only once can appreciably influence the fatigue strength, and this is discussed further on page 191. It is found, however, that a greater increase is obtained if the high load is repeated periodically. Figure 61 summarizes the results of tests made by Heywood [238] illustrating this behaviour. Tests were made in fluctuating tension on simple lugs, channel specimens and transverse hole specimens and in reversed bending on Meteor tailplanes. The periodic high loads were applied after every 20,000 cycles up to 500,000 cycles and then at less frequent intervals until failure occurred. The figure shows how the increase in fatigue life obtained depends on the magnitude of the high load, both for a single application at the beginning of a test and when applied periodically. The scatter bands shown contain most of the experimental results; the decrease in fatigue life resulting from a high static compressive load was determined only with transverse hole specimens. Heywood suggests two reasons why periodic application of a high load is more effective than a single application; firstly, the residual stresses may decrease during the fatigue test and secondly, fatigue cracks may form during the early stages of a fatigue test and the subsequent application of a high load may produce compressive residual stresses at the ends of the cracks, so preventing or retarding further progression.

### Programme Testing

The results of two-step tests show that despite the effect of such factors as residual stress and strain ageing, the linear damage law usually gives a reasonable approximation of the fatigue life. Such tests bear little resemblance to stressing conditions in practice, however, and to approach these more closely some investigators have adopted a method known as programme testing. The procedure is to subject a specimen, component or structure to interval or block tests incorporating a number of stress amplitudes, applying a number of cycles at each, in proportion to the distribution occurring in service [657].

The first step is to determine the load spectrum for service conditions, that is the distribution, magnitude and frequency of the loads which occur during the normal use of the part in service. Many load measurements during service have been made of aircraft and automobile parts and it is usually found that the frequency with which loads of different magnitude occur can be expressed approximately by a particular distribution law.

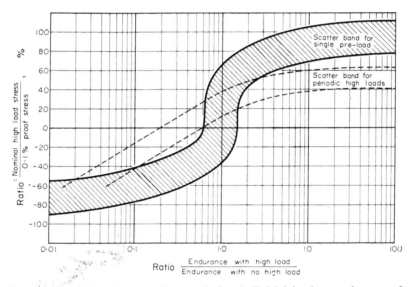

FIG. 61. The effect of one pre-load and of periodic high loads on endurance of aluminium alloy parts subjected to fluctuating tension. (Heywood [238])

Gassner [239, 240], for example, states that for vehicle components such as steering arms, steering pivots and springs and also for military aircraft wings and undercarriages, there is a binomial distribution function, while for the wings of passenger and transport aircraft there is a logarithmic binomial distribution function. A programme cycle pattern, used by Gassner is shown in Fig. 62. He has shown that the fatigue life is not much affected by the size of the programme cycle nor by increasing the number of stress levels above eight. The result may be considerably affected, however, if the lowest level of stress is omitted, even if it is below the fatigue limit. In tests on aluminium alloy specimens, each with a hole, elimination of the lowest level of stress (making up roughly 80% of the

total number of cycles) resulted in an increase of 2 to 3 times in the number
of programme cycles to fracture, even though the stress at this level was
only 5–6% of the maximum stress applied.

Even programme testing involves several simplifying assumptions, for
example, rest periods are omitted, positive and negative load cycles are
added to form complete load cycles and the complete load cycles are
arranged in some regular order of succession. Freudenthal [241], who has
designed a fatigue machine that applies a number of different stress
amplitudes in a random manner, has shown that the effect of the load
sequence can be quite pronounced. Nevertheless, Gassner, who has carried
out many programme tests on aircraft and road vehicle components, claims
that the results agree well with life in service.

As programme or spectrum tests are the closest approach in fatigue
testing to service conditions, it is interesting to compare the results of
such tests with the linear damage law; values of the cumulative cycle ratio
obtained from programme tests have therefore been listed in Table 25.
The results obtained in rotating bending mostly give a cumulative cycle
ratio of less than 1 and some of the values are very low indeed, so that the
linear damage law over-estimates the life, often by a very wide margin.
The greatest divergence occurs in the results quoted by Gassner [239],
probably because the stress range was varied between wide limits (see Fig.
62). The application of occasional high loads may have been sufficient to
start fatigue cracks which could then propagate at loads below the original
fatigue limit. The results of the programme tests in fluctuating tension, on
the other hand, are quite different from those in rotating bending. For
plain specimens, the results on aluminium alloys are in quite good agreement with the linear damage law, while for notched specimens and components the cumulative cycle ratio is, on average, significantly above one.

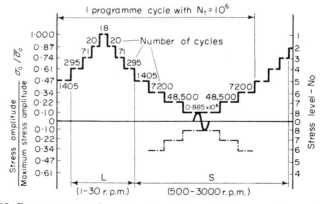

Fig. 62. Programme cycle pattern (log binomial) for a service endurance
test. (Gassner [239])

L, Low-speed drive of the fatigue testing machine; S, High-speed drive.

TABLE 25. CUMULATIVE CYCLE RATIOS DETERMINED FROM PROGRAMME OR SPECTRUM TESTS

| Material | Type of loading | No. of results obtained | No. of tests made for each result | Type of spectrum | Cumulative cycle ratio $\sum \frac{n}{N}$ | Ref. |
|---|---|---|---|---|---|---|
| | | | | *Plain testpieces* | | |
| 24S–T4 (Al–Cu) | R.B. | 14 | 10 | Sinusoidal | 0·43–1·41 | 242 |
| | | 13 | 10 | Exponential | 0·33–1·00 | |
| 75S–T (Al–Zn) | R.B. | 4 | 12 | Various, in random sequence | 0·37–1·25 | 243 |
| 24S–T Alclad sheet | Fluct. tension | 8 | 2–5 | Aircraft gust load | 0·69–1·35 | 244 |
| 75S–T Alclad sheet | Fluct. tension | 4 | 2 | Aircraft gust load | 0·79–0·98 | |
| 75S–T Alclad sheet | Fluct. tension | 4 | 2–3 | Aircraft manoeuvre load | 0·82–1·64 | |
| | | | | *Notched testpieces* | | |
| 24S–T | R.B. | 2 | 7–8 | Random* | 0·29–0·34 | 245 |
| 24S–T Alclad sheet | Fluct. tension | 4 | 3 | Aircraft gust load | 0·9–3·0 | 244 |
| DTD 363A (Al–Zn) | Fluct. tension | 3 | 6 | Aircraft gust load | 1·06–2·04 | 246 |
| | | | | *Components and structures* | | |
| Riveted joint 24S–T Alclad | Fluct. tension | 5 | 2–4 | Gust load | 0·64–2·3 | 244 |
| Riveted joint 24S–T Alclad | Fluct. tension | 3 | 2 | Manoeuvre load | 1·2–2·3 | |
| Riveted joint 75S–T Alclad | Fluct. tension | 5 | 2–4 | Gust load | 1·3–4·7 | |
| Riveted joint 75S–T Alclad | Fluct. tension | 3 | 2 | Manoeuvre load | 1·4–2·6 | 247 |
| Aircraft wing panel | Fluct. tension | 4 | 1 | 3 stress levels | 1·28–1·61 | |
| Automobile components— steel | R.B. | 3 | | Log. binomial | 0·3–0·6 | 239 |
| | R.B. | 3 | | Log. binomial | 0·1–0·12 | |
| | R.B. | 2 | | Log. binomial | 0·003–0·018 | |

* It was assumed that each stress peak was equivalent to a half cycle of a sine wave of the same peak amplitude about zero mean load.

This behaviour can be attributed to the beneficial residual stresses set up by the high loads.

It may be concluded that the linear damage law is, in general, a useful relation for making an approximate estimate of the fatigue life, but it clearly does not provide a reliable means of determining the life under all varying stress conditions. Several attempts have been made to derive non-linear laws [221, 248, 249], but none of these has been shown to be generally applicable and in view of the complex nature of the fatigue process and the effects of such factors as residual stress and strain ageing, no law of general application can be expected. For applications where a reliable estimate of the fatigue life is essential, programme testing of the actual components or structures must be undertaken.

## The effect of the frequency of the stress cycle

Most fatigue machines operate at a frequency between 500 and 10,000 cycles/min and in this range the fatigue strength of most materials, based on a given number of cycles to failure, is little affected by the frequency. In general, there is a slight decrease in the fatigue strength with decrease in the frequency. There are two factors which may contribute to this behaviour. Firstly, the endurance may be related to the amount of plastic deformation which occurs during a cycle of stress; at high frequencies there is less time during each stress cycle for deformation to occur, so that the resultant damage may be less. This effect is more important at high temperature (see page 251). Secondly, the corrosive effect of the atmosphere is known to reduce the fatigue strength of some materials and a bigger reduction would be expected at low frequencies. Another factor, which may influence the frequency effect is the rise in temperature of the material from hysteresis or internal damping; this will increase with increase of the frequency.

For steel, the fatigue limit is not affected by frequency between 200 and 5000 cycles/min, but there is a small effect at higher stresses. This is illustrated by some results, due to Wyss [250], shown in Table 26. The low speed tests were carried out in an Amsler 10-ton hydraulic universal testing machine and the high speed tests in an Amsler Vibrophore. The tests were made in pulsating tension on plain specimens and the results are based on failure in a million cycles.

The results at the bottom of the table show that the frequency effect is even smaller for aluminium alloys than for steel. A similar result has been obtained by Oberg and Trapp [166] from rotating bending tests at 90 and at 10,000 cycles/min on aluminium and magnesium alloys and by Smith and others [163] from axial stress tests on aluminium alloy sheet at 12 and 1000 cycles/min.

At frequencies above 10,000 cycles/min there is evidence that fatigue

TABLE 26. THE INFLUENCE OF TESTING FREQUENCY ON THE FATIGUE STRENGTH OF STEELS AND LIGHT ALLOYS (Wyss [250])

| Material | Fatigue strength at 10,000 c/min / Fatigue strength at 350 c/min |
|---|---|
| 0·12% C steel | 1·07 |
| 0·25% C steel | 1·05 |
| 0·35% C steel | 1·05 |
| 0·60% C steel | 1·00 |
| 3% Ni steel | 1·02 |
| 3% Ni 0·8% Cr steel | 1·03 |
| 3% Ni 0·8% Cr 0·3% Mo steel | 1·02 |
| 4% Ni 1% Cr steel | 1·01 |
|  | Fatigue strength at 8000 c/min / Fatigue strength at 350 c/min |
| Al–Cu alloy (17S–T) | 1·01 |
| Al–Cu alloy (24S–T) | 1·00 |
| Al–Zn alloy (75S–T) | 1·03 |
| Al–Mn alloy (A51S–T) | 1·00 |

strengths generally increase with increase in frequency. Testing at very high frequencies involves many experimental difficulties and there have been few investigations. The problem was first tackled by Jenkin, who achieved frequencies up to 1,000,000 cycles/min, as early as 1929, by means of a pneumatic resonant system [61], but no further attempts appear to have been made to achieve very high frequencies until the last few years [45, 60, 63]. There has been a renewed interest in the subject, both because high frequencies offer a means of reducing the time involved in fatigue testing and because of the direct practical application to components, such as turbine blades, which are subjected in service to vibrations of very high frequencies.

Lomas and others [63] have carried out fatigue tests on a number of steels at frequencies up to 150,000 cycles/min, using a resonant pneumatic system and their results are shown in Fig. 63. All the ferritic steels show a marked increase in fatigue strength up to about 100,000 cycles/min, but there is a sharp decline for frequencies above this. The authors argued that this behaviour did not arise from experimental error because the austenitic steels, tested in the same way, behaved in a different manner (see Fig. 63). Similar results were obtained by Jenkin [61]; for copper and

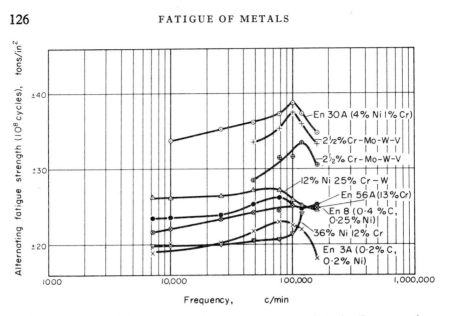

FIG. 63. Effect of frequency on the fatigue strength of steels. (Lomas and others [63])

aluminium the fatigue strength increased continuously with increase in frequency (see Fig. 64), but for a carbon steel and Armco iron the fatigue strength reached a maximum value and then decreased; the maximum value, however, occurred at about 600,000 cycles/min. It is possible that

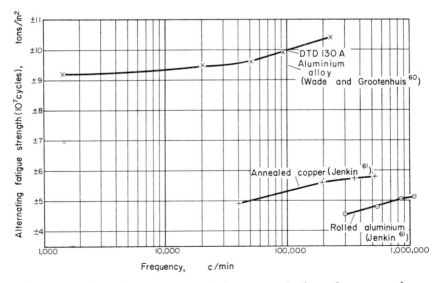

FIG. 64. Effect of frequency on the fatigue strength of non-ferrous metals.

this behaviour could result from some physical process occurring in the metal. (A similar result, arising from strain ageing, has been observed in a mild steel at lower frequencies between 200 and 300°C (see page 255).) However, if this were so, one would expect similar behaviour in static tensile properties, and this has not been observed. Further investigation on steels is clearly required and, if the present results are confirmed, it will be necessary to determine to what extent the fatigue strength decreases with still further increase in frequency.

In nearly all fatigue experiments the wave-form of the stress cycle is approximately simple harmonic. In some operating conditions the wave-form may be far from simple harmonic and the question of the effect of wave-form on fatigue strength may then arise. There is no direct experimental evidence to provide an answer to this question, but in view of the small effect of frequency on fatigue strength, it seems unlikely that the fatigue strength would be significantly influenced by the wave-form. The effect of frequency on fatigue strength has been reviewed recently by Stephenson [251].

## CHAPTER V

# STRESS CONCENTRATIONS

The detrimental effect of stress raisers on fatigue strength has already been mentioned in Chapter I and the importance of avoiding or reducing stress concentration in parts subjected to fluctuating stress was emphasized. In this chapter the magnitude of stress concentration arising from geometrical discontinuities is discussed briefly and the effect on fatigue behaviour is considered in some detail.

In a member under axial loading the stress may only be assumed uniform over the cross section when the member is long and of constant or gradually changing cross section. Any abrupt change, such as a notch, groove or hole, causes local variation in the elastic stress distribution which is dependent both on the reduction in cross-sectional area at the discontinuity and on the shape of the discontinuity. Similarly, for other loading conditions, stresses may only be assumed to be distributed in accordance with simple theory away from the point of application of load and where the members are of constant or gradually changing section.

A measure of the severity of a stress concentration is given by the stress concentration factor $K_t$, which is defined as the ratio of the maximum local stress in the region of the discontinuity to the nominal local stress, evaluated by simple theory. The nominal stress may be based either on the net cross section through the discontinuity or on the gross cross section of the member ignoring the discontinuity. In representing the effects of stress concentration, the nominal stress is usually based on the net section and this procedure is adopted unless otherwise stated. It is not always possible to express this simply, however, so that it is sometimes more convenient to use the nominal stress on the gross section. The maximum local stress at the discontinuity may be determined mathematically, by photo-elasticity or by direct measurement of deformation; it is assumed that the material involved is isotropic and obeys Hooke's law.

Although fatigue strengths are considerably reduced by geometrical stress concentrations, the reduction is often less than the stress concentration factor and a fatigue strength reduction factor, $K_f$, has therefore been introduced, which is defined as the ratio of the fatigue strength of a specimen with no stress concentration, to the fatigue strength with stress concentration.

128

A measure of the degree of agreement between $K_f$ and $K_t$ is given by the notch sensitivity factor $q$, which is defined as:

$$q = \frac{K_f - 1}{K_t - 1} \qquad (25)$$

The value of $q$ is usually between 0 and 1. When $K_f = K_t$, $q = 1$ and the material is said to be fully notch sensitive. If the presence of a notch does not affect the fatigue strength, $K_f = 1$ and $q = 0$ and the material is notch insensitive. It is found, however, that the value of $q$ depends not only on the material, but also on the stress conditions, the size of the specimen or part and the endurance, so that $q$ cannot be regarded as a material constant.

The effect of a notch on the fatigue strength of a mild steel and an aluminium alloy is illustrated in Fig. 65. The details of the notch and the

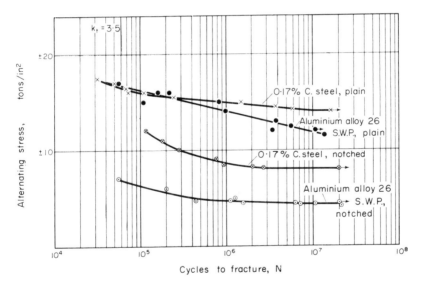

FIG. 65. *S–N* curves for plain and notched specimens of a mild steel and an aluminium alloy tested in direct stress. (Forrest [14])

stress distribution across the minimum section, determined from photo-elastic tests, are shown in Fig. 66. The maximum stress occurs at the root of the notch and $K_t = 3 \cdot 5$. It may be seen from Fig. 65 that for the mild steel

$$K_f = \frac{\text{plain fatigue strength}}{\text{notched fatigue strength}} = \frac{14 \cdot 0}{8 \cdot 0} \,(10^7 \text{ cycles}) = 1 \cdot 75$$

while for the aluminium alloy,

$$K_f = \frac{11 \cdot 9}{4 \cdot 3} \ (10^7 \text{ cycles}) = 2 \cdot 8.$$

For this particular notch and size of specimen, therefore, the notch sensitivity factors are:

for mild steel,
$$q = \frac{1 \cdot 75 - 1}{3 \cdot 5 - 1} = 0 \cdot 3,$$

and for the aluminium alloy, $q = \dfrac{2 \cdot 8 - 1}{3 \cdot 5 - 1} = 0 \cdot 72$

FIG. 66. Stress distribution at minimum section of circumferentially notched testpiece. (Forrest [14])

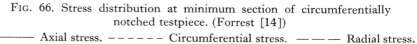
——————— Axial stress. –––––– Circumferential stress. ——— Radial stress.

There are two design problems to be solved in connection with stress concentrations. The first is to produce a design in which the values of the stress concentration factors are as low as possible and the second is to estimate the fatigue strength of the part. For the first, one must be able to determine $K_t$ and for the second to determine $K_f$.

## Determination of stress concentration factors

The determination of stress concentration factors mathematically is a difficult problem and solutions have been obtained only for a few simple geometrical shapes. These include solutions of two-dimensional problems such as an infinite sheet containing a circular or elliptical hole or groove, and axially symmetrical three-dimensional problems such as a deep hyperbolic groove in a solid shaft.

A solution for the stress distribution around a small elliptical hole in a large plate subjected to tension was determined mathematically by Inglis [252]. If the tension is applied in the plane of the plate at right angles to the major axis of the ellipse, then the maximum stress occurs at the edges of the hole on the major axis and the stress concentration factor is given by:

$$K_t = 1 + \frac{2a}{b}, \tag{26}$$

where $2a$ and $2b$ are the lengths of the major and minor axes respectively. This can be written alternatively as:

$$K_t = 1 + 2\sqrt{\frac{a}{R}} \tag{27}$$

where $R$ is the minimum radius of curvature of the ellipse. This equation is also approximately true for a shallow circumferential groove in a plate or in a shaft subjected to tension or bending; $a$ is then the depth of the groove and $R$ the radius of curvature at the bottom of the groove. For a shaft with a shallow circumferential groove subjected to torsion, the stress concentration factor is given by:

$$K_{t(\text{torsion})} = 1 + \sqrt{\frac{a}{R}} \tag{28}$$

Cox [204] has shown mathematically that the direct stress equation gives a good approximation to the stress concentration factor for grooves of various shapes, provided that the depth of the groove is small compared with the width of the plate. He found that the torsion equation was less reliable and suggested the alternative equation:

$$K_{t(\text{torsion})} = 1 + K\sqrt{\frac{a}{R}} \tag{29}$$

where the factor $K$ decreases from unity towards about $\frac{1}{2}$ as the groove is widened. For a "half-groove", represented for instance by the fillet at the root of a spline in a shaft under torsion, the stress concentration factor is given approximately by the equation:

$$K_{t(\text{torsion})} = 1 + \frac{1}{2}\sqrt{\frac{a}{R}} \tag{30}$$

It may be noted that the values of $K_t$ obtained from all the above equations, increase as the radius of the groove decreases. This behaviour is typical for all geometrical shapes, so that $K_t$ may always be reduced by increasing the radius of curvature.

Values of the stress concentration factors for a wide range of notches were obtained mathematically by Neuber [72]. He made use of the solutions for a shallow elliptical notch and for a deep hyperbolic notch in an infinite plate. For the intermediate region between shallow and deep notches, he used a quadratic relation, satisfying the end conditions, to give an approximate value of $K_t$. From his results it is possible to estimate $K_t$ for most grooves and notches with sufficient accuracy for most practical purposes [253].

There are many shapes, however, which are not amenable to mathematical analysis, so that other methods of stress analysis are required. Direct measurements of deformation may be made, using either short gauge-length mechanical–optical extensometers, or electrical resistance strain gauges. The difficulty with these methods is to make the gauge length sufficiently short to permit an accurate determination of the stress concentration factor, while retaining sufficient sensitivity. They are therefore most suitable for use with large pieces. A simple direct measure of stress concentration factor can be made by the application of a brittle laquer to the surface of a specimen or part [254]. On loading, the lacquer cracks when a certain strain is exceeded, thus indicating the position and magnitude of the stress concentration. Local strains can also be measured by X-ray diffraction, but the method is relatively insensitive and misleading results may be obtained from the presence of residual stresses in the surface layers of the specimen.

The most useful of the experimental methods is photo-elasticity. The technique depends on the principle that when a beam of plane polarized light enters a transparent model, its displacement vector is resolved into two components at right angles, which travel along the planes of principal stress. The speed of propagation of the light depends on the strain, so that the two rays emerge from the model out of phase by an amount depending on the difference between the principal stresses, the wavelength of the light and the thickness of the model. If, on emerging from the model, the rays are passed through another polarizer the resultant rays form interference fringes. The fringes represent contours of the differences of the principal stresses, that is of the shear stress. Photo-elastic models are usually two-dimensional, but it is possible, by a special technique, to obtain stress distributions from three-dimensional models. The method is to "freeze" the stresses in the model while it is loaded, by means of a heat treatment. The model is then cut into thin slices and each slice examined as a two-dimensional model. Great care is required to avoid distorting the fringes at the boundaries of models during machining, but it is possible, with care, to obtain accurate results for complex shapes.

The subject of stress analysis is dealt with comprehensively in the *Handbook of Experimental Stress Analysis* [2] and there are a number of books dealing with photo-elasticity [255–257]. Peterson [253] has correlated the results of mathematical analysis and experimental stress analysis in his compilation of stress concentration design factors. He deals fully with grooves, fillets and holes and gives additional information on engineering components, such as gear teeth and helical springs. Stress concentration factors are also given by Heywood [256] and in the Royal Aeronautical Society Data Sheets on Fatigue [81]. Some data for lugs, fillets and holes are also included in Chapter IX (see Figs. 127, 138 and 141).

## Factors influencing fatigue notch sensitivity

A great many experiments have been carried out to determine the reduction in fatigue strength caused by the introduction of a notch, so that there is considerable information available of the relation between the stress concentration factor $K_t$ and the fatigue strength reduction factor $K_f$ [258, 259]. This information is difficult to correlate because of the different testing conditions, such as size of specimen and shape of notch, used by different investigators. Some of the factors influencing notch sensitivity will therefore be discussed before the empirical relations available for estimating $K_f$ are considered.

If materials conformed to elastic theory and fatigue strength depended on the value of the maximum principal stress, then $K_f$ would be equal to $K_t$. In fact, $K_f$ is often less than $K_t$ and there are a number of factors which contribute to the discrepancy. Firstly, plastic deformation sometimes occurs during cyclic stressing, resulting in a lower maximum stress range than predicted by stress analysis. A more important factor is the size or stress gradient effect; it is found that the fatigue strength of a metal increases as the volume of material subjected to the maximum stress range is reduced, and since the region of high stress at a stress concentration is highly localized, this may result in a higher notched fatigue strength than predicted. In addition, the presence of biaxial or triaxial stresses at a notch and also residual stresses set up during production may influence the notched fatigue strength.

*The Influence of the Criterion of Failure on $K_t$*

$K_t$ is defined as the ratio of the maximum stress at the notch to the nominal stress, so that a discrepancy between $K_f$ and $K_t$ may arise if failure does not depend on the criterion of maximum principal stress. For most notches, however, the maximum stress occurs at the surface, where one of the principal stresses is zero, so that provided the other two principal stresses have the same sign, the criterion of maximum shear stress gives the same result as the maximum principal stress. A slightly different result is obtained if fatigue failure depends on the maximum shear strain energy. If $K_t'$ is the stress concentration factor, based on this criterion, then for the condition that one principal stress is zero:

$$K_t' = K_t \sqrt{(1 - c + c^2)}, \tag{31}$$

where $c = \dfrac{\text{second principal stress}}{\text{maximum principal stress}}$.

Values of $K_t'$ are quoted by Peterson [253]. The appropriate criterion for fatigue conditions is uncertain (see page 107), but the difference between $K_t$ and $K_t'$, given by the above equation, is always less than 15%.

*Plastic Deformation*

Under static loading, notches do not appreciably reduce the strength of a component unless the material is brittle. A small amount of yielding at the high stress regions will cause a redistribution of stress and a considerable reduction in the magnitude of the stress concentration. Under reversed stresses, on the other hand, the material must continue to deform plastically in every cycle if the range of stress at a notch is to remain reduced and the ability of materials to behave in this way is quite limited; this is, of course, why notches exert such a big influence on fatigue behaviour. Some materials do have the ability to deform plastically in every cycle to some extent, however, even at stress ranges below their fatigue limits and this may render them less notch sensitive than other materials.

An attempt has been made to predict the effect quantitatively by measuring the alternating strain during fatigue tests [14] (see page 17). Table 27 shows the values of $K_f$ predicted on this basis, for a range of materials, for a bar with a transverse hole, for which $K_t = 2.3$.

The values in the table show that, for an endurance of $10^7$ cycles, a significant benefit from plastic deformation is expected only for the 0·17% C steel and the austenitic steel. Moreover, it should be noted that the values quoted are applicable to direct stress conditions; in bending, plastic deformation influences both the plain and notched fatigue strengths and will therefore have less influence on $K_f$. A greater benefit from plastic deformation is expected for short endurances and also when a mean stress is applied; both of these factors are discussed later.

The values of $K_f$ observed experimentally from a comparison of the direct stress fatigue strengths on plain and notched specimens for the materials listed in Table 27 were mostly lower than the predicted values, which may be attributed to the small size of the specimens tested, but the correlation was sufficiently close to show that the ability of a material to

TABLE 27. ESTIMATED EFFECT OF PLASTIC DEFORMATION ON $K_f$ FOR SPECIMENS WITH A TRANSVERSE HOLE TESTED IN DIRECT STRESS

$$K_t = 2\cdot3$$

| Material | Heat treatment | Tensile strength tons/in² | Predicted value of $K_f$ for $N=$ | | |
|---|---|---|---|---|---|
| | | | $10^5$ | $10^6$ | $10^7$ |
| Austenitic steel, 18% Cr, 12% Ni, 1% Nb | Normalized | 39·6 | 1·3 | 1·7 | 1·7 |
| 0·17% C steel | Normalized | 29·9 | 1·5 | 1·7 | 1·9 |
| 0·5% C steel | Quenched and tempered | 90·0 | 2·1 | 2·3 | 2·3 |
| Ni, Cr, Mo steel | Hardened and tempered | 80·5 | 2·3 | 2·3 | 2·3 |
| Pure copper | Annealed | 16·2 | 1·5 | 1·9 | 2·2 |
| Aluminium–5% Mg alloy A 56 S | As rolled | 18·0 | 2·3 | 2·3 | 2·2 |
| Aluminium–copper alloy 26S | Fully heat-treated | 34·6 | 2·2 | 2·3 | 2·3 |

deform plastically under cyclic stressing results in reduced notch sensitivity. This was demonstrated by introducing a plastic stress concentration factor $K_{tpl}$, defined as the ratio of the greatest stress in the region of a notch, computed on the basis of the dynamic stress–strain curve (see page 18), to the corresponding nominal stress. Fig. 67 shows that there is a reasonably close correlation between $K_{tpl}$ and $K_f$.

The amount of plastic deformation which occurs during a cycle of stress is directly related to the damping capacity, but since the damping is markedly dependent on the stress range, correlation between damping and notch sensitivity can only be expected if the damping is measured at the same range of stress as that applied in the fatigue tests. Numerous attempts have been made to relate fatigue notch sensitivity to other mechanical properties, but without success.

### Size Effect

Probably the most important factor affecting $K_f$ and hence the notch sensitivity, is the size of the notched part, and this has been widely investigated [260]. Size effect in fatigue is a serious factor because tests on small laboratory test pieces may indicate values of fatigue strength which are higher than large components in service can withstand.

The influence of size can be illustrated by the results of some fatigue tests carried out by Phillips and Heywood [261] in direct stress on plain and

K

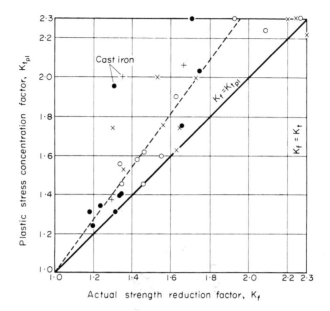

FIG. 67. Comparison of plastic stress concentration factor and strength
reduction factor. (P. G. Forrest [14])

Failure:   ×   in 10⁷ cycles          ○   in 10⁶ cycles
           ●   in 10⁵ cycles          +   in 10⁶ and 10⁷ cycles

transversely bored specimens of various sizes. The transversely bored
specimens were all geometrically similar, each with a hole of diameter
equal to one sixth that of the specimen. The results, for a mild steel, given
in Fig. 68, show that the fatigue limit of the plain specimens is independent
of the size, but that the fatigue limit for the transversely bored specimens
decreases as the size increases. A similar result was obtained with a nickel–
chromium steel and Fig. 69 shows $K_f$ plotted against the specimen diameter for each material. This illustrates the marked difference in notch
sensitivity between the two materials; the alloy steel is virtually fully
notch sensitive for sizes above 1 in. diameter, while for the mild steel, $K_f$ is
still considerably below $K_t$ at the maximum diameter of 2·4 in.

A further illustration of size effect is given by the results shown in Fig.
70 of fatigue tests on flat specimens with a central hole [262]. For a very
small hole $K_t$ is approximately equal to 3, but as the size of the hole is
increased, $K_t$ decreases, tending towards a value of 2 as the diameter of
the hole approaches the width of the bar. However, the fatigue strength
(based on the net section) decreases as the size of the hole is increased,
showing a minimum value when the diameter of the hole is about one
eighth the width of the bar and then increases again.

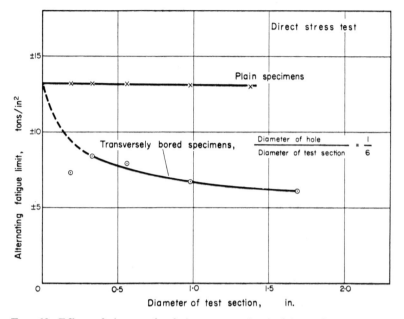

FIG. 68. Effect of size on the fatigue strength of plain and transversely bored specimens of mild steel. (Phillips and Heywood [261])

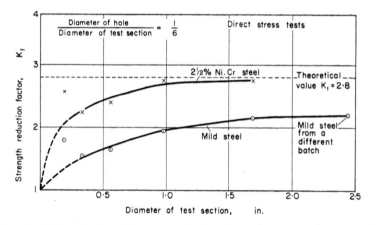

FIG. 69. Effect of size of transversely bored specimens on the strength reduction factor $K_f$. (Phillips and Heywood [261])

Although the fatigue strength of plain unnotched specimens is independent of size in direct stress tests, a size effect does occur in bending tests on plain specimens and some typical results are shown in Fig. 71. There is little change in fatigue strength between 1 in. and 2 in. diameter

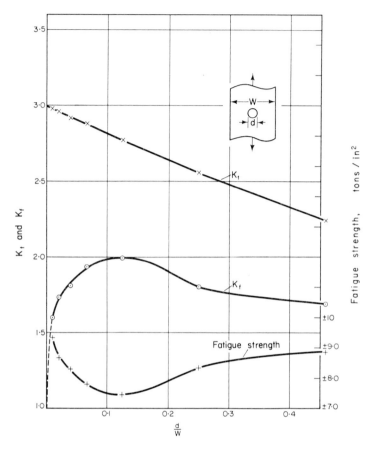

F𝐢ɢ. 70. Effect of size of hole on fatigue strength of flat bored specimens
of 0·36% C steel. (Massonnet [262])

but, on average, the fatigue strengths for steels are 3%, 10% and 15%
above the 1 in. diameter values at $\frac{1}{2}$, $\frac{1}{4}$ and $\frac{1}{8}$ in. diameter respectively.
Similar results have been obtained from fatigue tests in alternating torsion
[269]. The results for aluminium alloys and magnesium alloys are less
consistent, but are in general similar to those for steels.

It should be noted that the results shown for each material in Fig. 71
were obtained using specimens cut from the surface of bars of one diameter. There may be a further size effect if bars of different size are compared, depending on the size of the ingot and on the amount of reduction
from ingot to bar. In practice, the difference in fatigue strength between
large engineering parts and small specimens may be greater than expected
from the results in Fig. 71, and this is illustrated by the results shown in
Table 28 for large diameter shafts.

TABLE 28. THE EFFECT OF SIZE ON THE FATIGUE STRENGTH OF LARGE UNNOTCHED STEEL SHAFTS

| Type of specimen | Diameter of specimens in. | Type of fatigue test | Endurance | Fatigue strength tons/in² | Reference |
|---|---|---|---|---|---|
| Railway axles 0·4–0·5% C steel | 6–7 | R.B. | $85 \times 10^6$ | About 8* | Horger and Neifert [270] |
| 2¼ in. diameter bar to same specification | 1·5 | | $10^8$ | 12·5 | |
| Specimens from full size axles | 0·3 | | $10^7$ | 14·5 | |
| Ni Cr Mo steel | 9 | R.B. | $10^7$ | 17 | Eaton [271] |
| Ni Cr Mo steel | 0·469 | | | 25 | |
| 0·22% C steel, acid open-hearth | 4·9 | R.B. | $2 \times 10^7$ | 12·7 | Jiro and Junich [663] |
| | 0·39 | | | 13·8 | |
| 0·22% C steel, electric furnace | 4·9 | | | 14·9 | |
| | 0·39 | | | 17·5 | |
| 0·23% C steel shaft | 9¾ | Alternating torsion | $10^7$ | 10† | Bunyan [272] |
| | 5⅝ | | | 10† | |
| | 3 | | | 10† | |
| Ni Cr Mo shafts to SAE 86 B 45H and 4150 with ground surfaces, hardness Rockwell C-52 | 3 | Repeated torsion | $2 \times 10^5$ | 0 to 50 | Eckert [273] |
| C Mn steel, hardness Rockwell C-50 | ¾ | Repeated torsion | $2 \times 10^5$ | 0 to 55 | Watkinson [273] |

* There was considerable scatter.

† Extrapolated from results for shafts with different transition radii.

It would appear from the results in the table that the size effect in rotating bending is much greater than in torsion, but Lehr and Ruef [274] observed a considerable size effect on the torsional fatigue strength of crankshafts (see page 307). Horger and Neifert suggested that a number of factors may have attributed to the marked effect in their tests. Among these were residual stresses and directionality effects arising from the forging (the axles were machined but not heat-treated before testing), local variation in grain size, surface finish and rise in temperature during the tests. Whatever the explanation, the result demonstrates the necessity for full-scale fatigue testing.

Some results of the influence of size on the rotating bending fatigue strength of geometrically similar notched pieces of steels are shown in Fig. 72. The behaviour is similar to that for plain specimens tested in bending, there being a distinct size effect below $\frac{1}{2}$ in. diameter, but little effect above $\frac{1}{2}$ in. Phillips and Fenner [275], on the other hand, have

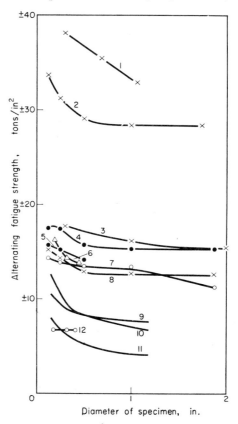

FIG. 71. Effect of specimen size on fatigue strength of unnotched rotating bending specimens.

reported a marked size effect in 14 S.W.G. sheet, both plain and with a drilled hole, in direct stress; and their results are summarized in the following table:

TABLE 29. FATIGUE STRENGTH OF ALUMINIUM ALLOY AND MILD STEEL SHEET WITH AND WITHOUT DRILLED HOLES (Phillips and Fenner [275])

14 S.W.G. Direct stress tests with minimum stress 2 tons/in²

| | Range of stress for failure in 10⁷ cycles | | | | |
|---|---|---|---|---|---|
| | Aluminium alloy DTD 646B | | | Mild steel | |
| Width of sheet, ins. | $\frac{3}{4}$ | $4\frac{1}{2}$ | 9 | $\frac{3}{4}$ | 9 |
| Plain specimens | 13·4 | 7·5 | 6·3 | 17·0 | 14·4 |
| Drilled specimens Ratio $\frac{\text{net width}}{\text{hole diameter}}$ | | | | | |
| 144 | | 7·5 | 6·0 | | 13·2 |
| 36 | | 6·3 | 4·5 | | 7·5 |
| 9 | 9·5 | 5·7 | 5·7 | 12·0 | 7·7 |
| 3 | | 5·0 | 4·5 | | 7·0 |

A number of suggestions were put forward in the discussion of the paper to explain the drastic reduction in fatigue strength observed on the large specimens. The most likely explanations are that the effect arose from residual stresses, when the sheets were flattened after heat-treatment, or from the presence of sparsely distributed flaws. These results again illustrate the danger of predicting the fatigue strength of large parts from the results of tests on small specimens. Another interesting feature of the results is the effect of the size of the hole on the fatigue strength. With a very small hole, for which $K_t$ is approximately equal to 3, the fatigue strength is scarcely affected and, in fact, some specimens failed at the fillet at the end of the test section and not through the hole. $K_t$ at the fillet was estimated mathematically to be 1·35 and by photo-elasticity to be 1·2.

### Theories of Size Effect

The experimental observations show that fatigue strength is independent of size for plain specimens tested in direct stress, but increases with a

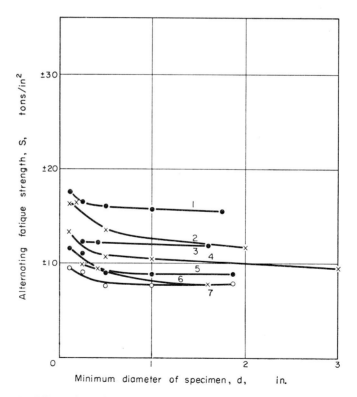

FIG. 72. Effect of specimen size on fatigue strength of notched rotating bending specimens of steels.

*Key to Fig. 72 :*

| Curve | Material | Notch | $K_t$ | $\dfrac{D}{d}$ | $\dfrac{r}{d}$ | Source | Ref. |
|---|---|---|---|---|---|---|---|
| 1 | Cr Mo Steel SAE X4130 | Semi-circular groove | 2 | 1·16 | 0·08 | Morkovin & Moore | [264] |
| 5 | 0·34% C Steel SAE 1035 | Semi-circular groove | 2 | 1·16 | 0·08 | Morkovin & Moore | |
| 7 | 0·22% C Steel SAE 1020 | Semi-circular groove | 2 | 1·16 | 0·08 | Morkovin & Moore | |
| 3 | 0·45% C Steel | Fillet | 1·43 | 2 | 0·25 | Peterson & Wahl | [265] |
| 6 | 0·45% C Steel | Fillet | 2·04 | 2 | 0·0625 | Peterson & Wahl | |
| 2 | Ni Mo Steel | Transverse Hole | 2 | | 0·125 | Peterson & Wahl | |
| 4 | 0·45% C Steel | Transverse Hole | 2 | | 0·125 | Peterson & Wahl | |

$d$ = Minimum diameter of shaft with groove or fillet or diameter of shaft with transverse hole.
$D$ = Maximum diameter of shaft with groove or fillet.
$r$ = Radius of groove, fillet or hole.

decrease in size for plain specimens tested in bending or torsion and for notched specimens under all stress conditions. The significance of this result is that only in plain specimens tested in direct stress is the stress uniformly distributed over the test section. It therefore appears that size effect is a consequence of the limiting of the maximum stress to a small volume of the material; the fatigue strength increases as the volume of material at the maximum stress is decreased or, to put it another way, the fatigue strength increases as the stress gradient is increased. Two hypotheses have been put forward to explain this behaviour, the inherent flaw concept and the elementary block concept [276].

The inherent flaw concept is that all materials contain internal discontinuities or stress concentrations and that their behaviour, including their response to a change in size, can be explained on this basis. Firstly, if the flaws are sparsely distributed, the fatigue strength will depend on the probability of a flaw being present in the region of maximum stress. Under uniform stress the presence of a flaw will be highly probable, while at the root of a sharp notch the probability will be low. This will result in a wide scatter between the fatigue life of different notched specimens. It has been suggested that some forms of porosity or intermetallic constituents may act in some materials as sparse flaws [276].

Secondly, the influence of internal flaws will depend on their size in relation to the region of high stress. This can be illustrated by considering the effect of an external notch on a material containing many internal flaws. If the notch is large compared with the flaws, then there will be a number of flaws wholly within the region of high stress at the root of the notch and $K_f$ would be expected to be nearly equal to $K_t$. If, on the other hand, the size of the notch is comparable with the size of the flaws, then the average stress across any flaw will be appreciably less than the maximum stress and a value of $K_f$ much lower than $K_t$ would be expected. In other words, if a material is full of stress raisers, the addition of one more of about the same size will not make much difference. In cast iron the graphite flakes may be regarded as inherent flaws and its behaviour in fatigue is consistent with the inherent flaw concept. Firstly, the fatigue strength of cast iron is almost completely insensitive to small external notches and, secondly, its fatigue behaviour under combined bending and torsion is that expected of a material containing flaws [277].

This argument may be used, conversely, as evidence that ductile metals do not conform to the inherent flaw concept. Cox [204] has shown that if fatigue failure results from the stress concentration at an inherent flaw, then the ratio of the fatigue strength in torsion to the fatigue strength in bending cannot be less than 0·75. Values greater than 0·75 are obtained for cast iron and also for ductile steels containing artificial flaws in the form of transverse round holes, but for plain specimens of ductile metals the value is usually less than 0·6 and always less than 0·75. Moreover, the size of inherent flaws required to account for the observed size effect in ductile metals is big enough for them to be detected microscopically, but no one has claimed to have seen them.

The elementary block concept is that fatigue failure is governed not by the maximum stress, but by the average stress over an elementary block of finite size. This implies that a higher maximum stress can be withstood when the stress gradient is high, than when it is low, which is in accord with the observed behaviour. The concept was first introduced by Neuber [72] because the classical theory of elasticity was clearly inapplicable to existing materials containing sharp notches. He cites as an example a bar containing a shallow notch under torsion for which the elastic theory gives $K_t = 1 + \sqrt{(a/R)}$ and points out that if the radius of curvature were only 1/10,000 of the depth, $K_t$ would have the unlikely value of 101. The failure of the classical theory of elasticity in this respect results from the assumption that materials are homogeneous and Neuber therefore reconsidered the theory on the basis that materials are composed of numerous small, but finite, particles. He showed that under these conditions, $K_t$

for sharp notches could be calculated from the equations of the elastic theory by substituting for the radius of the notch a length $A$ equal to half the width of the elementary particle. Then, because the ideal stress concentration factor for a small notch of radius $R$ is proportional to $\sqrt{(1/R)}$, he suggested the following empirical relation for the transition between sharp and shallow notches:

$$K_f = 1 + \frac{K_t - 1}{1 + \sqrt{(A/R)}}, \tag{32}$$

which may be rewritten:

$$\frac{K_f - 1}{K_t - 1} = q = \frac{1}{1 + \sqrt{(A/R)}}, \tag{33}$$

Neuber regarded $A$ as a material constant, not necessarily related to the microstructure, which could be determined experimentally. The equation has proved useful for correlating the results of notched fatigue tests and this is discussed further on page 150.

No quantitative relation has been established between values of $A$ determined experimentally and the microstructure of the materials tested, but this may be because $A$ is affected by other factors that influence the notch sensitivity, such as plastic deformation, cold work and residual stress. Nevertheless, Peterson [278], has shown that the response of a material to size effect is affected by the grain size. Figure 73 shows a relation found by him between the notch sensitivity, the size of the notch and the grain size. Further evidence of the influence of grain size has been obtained by Karry and Dolan [279] from the results of plain and notched fatigue tests on electropolished specimens of brass for a wide range of grain size. They

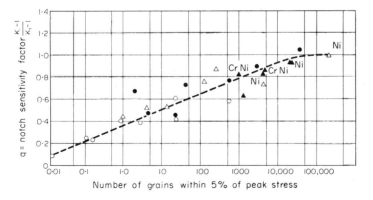

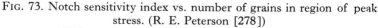

FIG. 73. Notch sensitivity index vs. number of grains in region of peak stress. (R. E. Peterson [278])

| Holes: | ○ carbon steel. | ● alloy steel. |
|---|---|---|
| Fillets: | △ carbon steel. | ▲ alloy steel. |

found that the difference observed between $K_f$ and $K_t$ could be accounted for, approximately, by assuming that failure was determined by the average stress acting across one grain.

## Work-hardening and Residual Stress

Processes such as grinding, machining or polishing are very likely both to work-harden a thin layer of material at the surface and to set up residual stresses. As fatigue failures nearly always propagate from the surface, these factors may appreciably influence the fatigue strength. The cold-working effect is usually beneficial and surface residual stresses can also increase the fatigue strength provided they are compressive, and these effects are discussed further in Chapter VI.

Notch sensitivity may also be affected, because the degree of cold-work and the magnitude of residual stress are likely to be greater at the root of a notch than elsewhere. The effects may also be greater on small pieces than on large ones and it has been suggested that this can account entirely for the size effect. However, experiments on specimens which have been stress-relieved or electropolished after machining have shown that this is not so, although the size effect was reduced considerably by these treatments [262, 264]. The influence of these factors will be smaller on materials which have been previously cold-worked and this may account for the greater notch sensitivity of cold-worked metals.

## Non-Propagating Cracks

It is sometimes found that fatigue cracks develop at the root of very sharp notches, reach a certain size, but do not propagate further. Fatigue cracks which have not propagated have been observed in engineering parts on occasions for many years, but their presence in laboratory specimens subjected to a constant stress amplitude has not been noticed until more recently. Their presence is consistent with Neuber's elementary block concept, because the stress concentration at the end of a crack is very high, but is localized in a very small volume. Once the crack has spread from the region of high stress in the vicinity of the notch, therefore, it is possible that despite the presence of the crack the average stress over the necessary volume may be less than it was initially at the root of the notch.

Non-propagating fatigue cracks occur when the fluctuating stress required to form a crack is less than the fluctuating stress required to propagate it, and under these circumstances it is the stress required to propagate the crack which determines the notched fatigue strength. This behaviour is thus another factor which must be considered in the interpretation of notch sensitivity. The full significance of non-propagating cracks is not yet clear, but considerable progress has been made in a recent series of experiments carried out by Frost at the National Engineering Laboratory [280, 281, 677].

The first experiments were concerned with the rate of growth of the cracks and it was clearly established that these reached their maximum length at an early stage in the test and then remained dormant. Some tests were made later on sharply notched plate specimens, in which it was possible to observe the cracks during the course of the test. The length to which the cracks finally propagated was dependent on the notch and also on the stress range, and lengths of up to 0·02 in. were observed.

Tests were then made to determine the conditions governing the initiation and propagation of fatigue cracks and the behaviour can be illustrated by the results obtained on notched specimens of mild steel which are shown in Fig. 74. All the specimens contained notches 0·05 in. deep, but different

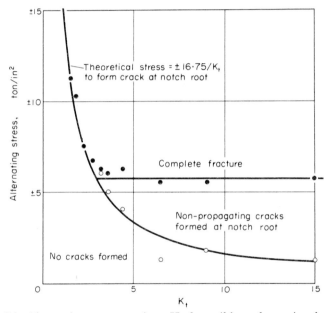

FIG. 74. Alternating stress against $K_t$ for mild steel rotating bending notched specimens. (Frost [280])

  O  Fatigue limit based on stress to initiate crack at notch root.
  ●  Fatigue limit based on complete fracture.

values of the radius at the root of the notch, from 0·09 in. to as sharp as possible, were used to obtain a range of values of $K_t$. The stress to start a fatigue crack was found to be in good agreement with the theoretical value, given by the plain fatigue limit, $\pm 16·75$ tons/in², divided by $K_t$. The stress to propagate the crack, on the other hand, was independent of $K_t$ and the root radius, and had a constant value of $\pm 5·75$ tons/in². Thus, when $K_t$ exceeded a critical value, $K_{t\ \mathrm{crit.}} = 16·75/5·75 = 2·9$, cracks were formed at the roots of the notches, but did not propagate.

Although the alternating stress required to propagate a crack is independent of the notch radius, Frost showed that it depends on the crack length and, provided the crack is small compared with the specimen size, is governed by the equation:

$$S^3 l = k \qquad\qquad (34)$$

where $S$ is the nominal alternating stress, $l$ is the combined length of the notch and the crack and $k$ is a material constant. The length of a non-propagating crack at the root of a sharp notch is usually small compared with the depth of the notch, so that the stress required to propagate a crack can be determined approximately by substituting the depth of the notch for $l$ in the above equation. It should be noted that, for a given depth of notch, this stress is the minimum fatigue strength of the material, and its relation to the notch depth for those materials tested by Frost, computed from equation 34, is shown in Fig. 75. The fatigue strength will be higher than these values, however, provided that $K_t < K_t$ crit. The relation between $K_t$ crit. and the notch depth is shown in Fig. 76 and this diagram can be used to indicate whether non-propagating cracks are likely to occur under particular conditions. It can be seen that $K_t$ crit. increases with the notch depth and, therefore, for geometrically similar notched pieces, there will be a critical size below which non-propagating cracks will occur and above which they will not occur. In general, therefore, non-propagating cracks are more likely to occur in small notched fatigue specimens than in large parts in service.

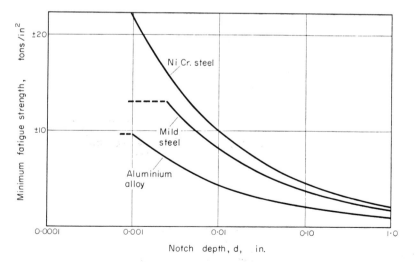

FIG. 75. Relation between minimum fatigue strength and notch depth $d$.
(Forrest, discussion of Ref. 280)

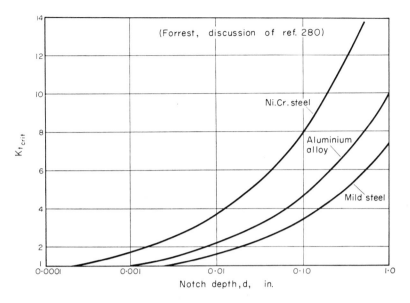

FIG. 76. Relation between $Kt$ crit and notch depth $d$ from relation $Kt$ crit $= \sqrt[3]{(d/c)}$.

For values of tensile mean stress, such that the crack remains open during the loading cycle, the range of stress at the tip of the crack is effectively doubled and Frost has found that for mild steel under these conditions, Equation 34 applies if $k/8$ is substituted for $k$.

It should be pointed out that although, under some conditions, fatigue cracks may be non-propagating in a laboratory test, the presence of a fatigue crack in an engineering part in service is almost always a source of danger. Fluctuating loads in service are seldom of constant amplitude and the occurrence of an unusually high load may be sufficient to propagate an existing fatigue crack or even to cause complete failure. Some examples of service failures which have occurred in this way have been discussed by Bennett [282].

### Determination of strength reduction factors

Notched fatigue data are difficult to interpret because of the many factors, particularly the size of the specimens, which influence the behaviour. Instead of tabulating the data, consideration will therefore be given primarily to empirical relations that have been derived from experimental data for predicting notched fatigue strengths. A considerable number of notched fatigue data are quoted by Grover, Gordon and Jackson [135] and by Kuhn and Hardrath [283].

The most widely used empirical relation is that suggested by Neuber, which has already been discussed in connection with size effect:

$$K_f = 1 + \frac{K_t - 1}{1 + \sqrt{(A/R)}} \tag{32}$$

This equation takes into account the effect of size by means of the notch radius $R$ and of differences between materials by the material constant $A$. Other similar relations have been suggested [284, 285], but these offer no significant advantage over Neuber's relation. The fatigue limit or fatigue strength for long endurances will be considered initially.

### Steel

Most of the experimental data available have been obtained on steels and these show clearly that to satisfy Neuber's relation, a different value of the material constant must be chosen for different steels. Figure 77 shows the relation between the plain and notched fatigue strengths of a large

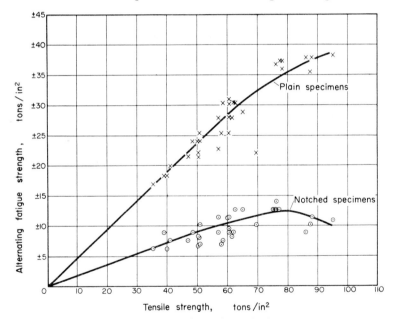

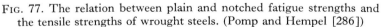

FIG. 77. The relation between plain and notched fatigue strengths and the tensile strengths of wrought steels. (Pomp and Hempel [286])

Axial load fatigue tests.
Notched specimen dimensions:—
Maximum Diameter 0·315 in.
Minimum Diameter 0·276 in.
60° V groove
Root Radius 0·004 in.
$K_t = 4·4$

number of steels plotted against the tensile strengths. All the results were obtained by Pomp and Hempel [286] from direct stress tests with the same shape and size of notch for all the notched tests. Both the plain and the notched results lie close to smooth curves which diverge as the tensile strength is increased, showing that the notch sensitivity is related approximately to the tensile strength and increases as the tensile strength is increased. Körber and Hempel [287] obtained similar results from tests on steel specimens with holes and notches in axial stress, bending and torsion, and similar behaviour has been observed by other investigators, although there is some evidence that the notch sensitivity may be reduced at very high tensile strengths, see, for example, reference [99]. This may be because the unnotched fatigue strength of very high strength steels is reduced by the presence of internal stress raisers, particularly inclusions.

Kuhn and Hardrath [283] have analysed experimental results for a large variety of steels (but excluding austenitic stainless steels), and determined an approximate relation between $A$ in Neuber's equation (equation 32) and the tensile strength, and this is shown in Fig. 78. The analysis included results obtained on transversely bored specimens and on specimens with fillets and circumferential grooves. (For the grooved specimens, equation 32 was modified to take account of the flank angle. The validity of this modification is doubtful [284], but it does not appreciably influence the result.) The data considered included results obtained on large shafts, up to $6\frac{1}{2}$ in. in diameter, and the prediction of the notched fatigue strength for these

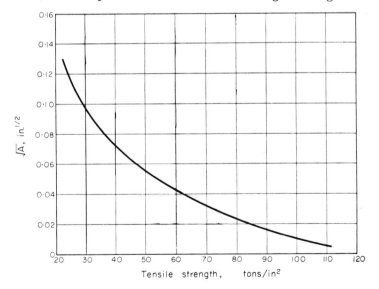

FIG. 78. Approximate values of the material constant $A$ in equation 32 for steels. (Kuhn and Hardrath [283])

L

was as accurate as for small specimens. Dorey and Smedley [288], by confining their attention only to the effect of fillets in shafts above 1 in. diameter, have derived an empirical equation which gives a closer fit to experimental results. Their relation has been criticized, however, because it cannot be applied either to small shafts or to very large shafts and because no account is taken of the ratio of the minimum diameter of shaft to the maximum diameter. The results of their tests on large steel shafts, showing the effect of fillet radius on the torsional fatigue strength, are discussed in Chapter IX (see Fig. 139). It has been claimed recently by Agerman [664] that a closer approximation to the experimental data can be obtained by relating Neuber's constant to the yield stress instead of the tensile strength.

The values of $A$, for four values of tensile strength, obtained from the curve given by Kuhn and Hardrath, have been used to determine the relation between the notch sensitivity factor $q$ and the notch radius, and this is shown in Fig. 79. This method was suggested by Peterson [285], and the

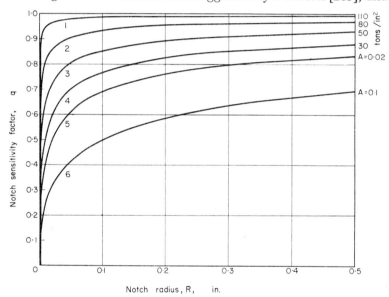

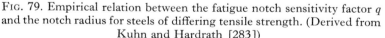

Notch radius, R, in.

Fig. 79. Empirical relation between the fatigue notch sensitivity factor $q$ and the notch radius for steels of differing tensile strength. (Derived from Kuhn and Hardrath [283])

| Curve | Tensile strength of steel, tons/in² | $A$ (from Kuhn and Hardrath), in. |
|---|---|---|
| 1 | 110 | 0·00003 |
| 2 | 80 | 0·0006 |
| 3 | 50 | 0·003 |
| 4 | 30 | 0·009 |
| 5 | — | 0·02 |
| 6 | — | 0·1 |

resulting curves are similar to those derived by him from his own experimental results. It is clear from Fig. 79 that for high tensile steels it is advisable in design to make allowance for the full stress concentration factor, $K_t$, unless the notch is very small. A similar procedure is also recommended for low-strength steels unless the notch is small, for the scatter in results, according to Heywood [284], even omitting some extreme values, is $\pm 20\%$. Results are sometimes quoted showing values of $K_f$ exceeding $K_t$. This could occur if the notch has been produced by grinding as a result of residual tensile stresses induced at the root of the notch or from non-axial loading in the fatigue testing machine. Such behaviour might therefore be attributed to experimental error, but both residual tensile stress and non-axial loading frequently occur in practice.

The results analysed by Kuhn and Hardrath were mostly obtained from relatively mild notches in which non-propagating fatigue cracks would not be expected and their empirical relation cannot, therefore, be expected to apply to sharp notches in which non-propagating cracks occur. With non-propagating cracks the value of $q$ may be considerably lower than those indicated by Fig. 79. Sharp notches should always be avoided if possible, of course, and the conditions for non-propagating cracks should occur only rarely in practice. It is possible to estimate approximately these conditions for a few materials, from the information given in Fig. 76.

There has been no systematic investigation of the influence of notches on the fatigue strength of austenitic stainless steel, but the data available show that it is less notch sensitive than almost any other metal. A number of results have been quoted showing a notched fatigue strength higher than the unnotched value. Two reasons for this are the ability of this material to be strengthened by work-hardening and its ability to deform plastically without failing by fatigue. The results quoted in the following table show that the notch sensitivity is increased if the material is initially cold-worked.

TABLE 30. INFLUENCE OF COLD-WORK ON THE NOTCH SENSITIVITY OF
STAINLESS STEEL (Oberg and Johnson [289])
Rotating bending tests at 10,600 cycles/min.
Root diameter of notch 0·25 in., depth of notch 0·025 in.
Angle of notch 60°. Radius at root of notch 0·01 in.
$K_t = 2\cdot6$, 20% Cr, 10% Ni Steel.

| Condition | Tensile strength tons/in² | Fatigue strength tons/in² | | $K_f$ | $q$ |
|---|---|---|---|---|---|
| | | Unnotched | Notched | | |
| Annealed | 37 | 15·6 | 18·8 | 0·8 | 0 |
| Cold drawn | 59 | 31·2 | 22·3 | 1·4 | 0·25 |

TABLE 31. EFFECT OF A CIRCUMFERENTIAL V-NOTCH ON THE BENDING FATIGUE STRENGTH OF CAST STEEL AND CAST IRON

| Material | Tensile strength tons/in² | Bending fatigue strength tons/in² | | $K_f$ | $K_t$ (Neuber) | Dimensions of notch | | | | Source | Ref. |
|---|---|---|---|---|---|---|---|---|---|---|---|
| | | Plain | Notched | | | Angle deg. | Root radius in. | Minimum diameter in. | Depth in. | | |
| Cast 0·4% C steel | 37·3 | 14·8 | 11·6 | 1·28 | 2·2 | 60 | 0·015 | 0·22 | 0·035 | Evans, Ebert and Briggs | 130 |
| | 42·1 | 16·8 | 12·5 | 1·34 | 2·2 | 60 | 0·015 | 0·22 | 0·035 | | |
| Cast alloy steel | 50·3 | 22·9 | 14·9 | 1·54 | 2·2 | 60 | 0·015 | 0·22 | 0·035 | | |
| | 56·5 | 28·1 | 15·6 | 1·80 | 2·2 | 60 | 0·015 | 0·22 | 0·035 | | |
| | 65·3 | 27·3 | 18·1 | 1·51 | 2·2 | 60 | 0·015 | 0·22 | 0·035 | | |
| | 75·1 | 34·6 | 21·5 | 1·61 | 2·2 | 60 | 0·015 | 0·22 | 0·035 | | |
| Cast alloy steel | 65·0 | 19·5 | 13·0 | 1·50 | 3·1 | 55 | 0·0086 | 0·300 | 0·0375 | Love | 290 |
| | 75·0 | 22·0 | 14·5 | 1·52 | 3·1 | 55 | 0·0086 | 0·300 | 0·0375 | | |
| | 82·0 | 23·0 | 15·0 | 1·53 | 3·1 | 55 | 0·0086 | 0·300 | 0·0375 | | |
| | 85·0 | 23·5 | 16·0 | 1·47 | 3·1 | 55 | 0·0086 | 0·300 | 0·0375 | | |
| Graphitic cast steel | 50·0 | 16·0 | 9·0 | 1·78 | 3·1 | 55 | 0·0086 | 0·300 | 0·0375 | Love | 290 |

| Material | | | | | | | | | | Reference | |
|---|---|---|---|---|---|---|---|---|---|---|---|
| Flake-graphite grey cast iron | 23·0 | 11·0 | 7·0 | 1·57 | 3·1 | 55 | 0·0086 | 0·300 | 0·0375 | Love | 290 |
| | 22·0 | 8·0 | 8·0 | 1·00 | 3·1 | 55 | 0·0086 | 0·300 | 0·0375 | | |
| | 26·0 | 12·0 | 11·0 | 1·09 | 3·1 | 55 | 0·0086 | 0·300 | 0·0375 | | |
| | 24·0 | 10·0 | 10·0 | 1·00 | 3·1 | 55 | 0·0086 | 0·300 | 0·0375 | | |
| | 25·0 | 10·5 | 10·5 | 1·00 | 3·1 | 55 | 0·0086 | 0·300 | 0·0375 | | |
| | 20·8 | 9·0 | 7·5 | 1·20 | 3·1 | 45 | 0·010 | 0·331 | 0·071 | Grant Gilbert | |
| | 30·3 | 11·5 | 10·5 | 1·09 | 3·1 | 45 | 0·010 | 0·331 | 0·071 | | |
| Nodular cast iron (as cast) | 40·0 | 19·0 | 11·0 | 1·73 | 3·1 | 45 | 0·010 | 0·301 | 0·086 | Palmer and Gilbert | 290 |
| | 43·0 | 18·5 | 10·5 | 1·76 | 3·1 | 45 | 0·010 | 0·301 | 0·086 | | |
| | 45·7 | 19·0 | 13·0 | 1·46 | 3·1 | 45 | 0·010 | 0·301 | 0·086 | | |
| | 38·9 | 19·0 | 10·0 | 1·90 | 3·5 | 45 | 0·010 | 0·417 | 0·142 | | |
| | 39·8 | 17·5 | 9·5 | 1·84 | 3·5 | 45 | 0·010 | 0·417 | 0·142 | | |
| | 40·5 | 18·5 | 10·5 | 1·76 | 3·5 | 45 | 0·010 | 0·417 | 0·142 | | |
| | 42·7 | 17·0 | 8·0 | 2·13 | 3·5 | 45 | 0·010 | 0·417 | 0·142 | | |
| Nodular cast iron (heat treated) | 23·1 | 12·0 | 10·5 | 1·14 | 3·1 | 45 | 0·010 | 0·301 | 0·086 | Palmer and Gilbert | 290 |
| | 30·7 | 14·5 | 8·5 | 1·70 | 3·1 | 45 | 0·010 | 0·301 | 0·086 | | |
| | 36·5 | 15·0 | 8·5 | 1·77 | 3·1 | 45 | 0·010 | 0·301 | 0·086 | | |
| | 38·8 | 16·0 | 8·5 | 1·88 | 3·1 | 45 | 0·010 | 0·301 | 0·086 | | |
| | 21·0 | 11·0 | 7·5 | 1·47 | 3·5 | 45 | 0·010 | 0·417 | 0·142 | | |
| | 23·0 | 11·5 | 9·0 | 1·28 | 3·5 | 45 | 0·010 | 0·417 | 0·142 | | |
| | 25·8 | 13·0 | 8·0 | 1·63 | 3·5 | 45 | 0·010 | 0·417 | 0·142 | | |

Even in the cold-drawn condition, however, $q$ has a value of only 0·25, which corresponds to a Neuber constant $A$ of about 0·1 (see Fig. 79), and the material would therefore be expected to be relatively insensitive to notches on large sizes. It should be noted that the data available have been obtained on simple austenitic steels and high-strength complex austenitic alloys may not behave in this way.

### Cast Steel and Cast Iron

Cast metals usually have a lower unnotched fatigue strength than wrought metals of the same composition, but they are usually less notch sensitive. This behaviour can be attributed to the presence of stress raisers in the cast material. These reduce the unnotched fatigue strength, but the presence of a mechanical notch has less effect on a material already containing stress raisers. The notch sensitivity will increase with the size of the notch, however, and if the notch is very much larger than the internal flaws, the reduction in fatigue strength will approach the theoretical value. Almost all of the data has been obtained on small specimens (except for tests on full-scale crankshafts which are described on page 307) and there is insufficient to warrant the use of an empirical relation. A collection of data of notched and unnotched fatigue results for cast steel and cast iron is therefore given in Table 31. Ordinary flake graphite cast iron is particularly insensitive to notches. High-strength and nodular cast iron and cast steel are more susceptible, but are still less affected, in general, than mild steel. The results of a few tests on wrought iron on specimens containing sharp notches, reported by Russell and Welcker [291], indicate that its notch sensitivity is comparable with that of high-strength cast iron and cast steel.

### Aluminium Alloys

An attempt to determine Neuber's constant in equation (32) from experimental data on aluminium alloys has been made by Kuhn [259, 292]. The amount of information is much less than for steels but he found greater inconsistencies in the results. From results of axial stress tests on sheet and rotating bending tests on cylindrical specimens he concluded that the Neuber constant was about the same for 24S–T (aluminium–copper alloy) and for 75S–T (aluminium–zinc–magnesium alloy) and that a value of $A = 0·02$ in. gave reasonable agreement with the experimental results for both materials. For sheet, most of the calculated values of $K_f$ were within ±10% of the experimental values and almost all the remainder gave conservative values. The rotating bending results, on the other hand, showed more scatter and many of the calculated values were unconservative. Kuhn suggested that this might be explained by differences in surface finish; most of the unnotched bending specimens were hand polished, which increases the fatigue strength and hence also increases $K_f$.

The relation between $q$ and $R$ for $A = 0.02$ in. is given in Fig. 79. This value indicates the surprising result that high-strength aluminium alloys are less notch sensitive than mild steel. This is contrary to general experience and may arise from the greater emphasis placed on the results of tests on sheet for the aluminium alloys. The results appear to justify the use of this curve to determine $K_f$ for sheet, but in view of the scatter in the bending results, it is advisable—as for steels—to make allowance in design for the full stress concentration factor $K_t$ for forgings and extrusions, except for very small notches. This point can be emphasized by reference to some results, quoted by Templin [134], which are given in Table 32.

TABLE 32. INFLUENCE OF CIRCUMFERENTIAL V-NOTCHES ON THE FATIGUE STRENGTH OF ALUMINIUM ALLOYS (Templin [134])

Root diameter at notches 0.33 in. Depth of notches 0.075 in.
Angle of notch 60°

| Material | Bending fatigue strength tons/in² ($5 \times 10^8$ cycles) | $K_f$ | $K_t$ | Root radius of notch in. |
|---|---|---|---|---|
| 25S–T6 | 7·6 | | 1 | Unnotched |
| | 5·4 | 1·41 | 1·38 | 0·106 |
| | 4·5 | 1·7 | 1·99 | 0·031 |
| | 3·6 | 2·1 | 16–20 | 0·0002 |
| 75S–T6 | 11·2 | | 1 | Unnotched |
| | 10·3 | 1·09 | 1·095 | 0·5 |
| | 7·6 | 1·47 | 1·38 | 0·106 |
| | 6·9 | 1·61 | 1·59 | 0·062 |
| | 5·6 | 2·0 | 1·99 | 0·031 |
| | 4·0 | 2·8 | 16–20 | 0·0002 |

For alloy 75S–T, $K_f$ is approximately equal to $K_t$ for all the notches, except the very sharp one, where non-propagating cracks were probably present.

The lower notch sensitivity of cast aluminium alloys is illustrated by the results of tests also carried out by Templin [144] which are summarized in the following table.

TABLE 33. INFLUENCE OF SHARP CIRCUMFERENTIAL V-NOTCH ON THE FATIGUE
STRENGTH OF WROUGHT AND CAST ALUMINIUM ALLOYS (Templin. [143, 144])

Root diameter of notch 0·33 in., depth of notch 0·075 in.,
angle of notch 60°, radius at root of notch less than 0·001 in.

| Material | No. of alloys tested | Bending fatigue strength tons/in² (5 × 10⁸ cycles) | |
|---|---|---|---|
| | | unnotched | notched |
| Wrought alloys | 4 | 6·7–12·5 | 2·7–6·5 |
| Sand-cast alloys | 28 | 2·7–5·8 | 1·8–4·5 |
| Permanent-mould cast alloys | 17 | 3·6–7·6 | 2·2–4·9 |

$K_t$ is greater than 9 for the notch used, so that non-propagating cracks were probably present, but results obtained by Frith [146] using a milder notch also show low notch sensitivity for cast aluminium alloys.

*Other Metals.*—Less data are available for other metals than for steel and aluminium alloys and it is only possible to give a general indication of their behaviour. For wrought magnesium alloys, results quoted by Buchmann [268] show quite low notch sensitivity, but other results show a reduction in fatigue strength approaching $K_t$ [166, 293, 294]; cast magnesium alloys are less notch sensitive [146, 293, 294]. The fatigue strength of pure copper is reduced by the presence of a notch more than might be expected in view of its ductility and a number of experimental results show that it is more notch sensitive than mild steel [14, 135, 295]. Most materials show an increasing notch sensitivity with increase in tensile strength and a survey of the data shows that for a number of materials the notch sensitivity is approximately equal to that of steel of the same tensile strength. This applies to copper alloys [150], though these show rather wide variation, to nickel alloys [295] and to titanium and some titanium alloys [296–298].

### Notch Sensitivity at Low Endurances

The static tensile strength of a notched specimen (based on the minimum section) is often higher than the unnotched tensile strength, because of the triaxial stress system at the notch and the smaller volume of material subjected to the maximum stress in the notched specimen. In fatigue the $S$–log $N$ curves for notched and unnotched specimens converge as the number of cycles to fracture is decreased and may cross at an endurance between 1 and 1000 cycles. There is thus a gradual decrease in notch sensitivity as $N$ is decreased and this may be explained partly by the increasing influence of plastic deformation as the stress range is increased and partly by the increased proportion of the fatigue life occupied by crack propagation in notched specimens at high ranges of stress.

In Fig. 80 the ratio of the bending fatigue strength to tensile strength is plotted against $N$ for both notched and unnotched specimens of a steel and three non-ferrous alloys. The results for the steels are similar to those from other sources quoted by Weisman and Kaplan [161], for notched specimens having values of $K_t$ between 2 and 2·5. The curves for the non-ferrous alloys are lower than for the steel, but for both unnotched and notched

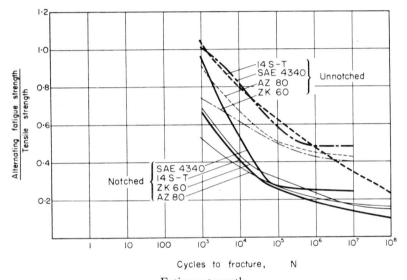

FIG. 80. Relation between $\dfrac{\text{Fatigue strength}}{\text{Tensile strength}}$ and endurance for notched and unnotched specimens tested in rotating bending

| Material | Tensile Strength, tons/in$^2$ | Reference |
|---|---|---|
| Ni Cr Mo Steel SAE 4340 | 71 | (Oberg and Ward [167]) |
| Aluminium Alloy 14S–T | 34 | (Oberg and Trapp [166]) |
| Magnesium Alloy ZK60 | 21 | (Oberg and Trapp [166]) |
| Magnesium Alloy AZ80 | 24 | (Oberg and Trapp [166]) |

*Details of Notch*

Root Radius $R = 0{\cdot}01$ in.
Depth $= 0{\cdot}025$ in., 60°V
Minimum Diam: 0·3 in.
$K_t = 2{\cdot}8$

results, a straight line from the point for failure in $10^4$ or $10^5$ cycles to the static tensile strength at a ¼ cycle usually gives a conservative estimate of the fatigue strength.

Notched fatigue strengths at low endurances are usually lower in direct stress than in bending[161]. Some results for high-strength steels are shown in Fig. 81 and for ferrous and non-ferrous sheet in Figs. 82 and 83. The tests on sheet specimens shown in Fig. 82 were made in alternating stress

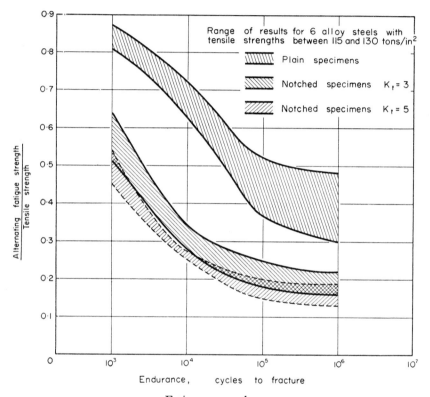

FIG. 81. Relation between $\dfrac{\text{Fatigue strength}}{\text{Tensile strength}}$ and endurance for plain and notched specimens of high-strength steels tested in direct stress. (Muvdi, Sachs and Klier [117])

Plain Specimens 0·2 in. dia.

*Details of notches*
Depth 0·0365 in. 60°V
Minimum Dia: 0·177 in.

Notch Root Radius:—
For $K_t = 3$, 0·009 in.
For $K_t = 5$, 0·003 in.

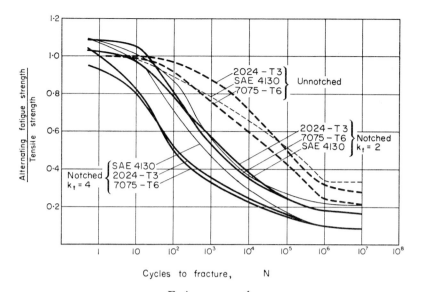

Cycles to fracture, N

FIG. 82. Relation between $\dfrac{\text{Fatigue strength}}{\text{Tensile strength}}$ and endurance for axially loaded notched and unnotched sheet specimens. (Illg [164])

|  | *Tensile strength tons/in²* |
| --- | --- |
| Steel SAE 4130 | 80 |
| Aluminium Alloy 2024–T3 | 32 |
| Aluminium Alloy 7075–T6 | 37 |

*Details of Notches*
Depth 0·375 in. Minimum width 1·5 in.
$K_t = 2$, Root radius $R = 0\cdot3175$ in.; $K_t = 4$, $R = 0\cdot057$ in.

Aluminium Specimens 0·09 in. thick
Steel specimens 0·075 in. thick

and guide plates were used to prevent buckling when the stress was compressive: those shown in Fig. 83 were made in pulsating tension.

## The Influence of Mean Stress on Notched Fatigue Strengths

The behaviour of notched pieces under fluctuating stresses can be represented on an *R–M* diagram similar to that used for unnotched pieces (see Fig. 48). Figure 84, due to Smith [189], shows the effect of a mean tensile stress and of a mean compressive stress on the axial fatigue strength. The results are from a number of sources, mostly for steels, and include tests on specimens with mechanical notches, bolts, specimens with as-cast surfaces and specimens undergoing corrosion fatigue. The behaviour is similar to that for unnotched specimens; under fluctuating tension the

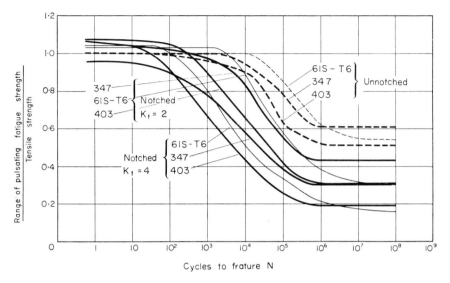

Cycles to frature N

FIG. 83. Relation between $\dfrac{\text{Range of pulsating fatigue strength}}{\text{Tensile strength}}$ and endurance for axially loaded notched and unnotched sheet specimens.
(Hardrath, Landers and Utley [299])

| | *Tensile strength tons/in²* |
|---|---|
| Aluminium Alloy 61S–T6 | 21 |
| 347 Stainless Steel | 40 |
| 403 Stainless Steel | 87 |

*Details of Notches*

| Depth 0·375 in. | Minimum width 1·5 in. |
|---|---|
| $K_t = 2$, | Root radius $R = 0·3175$ in. |
| $K_t = 4$, | Root radius $R = 0·057$ in. |

Aluminium Specimens 0·125 in. thick
347 Steel Specimens 0·064 in. thick
403 Steel Specimens 0·050 in. thick

Goodman line, drawn from the alternating notched fatigue strength to
the tensile strength, gives a conservative estimate of the fluctuating fatigue
strength for most of the results, while a mean compression increases the
fatigue range. The effect of a static torque on the torsional fatigue
strength, also due to Smith, is shown in Fig. 85. These results are also
from a number of sources, mostly for steels, and include a number of
spring steels, tested as springs and specimens with mechanical notches.
Unlike the behaviour in unnotched specimens, a steady torque reduces the
fatigue strength and most of the results lie close to the Goodman line

joining the notched alternating torsional fatigue strength to the torsional modulus of rupture.

The use in design of the Goodman line, drawn from the unnotched alternating fatigue strength divided by $K_t$, to the unnotched tensile (or torsional) strength is justified by the experimental results for most materials, but can lead to unsafe predictions of the fluctuating fatigue strength for notched pieces of alloys with a high ratio of yield strength to tensile strength. For these materials, fatigue failures can occur without the stress at the root of the notch exceeding the yield stress, and in these circumstances both the mean stress and the alternating stress that the material can withstand will be reduced by the presence of a notch. Gunn [300] has described a method by which the notched $R$–$M$ diagram for these materials may be predicted from the stress–strain curve and has shown that this gives a more reliable guide to the notched fatigue behaviour than the Goodman line.

A simplified procedure, described by Gunn, for predicting the notched $R$–$M$ diagram graphically is illustrated in Fig. 86. Firstly, the $R$–$M$ diagram for unnotched specimens is drawn—in this diagram it is assumed that the unnotched alternating fatigue strength is 10 tons/in² and the tensile strength, $U$, 30 tons/in². The yield stress, $Y$, is assumed to be 20 tons/in² and dotted lines are drawn to indicate the regions in which $Y$ and $Y/K_t$ are not exceeded. The first part of the notched $R$–$M$ diagram, $AB$, is then drawn from the unnotched curve by reducing both the alternating stress and the mean stress by the stress concentration factor $K_t$ (here assumed to be 3). The point of local yielding, $B$, is obtained by the intersection of this $R$–$M$ curve and the dotted straight line representing the locus of maximum stress = yield stress/$K_t$. It is then assumed that because of yielding, the mean stress at the notch does not increase with further increase of static load, so that the predicted $R$–$M$ diagram is given by $ABC$. There is little error in this assumption until general yielding is approached and this is outside the scope of normal design. The dotted curve was obtained by calculation from a stress–strain curve and it is apparent that the simplified procedure leading to the curve $ABC$ is sufficiently accurate for practical purposes.

In Figs. 87 and 88 Gunn's construction is compared with some experimental results quoted by Grover, Bishop and Jackson [301] for notched sheet specimens of the aluminium alloys 24S–T3 and 75S–T6. The yield stresses used for the construction are those quoted by the authors and are probably 0·2% proof stresses. It will be seen that for both materials the construction is in quite good agreement with the experimental results, particularly for low mean stresses. The construction gives a conservative estimate for all the results; this is partly because it is assumed that the stress concentration will be fully effective and no allowance is made for

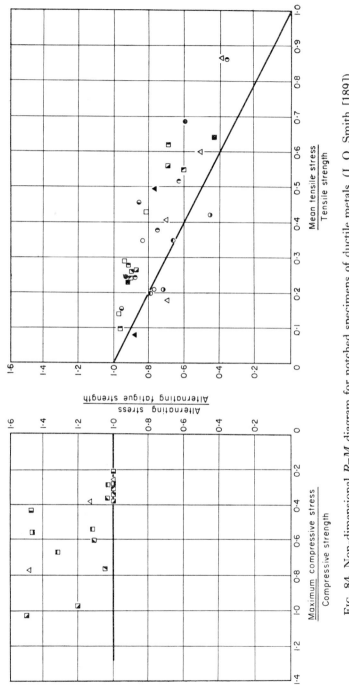

Fig. 84. Non-dimensional *R–M* diagram for notched specimens of ductile metals. (J. O. Smith [189])

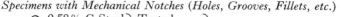

*Key to Fig 84 :*

### Specimens with Mechanical Notches (Holes, Grooves, Fillets, etc.)

◑ 0·58% C Steel ⎤ Tested
◓ 0·47% C Steel ⎬ as
◐ 0·07% C Steel ⎦ Bolts      A. Pomp
○ Spring Steel                   and
◪ Malleable Iron, Tempered     M. Hempel
◩ Malleable Iron, Untempered ⎦
◧ ST.50.11 Steel, Tempered ⎤
◪ ST.50.11 Steel, Annealed  ⎬ G. Seeger
◑ Cr–Ni Steel—P. Ludwik and J. Krystok
□ 0·7% C Steel—Schenck
△ SAE 3140 Steel, Heat treated—J. O. Smith
◪ 0·12% C Steel—A. Thum and W. Bautz

### Specimens with Chemical Notches (Corrosion Fatigue)

● 17-1 Cr–Ni Steel ⎤ H. J. Gough and
■ 18-8 Cr–Ni Steel ⎦ D. G. Sopwith
▲ Duralumin—H. J. Gough and D. G. Sopwith
◪ Cr–Ni Steel—P. Ludwik and J. Krystok
◪ Cr–Ni Steel, Annealed       ⎫ G. Seeger
◪ ST.50.11 Steel, Annealed     ⎭

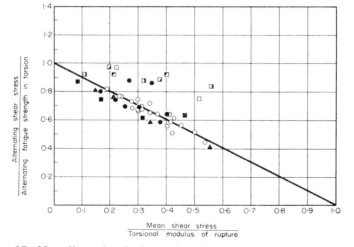

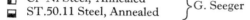

FIG. 85. Non-dimensional alternating shear stress–mean shear stress diagram for notched specimens of ductile metals in torsion. (Smith [189])

■ SAE 3140 Heat treated steel, Notched (transverse hole) ⎫ J. O. Smith
▲ Tobin Bronze, Notched (transverse hole)               ⎭
● 2 Spring steels, tested as coiled springs—Lea and Heywood
○ 9 Spring steels, tested as coiled springs—Zimmerli
□ Cr–Ni steel, Circumferential Notch ⎫ P. Ludwik and
◪ Cr–Ni steel, Corrosion             ⎭  J. Krystok
◪ Malleable cast iron, untempered, surface as cast ⎫ A. Pomp and
◪ Malleable cast iron, tempered, surface as cast   ⎭   M. Hempel

size and other effects which may reduce the notch sensitivity. A closer fit to the experimental results would be obtained by basing the construction on the alternating notched fatigue strength and this is shown for $K_t = 2$ in Fig. 87. This procedure is not recommended, however, if design data for large-scale components and structures are required. It may be noted that the Goodman line predicts an unsafe fatigue strength for many of the results in Figs. 87 and 88.

It is also apparent from Gunn's construction that a higher notched fluctuating fatigue strength would be expected from a material with a low ratio of yield strength to tensile strength than from one with a high

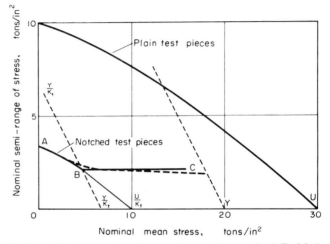

FIG. 86. Simplified procedure for predicting the notched $R-M$ diagram. (Gunn [300])

ratio. This is confirmed by a comparison of the results for the two alloys. The ratios of yield strength to tensile strength are 0·74 for the alloy 24S–T3 and 0·92 for the alloy 75S–T6, and, despite the higher tensile strength and unnotched fatigue strength of the latter, the former shows a higher notched fatigue strength at high mean stresses.

Some confusion may arise about the meaning of the strength reduction factor $K_f$ under fluctuating stresses. The *A.S.T.M. Manual on Fatigue Testing* [39] gives the following two alternative definitions:

1. The ratio between the stress amplitude for a polished unnotched test specimen and that of a notched test specimen, at the same nominal value of the mean stress and at the same value of $N$.

2. The ratio between the maximum stress for a polished unnotched specimen and that for a notched specimen at the same values of $R$ (ratio of minimum stress to maximum stress) and $N$.

The first definition is based on the assumption that the presence of a

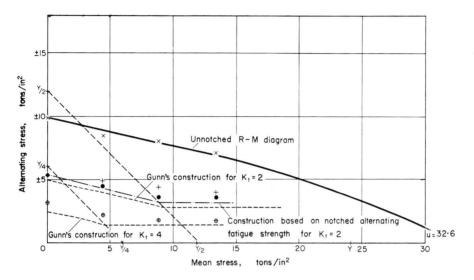

FIG. 87. Gunn's construction for the notched $R$–$M$ diagram compared with experimental results for axially loaded sheet specimens of the aluminium alloy 24S–T3. (Grover, Bishop and Jackson [301])

Yield stress 24·1 tons/in²
Tensile strength 32·6 tons/in²
Fatigue results are for failure in 10⁷ cycles
Thickness of sheet 0·090 in.

*Details of Notches*

● Hole 1·5 in. $R$. Width of sheet 4·5 in. $K_t = 2$

+ ⎧ Edge notches. Root radius $R = 0·3175$ in.
⎨ Depth of notches 0·375 in.
⎩ Width of sheet 2·25 in. $K_t = 2$

⊕ ⎰ Edge Notches
⎱ As above, but $R = 0·057$ in. $K_t = 4$

notch affects only the stress amplitude and not the mean stress. Values of $K_f$ defined in this way may exceed $K_t$ (see, for example, Fig. 88). The second definition is based on the assumption that a notch affects both the mean and the alternating stress. Values of $K_f$ defined in this way are lower than that for the first definition and would not normally be expected to exceed $K_t$. Other definitions have been suggested and if values of $K_f$ are quoted for fluctuating stress conditions, the definition used should be made clear.

## Crack propagation in fatigue

It is not always practicable to limit the fluctuating stresses on components and structures so that fatigue cracks never occur. It is sometimes

M

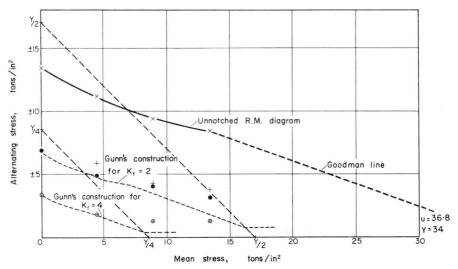

FIG. 88. Gunn's construction for the notched $R$–$M$ diagram compared with experimental results for axially loaded sheet specimens of the aluminium alloy 75S–T6. (Grover, Bishop and Jackson [301])

Yield stress 34 tons/in²
Tensile strength 36·8 tons/in²
Fatigue results are for failure in $10^7$ cycles
Thickness of sheet 0·090 in.

Details of notches as on Fig. 87.

necessary, therefore, to carry out periodic inspections of service parts to ensure that fatigue cracks do not propagate to cause complete failure. In these circumstances, information is required of the rate at which fatigue cracks are likely to propagate. There is no simple answer to this problem, because the rate of crack propagation depends on the material, the presence of stress raisers and the loading conditions. Relatively few investigations have been made and it is possible only to indicate in a general way the effects of the variables involved.

The first question to be considered is at what stage in the life of a part does a fatigue crack appear. Recent metallographic research has shown that fatigue cracks can be observed microscopically at a very early stage in the life. However, this is not relevant to the practical problem of detecting fatigue cracks in service and it is more useful (following a suggestion by Schijve [302] in a review of fatigue crack propagation in light alloys), to distinguish between micro-cracks and macro-cracks. The distinction between the two is arbitrary, and for the present purpose a macro-crack is considered to be one that can be detected either with the naked eye or a magnifying glass with the aid of crack detectors of the magnetic or penetrant dye type; this corresponds roughly with fatigue cracks of about 0·001 in. or more in length.

The stage at which macro-fatigue cracks occur in rotating bending fatigue tests at constant amplitude has been determined by Demer [303] for a number of materials using both unnotched and notched specimens and some of his results are shown in Figs. 89 and 90. $N_c$ is the number of cycles required to produce a fatigue crack and $N_f$ the total number of cycles to complete fracture. These results illustrate the influence of a number of factors.

1. The proportion of the fatigue life occupied by propagation of a fatigue crack (equal to $(N_f - N_c)/N_f$), increases with increase in the stress range. This is consistent with the observation that more cracks are found in a specimen fatigued at a high stress range than at a low stress range.

2. The proportion of the fatigue life occupied by propagation of a fatigue crack compared on the basis of the same total life, increases, in general, with increasing ductility of the material: that is to say, fatigue cracks tend to propagate more quickly in brittle materials. The exceptional behaviour of cast iron in this respect (see Fig. 89) may be attributed to the presence of graphite flakes acting as internal flaws.

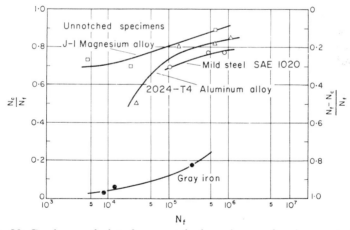

Fig. 89. Crack growth data for unnotched specimens of various materials as a function of number of cycles to fracture. (L. J. Demer [303])

3. The proportion of the fatigue life occupied by propagation of a fatigue crack, again compared on the basis of the same total life, increases with increase in the stress concentration; this is illustrated by the results in Fig. 90. Such behaviour is expected, for in a notched part the fatigue crack is propagating from a region of high local stress to a region of lower stress and, indeed, if the notch is very sharp the crack may cease to propagate once it has grown beyond the region of stress concentration

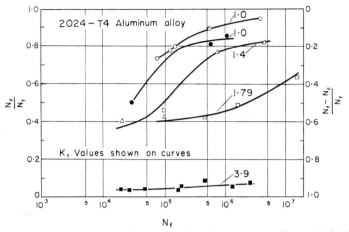

FIG. 90. Comparison of crack growth data from two studies on 2024–T4
aluminium alloy in various specimen forms. (L. J. Demer [303])
○, △ and □, Bennett and Weinberg
●, ■, Demer

(see page 146). This leads to the somewhat paradoxical result that if a
fatigue crack is found in service, it is likely to be more dangerous if it
has started from a mild notch than from a severe notch.

There is some evidence to show that there is appreciably less scatter
in the number of cycles required to propagate a crack to fracture than in
the number of cycles required to initiate a crack. This may explain the
observations that there is less scatter in fatigue endurance at high stress
ranges than at low and in notched specimens than in unnotched, because
the crack propagation stage represents a greater proportion of the life at
high stresses and in notched pieces.

The fractured surfaces of specimens or components which have been
subjected to interval or to programme tests show that fatigue cracks often
propagate in a comparatively regular manner. This is illustrated in Fig. 91
by a photograph, due to Forsyth and Ryder [304], of the fracture surface
of an L65 aluminium alloy bolted joint. The joint had been subjected to an
axial stress fatigue programme, each programme cycle consisting of the
following sequence of stress applications:

$$14,000 \pm 3950 \text{ lb/in}^2 \ 8940 \text{ cycles}$$
$$14,000 \pm 6550 \text{ lb/in}^2 \ 1790 \text{ cycles}$$
$$14,000 \pm 9200 \text{ lb/in}^2 \ 350 \text{ cycles}$$
$$14,000 \pm 11,700 \text{ lb/in}^2 \ 80 \text{ cycles}$$
$$14,000 \pm 14,400 \text{ lb/in}^2 \ 20 \text{ cycles}$$

The specimen failed after 98 of these programme cycles and each ring on
the fracture surface represents the progression of a crack during 1 programme cycle. Separate cracks had started from the four points A, B, C

and $D$ (Fig. 91) and probably from several other points between $C$ and $D$. Part of the fracture passed through a transverse bolt hole and all the cracks propagated from regions of heavy fretting damage.

A number of measurements have been made recently of the rate of propagation of fatigue cracks in sheet and a number of empirical relations have been derived to correlate the results [678]. One of the simplest is that derived by Frost and Dugdale [305] from the results of fluctuating tensile tests on 1 in. wide sheets about 0·1 in. thick, containing a small central slit. They found that the crack growth may be discontinuous,

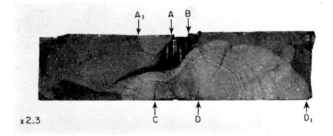

FIG. 91. Fatigue fracture of an L65 aluminium alloy bolted joint subjected to programme loading size 3⅜ in. by 1⅜ in. (Forsyth and Ryder [304]).

particularly at low ranges of stress, but that when the growth was continuous, the growth rate for crack lengths up to one-eighth of the sheet width could be represented by the following relation for all the materials tested:

$$\frac{\mathrm{d}l}{\mathrm{d}N} = \frac{lS^3}{N_s} \tag{35}$$

where $l$ is half the total length of the crack, including the initial slit, $S$ is the nominal alternating stress on the gross section, $N$ is the number of cycles and $N_s$ is a material constant which may depend on the mean stress. $N_s$ was found to be 11·6 ton-in. units for annealed mild steel for values of mean stress between 2 and 10 tons/in². The relative rates of crack growth for the ten materials tested are summarized in Table 34. It can be seen that there is no correlation between the susceptibility to crack propagation and the static mechanical properties.

As crack propagation proceeds, a stage is reached at which the relatively slow rate of propagation described by equation 35 suddenly changes to a much higher rate of propagation, leading quickly to fracture. The factors governing the onset of fast crack propagation are not yet established. There is considerable information available from static tests which indicates that it is dependent primarily on the nominal stress on the uncracked area of the

TABLE 34. RELATIVE RATES OF FATIGUE CRACK GROWTH (Frost [306])

| Material | 0.1% proof stress tons/in² | Tensile strength tons/in² | Elongation percent on 2 in. | Relative growth rate | | Remarks |
|---|---|---|---|---|---|---|
| | | | | For unit alternating stress | For a working stress which is a constant proportion of the 0.1% proof stress | |
| Austenitic steel | 16·5 | 43 | 56½ | 0·7 | 0·9 | Some dependence on mean stress. Fast cyclic fracture occurs at small crack lengths. |
| Mild steel (annealed) | 15 | 20·5 | 38½ | 1·0 | 1·0 | |
| Cold-rolled mild steel | 42·5 | 45 | 4 | 1·5 | 34 | |
| Cold-rolled copper | 14·5 | 20 | 11 | 4·3 | 3·9 | |
| Annealed copper | 1·7 | 14 | 62 | 4·3 | 0·006 | |
| Cold-rolled pure aluminium | 5·5 | 7·3 | 14½ | 12·5 | 0·6 | |
| Aluminium 4% copper alloy (BS L 71) | 27 | 31 | 9½ | 30 | 180 | Some dependence on mean stress |
| Tufnol (Kite brand paper base) | — | 6·1 | 0 | 55 | 3·5 | Very approximate. Brittle fracture occurs at small crack lengths. |
| Zinc | 3·4 | 8 | 65½ | 150 | 1·8 | Some dependence on mean stress. Fast cyclic fracture occurs at small crack lengths. |
| Aluminium 5½% zinc alloy Alclad (DTD 687a) | 32 | 35 | 13 | 163 | 1580 | Some dependence on mean stress. Initial period of crack growth at low stresses gives relative growth rates of 90 and 870. |

sheet and, in fatigue, Frost and Dugdale [305] have shown that it is dependent primarily on the maximum value of the nominal stress on the uncracked area $S_{max}$, and to some extent on the value of the mean stress, $S_m$, increasing with increase in mean stress. Their results showed that, for mild steel, rapid crack growth ensued when $S_{max}$ was about equal to the tensile strength, but for an aluminium–copper alloy the value was only about half the tensile strength.

The influence of fatigue cracks on the residual static strength of sheet

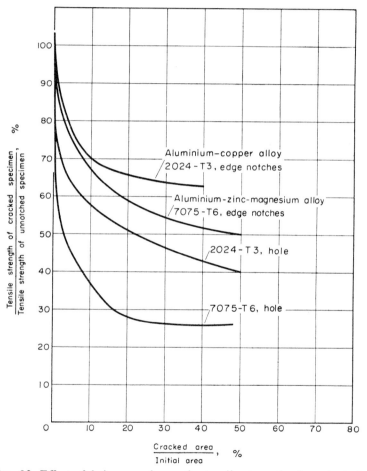

FIG. 92. Effect of fatigue cracks on the tensile strength of notched aluminium alloy sheet specimens. (McEvily, Illg and Hardrath [307]). The tensile strength is based on the uncracked area.

*Dimensions of Notches*
1.  Edge semi-circular notches. Minimum width 1·5 in. Radius 0·375 in.
2.  Central hole. Sheet width 35 in. Radius 0·5 in.

used in aircraft structures has also been studied in considerable detail recently [678]. The reduction in static tensile strength of aluminium alloy sheet resulting from the presence of fatigue cracks is shown in Fig. 92 and these results illustrate the importance of the crack length; the curves for the large specimens with a central hole are considerably below those for the relatively small specimens with edge notches. The results also show that the higher strength alloy 7075–T6 is affected more than the lower strength alloy 2024–T3. In general, ductile materials are less adversely affected. For example, in unnotched cylindrical specimens of mild steel, the presence of a fatigue crack covering between 10 and 20% of the section caused no reduction in the room temperature tensile strength (based on the uncracked area) but reduced the tensile strength at $-196°C$ by as much as 75% [308].

In steels the presence of a fatigue crack may seriously reduce the resistance to brittle fracture. For example, MacGregor [128] showed that fatigue cracks in mild steel could increase the transition temperature between ductile and brittle fracture by as much as 50°C. Kies and Holshouser [309] carried out tension impact tests after cyclic stressing on specimens of an alloy steel and showed that the smallest detectable fatigue crack resulted in important losses in impact strength.

## CHAPTER VI

# THE INFLUENCE OF SURFACE TREATMENT ON FATIGUE STRENGTH

FATIGUE failures almost always propagate from a free surface, so that the surface condition has a considerable effect on fatigue strength. This is because the stress is usually greatest at the surface, particularly when stress concentrations are present; moreover, the surface may be inherently weaker and may be further weakened by corrosive attack. It is therefore possible to achieve considerable improvement in the fatigue strength of engineering parts by the application of suitable surface treatments [120, 310, 311, 679].

There are basically three ways in which surface treatment influences fatigue strength, firstly, by affecting the intrinsic fatigue strength of the material near the surface, for example by strain-hardening or by a surface coating, secondly by introducing or removing residual stresses in the surface layers and thirdly, by introducing or removing irregularities in the surface which act as stress raisers. In practice we have usually to deal with the combined effect of these three factors, but the results of surface treatments can only be understood by considering them separately.

## Residual stress

There are two distinct types of residual or internal stresses in metals, micro-stresses and macro-stresses. Micro-stresses arise from differences in elastic and thermal properties of the various constituents in the metal and from the anisotropic properties of the grains. These are metallurgical factors which are influenced by the composition and heat treatment of the metal and their influence on fatigue strength has been considered in Chapter III. Macro-stresses are distributed uniformly over much wider areas and result either from plastic deformation produced by mechanical or thermal stress or by electrodeposition. The influence of surface treatment on fatigue strength is governed to a large extent by the effect of these long-range internal stresses.

The production of residual stresses by the application of external loads can be illustrated simply, by consideration of a rectangular beam subjected to pure bending, see Fig. 93 [312]. If the applied bending moment is

sufficient to cause yield in the outer fibres of the beam, the stress distribution will be of the form *BAOCD*, where *OAB*, *OCD* represent the tensile
and compressive stress–strain curves for the material. When the bending
moment is removed, the strain in the opposite direction, or spring-back,
is approximately elastic and this is represented by the line *FOE*. The
resultant internal stress system (which must satisfy the condition that the
total axial load and total resisting moment are both zero) is given by the
difference between *BAOCD* and *EOF*, and this is shown in Fig. 93b. It
should be noted that overstraining the material in tension results in a
residual compressive stress at the surface and vice-versa.

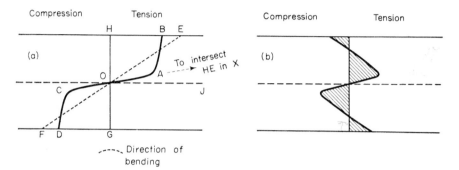

FIG. 93. Development of residual stresses in a beam of rectangular section
due to plastic bending. (G. Forrest [312])

The influence of a residual stress on fatigue strength is, in principle,
similar to that of an externally applied static stress, because the total stress
is equal to the algebraic sum of the internal and the external stresses.
Compressive residual stresses at the surface are therefore beneficial and
tensile residual stresses detrimental, because a static compressive stress
increases fatigue strength while a static tensile stress reduces it. For parts
stressed in torsion, residual stress has a smaller effect because torsional
fatigue strength is less affected by a static torque. It is difficult, however, to
assess the effect of residual stress on fatigue strength, partly because
residual stresses are difficult to measure and may alter in magnitude as a
result of further stressing and partly because whatever method is used to
produce the residual stress also influences the intrinsic fatigue strength of
the metal.

Residual stresses can be measured either by mechanical methods or by
means of X-rays, but both methods involve difficulties of technique and
interpretation. With the mechanical method successive layers of material
are removed from the specimen and the deformation of the remainder of the
specimen is measured as each layer is removed. The original residual
stresses in the specimen are then calculated from these measurements. This

method is well established [313–316], but care is required to avoid inducing thermal stresses which may alter the residual stresses. It is particularly difficult to determine the stress distribution if the stress gradients are high, as they often are near the surface. The principal advantages of the X-ray method are that it is non-destructive and may be used to determine the stress in a small region, for example at the root of a notch. Only the stress in the surface layer is determined, but it is the surface stress which is of major importance for resistance to fatigue. On the other hand, the measurements obtained are difficult to interpret, particularly when plastic deformation has occurred.

If further plastic deformation occurs during cyclic stressing there may be a gradual reduction in the magnitude of the residual stresses. Bühler and Buchholtz [317] showed by measurements on quenched specimens of various steels that this could occur even though the maximum stress applied was considerably below the initial yield stress. These authors also showed that residual stresses developed during the course of rotating bending fatigue tests in initially stress-free specimens of steel. Compressive residual stresses in the surface ranging from about 6 to 16 tons/in$^2$ longitudinally and about 2·5 to 8 tons/in$^2$ tangentially occurred after fatigue testing close to the fatigue limit. These effects were found not only for mild steel but for high-carbon steels for which the fatigue limit was far below the initial yield stress.

The effect of residual stresses on fatigue strength has been demonstrated most effectively by Rosenthal and Sines [318]. They carried out a series of bending fatigue tests on notched specimens of an aluminium–magnesium–silicon alloy, both in the fully heat-treated and annealed conditions. A residual compressive stress was induced at the root of the notch by pre-loading the specimens in tension and a residual tensile stress by pre-loading in compression. For heat-treated material, the fatigue strength was increased by about 30% when the residual stress at the notch was compressive and was reduced by about 30% when the residual stress at the notch was tensile. Almost the whole of this effect can be attributed to residual stress, because the amount of cold-work introduced by the pre-loading was very small and, moreover, any effect of the cold-work would be independent of the direction of the pre-load. For the annealed material, pre-loading had no significant effect on the fatigue strength and this was shown by X-ray stress measurements to be caused by the gradual disappearance of the residual stresses during the course of the fatigue tests.

Similar experiments have been carried out by Dugdale [319] and his results are summarized in Table 35. The tests were made on specimens containing round notches with a value of $K_t$ of about 1·5 and on specimens with a V-notch sufficiently sharp to produce non-propagating cracks. High pre-loads were applied to ensure that the greatest possible residual

TABLE 35. EFFECT OF PRE-STRAINING ON THE FATIGUE STRENGTH OF NOTCHED BARS
(Dugdale [319])

| Material | Yield stress or 0·1% proof stress tons/in² | Tensile strength tons/in² | Round notch * | | | | | V-notch † | | | | |
|---|---|---|---|---|---|---|---|---|---|---|---|---|
| | | | Fatigue strength, tons/in² (10⁷ cycles) | | | Change in fatigue strength | | Fatigue strength, tons/in² (10⁷ cycles) | | | Change in fatigue strength | |
| | | | As machined | Pre-stretched | Pre-compressed | Pre-stretched | Pre-compressed | As machined | Pre-stretched | Pre-compressed | Pre-stretched | Pre-compressed |
| 0·2% C steel | 19·0 | 30·5 | 12 | 12·5 | 11·5 | +4% | −4% | 7‡ | 11 | 6 | +57% | −14% |
| 0·45% C steel | 23·0 | 42·5 | 13·5 | 14 | 12·5 | +4% | −7% | 7‡ | 10·5 | 6·5 | +50% | −7% |
| 4% Ni steel | 76·0 | 112·0 | 37 | 44 | 13 | +19% | −65% | 22 | 34 | 4 | +54% | −82% |
| Aluminium alloy L65 (Al–Cu) | 30·5 | 34·0 | 10 | 13 | 5 | +30% | −50% | 4·5 | 8·5 | <0·75 | +89% | −>85% |

* Minimum diameter 0·4 in., maximum diameter 0·8 in., root radius 0·1 in. $K_t$ = 1·5.
† Minimum diameter 0·55 in., maximum diameter 0·85 in., root radius approx. 0·001 in.
‡ Stress relieved.

stress was induced at the root of the notch. The results show that the beneficial effect of pre-stretching and the detrimental effect of pre-compression is much greater for a high-strength nickel steel and aluminium alloy than for carbon steels. The effect was more marked with the V-notched specimens, and it may be noted that the fatigue strengths of the nickel steel and the aluminium alloy were reduced to very low values indeed by the presence of residual tensile stress at the root of the notch.

A compressive residual stress may be induced in the surface of a part if it is rapidly cooled from a high temperature. Becker and Phillips [320] applied a quenching treatment from the tempering temperature, known as temper stressing, to specimens of spring steel and obtained increases in fatigue strength. A more pronounced effect can be obtained on parts containing stress concentrations and this has been demonstrated by G. Forrest [312, 321] for aluminium alloys. He found little effect on unnotched specimens, but an improvement in fatigue strength of up to 80% for notched specimens.

There has been a certain amount of controversy about the relative contributions of work-hardening and residual stress towards the improvement in fatigue strength resulting from surface mechanical treatments. The results of Rosenthal and Sines [318] on a heat-treated aluminium alloy and of Mattson and Roberts [322] on a spring steel (see page 188) demonstrate clearly the pronounced effect of residual stress, but there is evidence that for softer materials the increase in fatigue strength produced by surface mechanical treatments results predominantly from work-hardening and not residual stress. For example, it has been shown by Horger [266] that the fatigue strength of large 0·45% carbon steel shafts could be increased 40% by surface rolling and this corresponded approximately to the increase in surface hardness of the shafts. As fatigue strength is closely related to hardness, this provides evidence that the benefit was derived mainly from work-hardening. (The relatively small effect of residual stress on carbon steels is also apparent from the results in Table 35.) Fatigue tests on titanium alloys, subjected to a variety of surface treatments, have also shown a close correlation between fatigue strength and the micro-hardness of the surface layers [323]. It may therefore be concluded that both beneficial residual stress and work-hardening of the surface can produce considerable improvements in fatigue strength and that, in general, the effect of residual stress predominates on hard materials and the effect of work-hardening on soft materials.

## Surface roughness

The roughness of the surface can also have an appreciable effect on fatigue strength [324]. The evidence for this is based mainly on the results of tests on steels and some of these are summarized in Table 36. The

TABLE 36. THE EFFECT OF SURFACE ROUGHNESS ON FATIGUE STRENGTH

| Material | Tensile strength tons/in$^2$ | Testing conditions | Fatigue strength, as percentage of maximum value (and in tons/in$^2$) | | | | | | Investigator | Ref. |
|---|---|---|---|---|---|---|---|---|---|---|
| | | | Highly polished | Polished | Ground | Smooth turned | Rough turned | Very rough turned | | |
| 0·02% C steel | 19 | R.B. | | 100 (±11·6, 00 emery) | | 92 | 88 | | Moore and Kommers | 120 |
| 0·45% C steel | | R.B. | 100 (±14, superfinished) | 100 (000 emery) | | 90 | 90 | | Horger and Neifert | 325 |
| 0·49% C steel | 43 | R.B. | | 94 | | 84 | 82 | | Moore and Kommers | 120 |
| 0·6% C steel | 47 | R.B. | 100 (±23, rouge) | 100 (00 emery) | 88 | 84 | 72 | | Glaubitz | 120 |
| 4 S 11 (3% Ni Cr steel) | 54–59 | R.B. | 100 (±29, superfinished) | 100 (±24) | 92 | 97 | | | Roberts and Grayshon | 120 |
| Cr Mo steel | 62 | R.B. | | 100 (0 emery) | 96 | 74 | 65 | | Glaubitz | 120 |
| DTD 331 Ni Cr Mo W steel | 80–90 | R.B. | 100 (±38, superfinished) | 100 (±34) | 93 | | | | Roberts and Grayshon | 120 |
| Ni Cr steel | 118 | R.B. ($10^7$) | 100 (±52, 0000 emery longt.) 100 | 94 (00 emery) | 99 | | | | Hankins, Becker and Mills | 326 |
| Ni Cr Mo steel | 138 | R.B. ($10^7$) | 100 (±65, 0000 emery longt.) | 76 (00 emery) | | | | | | |
| Brass, annealed | | Ax (60–80 × $10^6$) | | 100 (±12) | | 93 | 86 | 81 | Siebel and Gaier | 327 |
| Al Cu alloy, aged | | Ax (60–80 × $10^6$) | | 100 (±11) | | 93 | 72 | 68 | | |
| Al Mg alloy, annealed | | Ax (60–80 × $10^6$) | | 100 (±9·3) | | 100 | 77 | | | |
| Mg alloy, annealed | | | | 100 (±7·6) | | | 100 | | | |
| DTD 683 Al Zn Mg alloy | 35–37 | R.B. ($10^7$ cycles) | 100 (±12, longt. polish) | 94 (circumferential polish) | | 88 | 88 | | N. J. F. Gunn | 328 |

R.B. = rotating bending
Ax = axial

fatigue strengths for various surface finishes are quoted as a percentage of the polished or highly polished strengths (following Love [120]). The fatigue strength increases as the quality of a polished surface is improved and, in general, is higher when the direction of polishing is parallel to the direction of the applied stress than when it is perpendicular to it. It is clear from the results in the table that the effect of surface roughness is more pronounced in high strength steels. This is also illustrated in Fig. 94 by the results of fatigue tests on polished and rough-turned specimens carried out by Houdremont and Mailänder [329] on many steels with tensile strengths ranging from 20 to 70 tons/in².

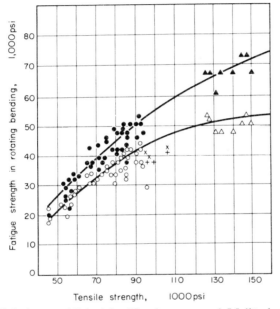

FIG. 94. Relation established by Houdremont and Mailänder between endurance limit and tensile strength for various steels. (Hanley and Dolan [324])

| ● Polished | ⎫ | ▲ Polished | ⎫ Quenched | × Polished | ⎫ Acid |
|---|---|---|---|---|---|
| ○ Rough-turned | ⎬ Annealed | △ Rough-turned | ⎬ and tempered | + Rough-turned | ⎬ Steel |

It is difficult, however, to determine how much of the observed effect results simply from the stress concentration effect of the surface discontinuities, for the surface treatments may also work-harden the surface and introduce residual stress. This probably explains the observation that the fatigue strengths of electropolished specimens are lower than for those mechanically polished, despite the smoother surface of the former. From rotating bending fatigue tests on four low alloy steels, Hempel [330] found that the ratio of the fatigue strengths of electropolished to mechanically polished specimens averaged 0·92 and from similar tests on eight alloy steels, mostly stainless, Cina [331] obtained an average ratio of 0·83. Both investigators found, however, that if the mechanically polished specimens were stress relieved after polishing, their fatigue strength was reduced to about the same value as the electropolished specimens. Thus, the fatigue strengths of these steels were apparently little affected by the differences in roughness between electro- and mechanically polished surfaces.

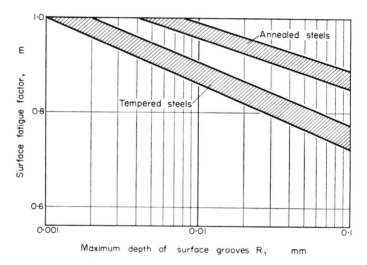

FIG. 95. The influence of surface roughness on the alternating fatigue strength of steels. (Siebel and Gaier [327])

$$m = \frac{\text{Fatigue strength for given roughness}}{\text{Smooth fatigue strength}}$$

A thorough investigation of the effect of surface roughness was made by Siebel and Gaier [327] for a number of steels and non-ferrous alloys. The roughness of each specimen was measured and the fatigue strength was compared with the maximum depth of groove $R$. They found that provided the maximum depth of groove was below a certain critical value $R_0$, which was dependent on the material, there was no change in fatigue strength and that above this value there was a linear drop in fatigue strength with log $R$. Tempered steels were more sensitive to surface roughness than annealed steels and all their experimental results in alternating stress, for both rotating bending and direct stress tests, lay within the bands shown in Fig. 95. A greater effect was found in pulsating tests, as shown by the bands in Fig. 96. Their results for non-ferrous alloys are given in

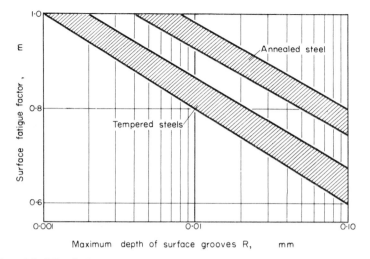

Fig. 96. The influence of surface roughness on the pulsating tension fatigue strength of steels. (Siebel and Gaier [327])

Table 36. The maximum depths of grooves R obtained for the various machining methods are shown in the following table:

TABLE 37. MAXIMUM DEPTH OF GROOVE FOR VARIOUS
MACHINING METHODS (mm)
(Siebel and Gaier [327])

| Surface | Steels | Non-ferrous alloys |
|---|---|---|
| Polished | <0·001 | <0·001 |
| Fine-ground | 0·002 | — |
| Rough-ground | 0·005–0·010 | — |
| Fine-turned | 0·010–0·020 | 0·005–0·010 |
| Rough-turned | 0·025–0·050 | 0·020–0·030 |
| Very rough-turned | >0·050 | >0·050 |

It can be inferred from the results of Siebel and Gaier that the fatigue strength of ground specimens is comparable with the fatigue strength of machined specimens of the same surface roughness. Severe grinding, however, can result in a reduction of fatigue strength [332], and this can be attributed to residual tensile stresses induced in the surface by severe local heating.

## The influence of specific surface treatments on fatigue strength

Metal surfaces may be treated in many different ways. Firstly, there are

N

mechanical treatments, including the normal processes of machining, grinding and polishing and also special treatments like shot-peening and surface rolling that are used primarily for their beneficial effect on fatigue strength. Secondly, there are thermal treatments such as flame- and induction-hardening and thirdly, surface coatings, including case-hardening and plating processes. Before discussing the effects of specific surface treatments, however, some consideration should be given to the fatigue behaviour of parts which are given no surface treatment after processing. All metals may show a reduced fatigue strength in these circumstances because of surface imperfections, but the effect is particularly serious in steels, owing to the decarburization of the surface which occurs during heat-treatment or forging, in an oxidizing atmosphere.

*Decarburization*

The marked reduction in fatigue strength that can result from surface decarburization is illustrated in Fig. 97 by some results obtained by Hankins and others [326, 333] on spring steels. Fatigue tests were made on specimens receiving no treatment after forging and on polished specimens from which the decarburized surface layer had been machined. When the strength is low the difference in fatigue strength is small, but the effect becomes increasingly important with increase in tensile strength. At 60

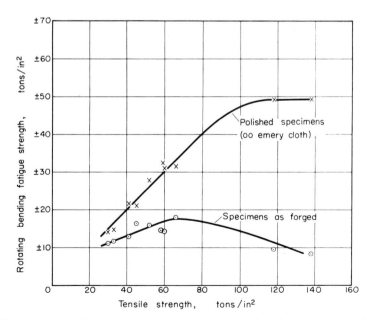

FIG. 97. The effect of decarburization on the fatigue strength of steels.
(Hankins and others [326, 333])

tons/in$^2$ tensile strength, the fatigue strength of the as-forged specimens was about half that of the polished specimens and for the very high strength steels the ratio was below one-fifth. In fact, the fatigue strength of a high-tensile steel in the as-forged condition is not significantly greater than that of mild steel.

A more recent investigation of the influence of decarburization on spring steels has been carried out by Watkinson [334], and his results are summarized in Table 38. These show that the reduction in fatigue strength results both from loss of carbon and from grain boundary oxidation. A carbon restoration treatment produced little improvement if the surface was oxidized; shot-peening, on the other hand, increased the fatigue strength considerably, while carbon restoration, followed by shot-peening, improved the strength of the surface to such an extent that fatigue failure was transferred to a point below the surface.

*Shot-Peening*

Shot-peening is a process involving the hammering of a metal surface with a relatively high velocity stream of steel or chilled iron spherical particles, with the object of increasing the resistance to fatigue failure. The principal effects of the treatment are to cold-work the surface layer of the material and to induce in it a residual compressive stress. Although the surface finish produced by shot-peening is much rougher than by machining or grinding, the resulting stress concentrations are quite small, because the depth of the indentations is only a small proportion of their radius.

The use of shot-peening has been restricted almost entirely to steel, but it is widely used and a number of reviews have been written of its influence on fatigue strength [335-337]. It has little effect on the fatigue strength of unnotched polished specimens. A summary of data by Love [120] shows that the improvement is usually less than 20% and in some instances shot-peened specimens have shown a lower fatigue strength than polished specimens. Considerable increases can be obtained, however, by shot-peening as-forged or roughly machined surfaces. The improvement that can be obtained on oxidized and decarburized surfaces is illustrated in Table 38. The process is used most widely for treating springs, both helical and laminated; it is particularly suitable for this because springs often have a decarburized surface and shot-peening can restore the fatigue strength more effectively and much more economically than machining or grinding. It can also be used effectively on imperfectly machined surfaces containing tool marks, scratches or other stress raisers, or on ground surfaces containing residual tensile stresses. Love [120] reports improvements in fatigue strength ranging from 5% up to 100% or more as a result of shot-peening full-scale components including crankshafts, axles, gears,

TABLE 38. THE INFLUENCE OF SURFACE TREATMENTS ON THE TORSIONAL FATIGUE STRENGTH OF SPRING STEELS
(Watkinson [334])

Range of repeated torsional fatigue strengths, based on $10^6$ cycles on $\frac{3}{4}$ in. diameter plain specimens

| Steel | A | B (En 42) | D (En 44) | E (En 45) |
|---|---|---|---|---|
| Chemical composition | 0.47% C 1.32% Mn | 0.77% C 0.63% Mn | 0.95% C 0.65% Mn | 0.60% C 0.92% Mn 1.87% Si |
| Fatigue strengths *tons/in²*: | | | | |
| Polished | 52.5* | 50.7 | 50.5 | 51.4 |
| Polished and shot-peened | 63.5 | 59.8 | 60.1 | 62.4 |
| Oxidized at 830 or 850°C. | 29.6 | 38.5 | 40.2 | 33.0 |
| Oxidized at 830 or 850°C. and recarburized | — | 42.0 | — | 37.3 |
| Oxidized at 830 or 850°C. and shot-peened | 59.4 | 58.2 | 57.0 | 55.2 |
| Oxidized at 830 or 850°C. and recarburized and shot-peened | — | 58.1 | — | 58.0 |
| Decarburized in dry hydrogen | 26.5 | 35.5 | 33.5 | 42.7 |
| Decarburized in dry hydrogen and recarburized | — | 46.1 | — | 46.0 |
| Decarburized in dry hydrogen and shot-peened | 40.7 | 54.4 | 49.0 | 52.5 |
| Decarburized in dry hydrogen and recarburized and shot-peened | — | 59.8 | — | 58.4 |
| Oxidized at 980 or 1040°C. | 22.2 | 22.5 | 21.8 | 33.7 |
| Oxidized at 980 or 1040°C. and recarburized | — | 25.7 | — | 36.8 |
| Oxidized at 980 or 1040°C. and shot-peened | 37.5 | 30.9 | 45.1 | 47.4 |
| Oxidized at 980 or 1040°C. and recarburized and shot-peened | — | 54.0 | — | 57.5 |

* Estimated value.

helical springs and leaf springs. Some results showing the effect of surface treatments, including shot-peening, on the fatigue strength of components are quoted in Chapter IX. Shot-peening also increases the resistance to corrosion fatigue and fretting corrosion (see Chapter VII).

There are no hard and fast rules for shot-peening procedure and the optimum conditions can best be determined for a particular material and component by carrying out actual fatigue tests or service trials. The variable factors are the type and size of shot, the pressure and velocity imparted to it and the time of application. The disadvantage of chilled iron shot is that it is brittle and breaks up during use, thus rendering the peening less effective. Steel shot cut from high strength steel wire has a much longer life so that a closer control of the process can be maintained; the cut shot rapidly becomes rounded in use. Shot between 0·025 and 0·03 in. diameter has been found satisfactory for a wide range of components, large and small, but the size of shot does not appear to be critical [335, 336]. Much smaller shot has proved effective for small sections, such as light springs, and may be more suitable for components with sharp changes of section, although there is evidence that shot-peening is effective even when the shot does not penetrate to the root of a notch [338]. Lessells and Brodrick [339] have shown that for an alloy steel treated to tensile strengths between 58 and 115 tons/in², the maximum residual stress developed was independent of the shot size in the range 0·003 to 0·025 in. diameter, but the depth of the residual compressive layer increased with the size of shot.

Jones [336] has stated that for shot-peening by the air blast method, pressures of the order of 30–40 lb/in² are commonly used, producing a velocity of about 180 ft/sec with shot 0·03 in. dia., and this has proved effective for steels of 85–100 tons/in² tensile strength. To be completely effective the treatment should be continued until the surface has been completely covered; prolonged treatment or use of too high a pressure can result in "over-peening", causing surface cracks and a consequent reduction in fatigue strength. Some measure of the intensity of shot-peening can be obtained using an "Almen strip". This is a thin strip of steel which is subjected to the peening treatment on one side only, the resulting curvature indicating the degree of residual stress [337, 340].

Almen [341] has shown that the maximum compressive residual stress produced by normal shot-peening is equal to approximately half the yield stress of the material, but that this can be increased if the treatment is carried out while the surface is subjected to a tensile stress; this process is known as stress- or strain-peening. A compressive residual stress equal to the yield stress $Y$ can be obtained by applying a tensile stress of about $Y/2$, and Almen considered this the optimum condition. The maximum benefit from this treatment will be obtained only in parts subjected subsequently to tensile stress, for otherwise the residual stress will be reduced by subsequent plastic deformation. The influence of strain-peening on the fatigue strength of leaf springs is illustrated in Fig. 98. In these experiments some tests were made on specimens strain-peened in compression in order to introduce adverse tensile residual stresses in the surface. The resulting residual stress pattern is shown in the right hand part of the diagram and the fatigue results demonstrate the marked effect of the residual stress.

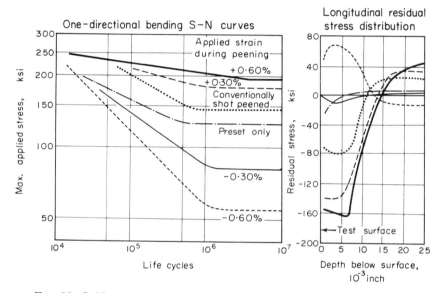

FIG. 98. *S–N* curves and residual stresses for variously shot-peened leaf springs (Mattson and Roberts [322]).

For some applications it may be necessary or desirable to apply a further surface treatment after shot-peening. If a smoother finish is required, as for example for a shaft working in a bearing, a light honing treatment sufficient to remove the high sharp peaks, only slightly reduces the improved fatigue strength induced by shot-peening [335]. It has been shown that the fatigue strength may be increased by as much as 20% by polishing after shot-peening, the optimum depth of polishing being about 0·005 in. [342]. It was claimed that this improvement was obtained because the maximum residual stress occurs below the surface, but this view is not wholly accepted and it is possible that the decrease in surface roughness as a result of polishing may be responsible. Heat treatment above 250°C should be avoided after shot-peening, because this may eliminate the residual stresses and reduce the fatigue strength.

Although shot-peening is used primarily on steel parts, it can also be used to improve the fatigue strength of other metals. Found [343] investigated the effect of shot-peening on magnesium alloy castings; he showed that the conventional treatment damaged the surface, but he obtained a significant improvement in fatigue strength by dropping large diameter shot freely from between 24 and 48 feet. A beneficial effect from shot-peening has also been demonstrated for titanium alloys [344] and aluminium alloys [337].

*Surface Rolling*

Rolling the surface of a metal can considerably improve its fatigue strength. This process may be more effective than shot-peening, because with a suitable pressure it is possible to achieve a greater degree of work-hardening and a higher residual compressive stress at the surface. The material can be hardened to a greater depth by surface rolling and there is the additional advantage that no roughening of the surface is introduced.

The use of surface rolling to improve fatigue strength has been discussed by Horger [314]. He showed that the depth of the hardened surface layer increases with increase of the roller pressure and in one crankpin examined he found this depth to be as much as 1 in. From experiments on unnotched shafts, he obtained increases in fatigue strength ranging from 20% to more than 80% as a result of surface rolling. The process is particularly effective, however, on parts containing stress concentrations. A well-known illustration of this is the higher fatigue strength obtained with screw threads formed by rolling than with those produced by cutting and grinding (see page 266). The fatigue strength of components such as crankshafts can be increased by cold rolling the fillets with steel balls. For cast crankshafts, Love [345] obtained an increase of 60% under completely reversed bending and of 80% under repeated bending, using a pressure sufficient to produce a small but detectable deformation of the fillet; similar improvements were obtained on forged and cast steel shafts. From the results of tests on V-notched specimens of cast irons, Gilbert and Palmer [346] showed that the benefit derived from surface rolling was dependent on the ability of the material to deform without developing surface failure. Their results are shown in Table 39.

The fatigue strength of a part containing a hole can be increased by pressing a steel ball into the edge of the hole. This is not so effective as rolling a fillet, but improvements in fatigue strength ranging from 20–60% have been reported [120].

Surface rolling can be applied equally well to non-ferrous metals, but there are few data available. An increase in fatigue strength of 50% has been obtained by surface rolling a 3 in. diameter specimen of a magnesium alloy and the process has been used to improve the fatigue resistance of magnesium alloy propellers [347].

TABLE 39. THE EFFECT OF SURFACE ROLLING ON THE NOTCHED FATIGUE STRENGTH OF CAST IRON IN ROTATING BENDING (Gilbert and Palmer [346])

Minimum diameter of notch 0·417 in., depth of notch 0·141 in., root radius 0·25 mm, angle of notch 45°.

| Material | Optimum rolling pressure lb | Notched fatigue limit, tons/in² | | % Increase in fatigue limit | Decrease in notch diameter, in. |
|---|---|---|---|---|---|
| | | unrolled | rolled | | |
| Pearlitic flake graphite cast iron | 79 | 7·5 | 9·0 | 20 | 0 |
| Ferritic flake graphite cast iron | 110 | 4·0 | 8·5 | 111 | 0·009 |
| Pearlitic nodular graphite cast iron | 406 | 12·5 | 30·4 | 143 | 0·014 |
| Ferritic nodular graphite cast iron | 327* | 8·0 | 23·4 | 193 | 0·021 |

* Maximum pressure used.

*Overstraining*

The beneficial effect of tensile overstraining on the fatigue strength of a notched bar was first demonstrated by G. Forrest [321]. He preloaded notched specimens of the aluminium alloy BS 6 L1 to three-quarters of their tensile strength and this doubled the fatigue strength at $10^8$ cycles. Similar experiments by Rosenthal and Sines [318] and by Dugdale [319] have already been described to illustrate the effects of residual stress. As the improvement in fatigue strength depends predominantly on residual stress, greater benefit is obtained in general with high mean stresses and for materials with a high ratio of yield strength to tensile strength. The prestraining of components and structures has not been much used in practice (except for the scragging of springs, see page 300), yet this treatment offers a simple means of improving resistance to fatigue. It has been shown, for example, that preloading a complete aircraft wing can appreciably increase its fatigue life (see page 319). As with surface rolling, the optimum preload for a given application can be determined only by direct experiment. The limited information available indicates that it may be as much as 90% or more of the tensile strength, which is well above the stress required to cause yielding in regions of stress concentrations [348]. It must be remembered, however, that residual compressive stresses are always balanced by residual tensile stresses at other places and one must be careful that these do not reduce the fatigue strength.

*Straightening*

Cold straightening operations are usually detrimental because of the tensile residual stresses that are introduced in regions where the material has been overstrained in compression. Love [120] quotes reductions in fatigue strength ranging from 20 to 50% as a result of cold straightening, but he also quotes evidence that such reductions may be avoided if hammer-peening is used for the straightening operation.

*Flame Hardening and Induction Hardening*

For steels, the thermal treatments flame-hardening and induction-hardening are often used for providing wear-resistant surfaces. The steel is heated to a temperature above the transformation range, either by means of a flame or by high-frequency alternating current, and then immediately quenched. It is possible to introduce residual tensile stresses at the surface on heating, but this is more than counterbalanced on cooling by the increase in volume associated with the phase change [349]. The resultant residual compressive stress on the surface, together with the surface-hardening can considerably increase the fatigue strength, particularly for notched parts. This is illustrated by some experimental data in Table 40 mostly taken from the review by Love [120]. It is necessary when using these treatments

TABLE 40 THE EFFECT OF FLAME- AND INDUCTION-HARDENING ON THE FATIGUE STRENGTH OF STEEL

| Material | Test conditions | Fatigue strength untreated tons/in$^2$ | Change of fatigue strength due to flame-hardening % | Change of fatigue strength due to induction-hardening % | Investigator | Ref. |
|---|---|---|---|---|---|---|
| C steel | *Unnotched* R.B. / T | 25·4 / 14·0 | + 60 to + 88 / + 18 | | Wiegand | 120 |
| En 12 0·35–0·45% C steel / En 16 Mn Mo steel | R.B. / R.B. | 21 / 26 | | + 19 / + 54 | R. J. Brown | 350 |
| En 24 1½% Ni Cr Mo steel | R.B. | 30 | | + 40 | | |
| SAE 1045 0·45% C steel | *Notched* ½ in. dia. R.B. Specimen with very sharp fillet | 8·0 | + 80 (Fillets only treated) + 190 (whole part treated) | | Zimmerman | 120 |
| 2½% Ni ½% Mo steel | R.B. Specimen with moderate fillet | 15·6 | + 40 | | Gross | 120 |
| Ni Cr Mo steel | T. 2·36 in. dia. specimens / T. 2·36 in. dia. specimens with transverse hole | 10·2 / 13·3 | + 6 / − 19 | | Cornelius and Bollenrath | 120 |
| SAE 1045 0·45% C steel / 0·52% C steel | *Rotating bending tests on axle with press-fitted wheel* 2 in. dia. / 7 9/16 in. dia. / 9½ in. dia. | 5·8 / 5·4 / 4·9 | > + 246 / > + 83 / + 46 to + 64 | | Horger and Buckwalter / Horger and Cantley | 120 / 120 |

R.B. = rotating bending
T  = torsion

to ensure that fatigue failures do not occur at the edge of the hardened regions, where very high tensile residual stresses are likely. This may account for the low fatigue strength sometimes found for parts surface-hardened by these treatments.

## Case-Hardening Steel by Carburizing, Nitriding and Cyaniding

Case-hardening is used primarily to produce a wear-resistant surface on steel parts, but it is also an effective means of increasing the resistance to fatigue, particularly to corrosion fatigue and fretting. In carburizing, the hardened case is obtained by heating the metal in contact with a carbonaceous material so that carbon diffuses into the surface, the metal then being quenched. In nitriding, the metal is heated in an atmosphere of ammonia and hardening is achieved by the absorption of nitrogen without quenching. By heating in molten cyanide, both carbon and nitrogen are absorbed and this is usually followed by quenching to obtain a hard case [351].

The improvement in fatigue strength obtained by any of these processes arises both from the higher intrinsic fatigue strength of the hardened case and from the compressive residual stress induced in it by the treatment. The combined effect of these two factors is usually sufficient to render the case more resistant to fatigue than the core and, consequently, fatigue failures in case-hardened parts are usually found to start in the region of the junction between the case and the core. Under these conditions the improvement in fatigue strength imparted by the surface treatment is dependent on the stress conditions and on the depth of the hardened layer in relation to the size of the piece. Under axial stress and in the absence of stress raisers, the stress below the surface is approximately the same as the surface stress and consequently case-hardening has little effect on the fatigue strength. There is an appreciable improvement in the unnotched bending or torsional fatigue strength as a result of case-hardening, particularly on small pieces, but the most striking improvements are obtained on notched pieces because the core is practically unaffected by stress concentrations at the surface. (This, of course, will not apply if stress concentrations, extending below the hardened surface layer, are introduced after the case-hardening treatment.)

Some typical data, showing the effect of carburizing and nitriding, mostly from Love's review [120], are shown in Tables 41 and 42. There are few data available on the effect of cyaniding; Lea [352] obtained an increase in fatigue strength of 97% for mild steel and Hankins and others obtained increases ranging from 5 to 74% on various steels, initially in the decarburized condition [326, 333].

The most suitable case-hardening treatment for a given application depends on the type of steel, the depth of case required, the amount of distortion permitted and the temperature attained by the part in service.

TABLE 41. THE EFFECT OF CARBURIZING ON THE FATIGUE STRENGTH OF STEEL (Love [120])

| Material | Tensile strength tons/in² | Testing conditions | Specimen details | Fatigue strength untreated tons/in² Plain | Notched | (Treatment) | Change in fatigue strength due to treatment % Plain | Notched | Investigator |
|---|---|---|---|---|---|---|---|---|---|
| 0·16% C | 30 | R.B. | 0·26 in. dia. 0·5 mm radius notch | 16·5 | 14·0 | | +88 | +82 | Wiegand |
| 1·0% Cr | 60 | | | 26·0 | 12·7 | | +105 | +95 | |
| 1·4% Cr 1·4% Mn | | | | 35·0 | 15·9 | | +75 | +120 | |
| 1·2% Cr 1·0% Mn 0·25% Mo | 65 | | | 28·0 | 12·7 | | +68 | +120 | |
| 1·2% Cr 1·0% Mn 0·25% Mo | | | | 29·0 | 8·9 | | +72 | +230 | |
| 2·0% Cr 0·2% Mo 2·0% Ni | 80 | | | 38·0 | 10·2 | | +32 | +219 | |
| 2·0% Cr 2·0% Ni 0·25% Mo | 80 | R.B. | 0·55 in. dia. transverse hole | 39·0 | 21·6 | Ground after carburizing | +13 | | Wiegand and Scheinost |
| | | | | | | Hole drilled after carburizing | | −38 | |
| | | | | | | Hole drilled before carburizing | | +29 | |
| | | T | | 15·9 | 7·6 | Ground after carburizing | +26 | | |
| | | | | | | Hole drilled after carburizing | | −17 | |
| | | | | | | Hole drilled before carburizing | | +142 | |
| C steel | — | R.B. | 5/16 in. dia. | 20·8 | | | +83 | | Woodvine |
| 3·5% Ni steel | 62 | | | 29·0 | | | +85 | | |
| 5·0% Ni steel | 72 | | | 34·0 | | | +62 | | |

TABLE 42. THE EFFECT OF NITRIDING ON THE FATIGUE STRENGTH OF STEEL

| Material | Tensile strength tons/in² | Testing conditions | Specimen details | Fatigue strength untreated tons/in² | | Change in fatigue strength due to treatment % | | Investigator | Ref. |
|---|---|---|---|---|---|---|---|---|---|
| | | | | Plain | Notched | Plain | Notched | | |
| Cr Mo V steel | 90 | Ax | | 40·0 | 10·5 | −5 | +142 | Bardgett | 120 |
| 1·7% Cr 1·3% Al steel | 62 | Ax R.B. | | 22·9 31·9 | | +2 +20 | | Sutton | 120 |
| Cr Mo Cr Mo Cr Mo V | 68 85 90 | R.B. | 0·355 in. dia. | 38·2 47·5 41·5 | 12·5 17·7 18·7 | +36 +20 +24 | +300 +189 +170 | Bardgett | 120 |
| Cr Mo | 62 | B T | 0·6 in. dia. Hollow with transverse hole | 33·0 19·9 | 14·5 10·5 | +23 +20 | +90 +88 | Frith | 196 |
| Cr Mo V | 90 | B T | | 43·3 25·3 | 19·3 14·3 | +10 +14 | +50 +60 | Gadd | 311 |
| Stainless steel 18·7% Cr 9·3% Ni | 40 | R.B. | | 15 | | +30 | | Malcolm and Low | 120 |
| Stainless steel 12·3% Cr | 58 | | | 28 | 5 | +15 | +750 | | |

R.B. = rotating bending          B = plane bending
Ax  = axial                      T = torsion

Carburizing produces a thicker case than nitriding; the depth of a carburized case is usually between 0·03 and 0·1 in., while a typical nitriding treatment, say 72 hr at 485°C, produces a case of 0·015 to 0·02 in. depth [351]. There is evidence to show that fatigue strength increases with case depth, but Frith [196] attributes this primarily to the effect of small specimen size—failure occurs between the case and the core, where the stress is appreciably less than the maximum, if the case depth is a significant proportion of the specimen radius. Little benefit will be obtained from this effect on large components and Frith therefore recommended that the effect of different treatments should be compared in terms of the stress at the fracture position. On this basis, he found for a chrome–molybdenum steel that a thin nitrided case (0·004 in., produced by 10 hours at 485°C) was almost as resistant to fatigue as a thick one (0·014–0·020 in., produced by 72 hours at 485°C) and he recommended the former treatment for components because only honing or lapping was required subsequently instead of grinding. There is generally more distortion from carburizing than from nitriding so that a final grinding operation is usually required after carburizing and, in addition, there is a danger of cracks being formed during quenching.

*Non-Ferrous Coatings on Steel*

Non-ferrous coatings deposited electrolytically or by other means on steel are used for improving resistance to wear or to corrosion or corrosion fatigue and also for building up worn and undersized machine parts. Their effect on fatigue strength has been reviewed recently by Hammond and Williams [353]. Electroplating with soft non-ferrous metals, such as cadmium, lead, tin and zinc have little effect, in general, on fatigue strength, but with the two harder metals, nickel and chromium, there may be serious reductions in fatigue strength. Some typical data are shown in Tables 43, 44 and 45 for chromium plating, nickel plating and zinc coatings respectively. Further data, showing the effect of surface coatings on air and corrosion fatigue strengths are quoted in Chapter VII (see Tables 50 and 51, and Fig. 107).

The reduction in fatigue strength resulting from chromium plating is dependent, to some extent, on the plating conditions, but there is insufficient evidence to establish the optimum conditions. The fatigue strength is generally little affected by the thickness of chromium plate and this is shown by several of the results quoted in Table 43. In contrast to these results, however, Williams and Hammond [359] found an appreciable effect of the thickness on material subsequently heat-treated (see Fig. 99). With nickel plating the fatigue strength is considerably reduced by increasing the thickness of the deposited layer, see Table 44.

It is well established that the reductions in fatigue strength resulting from chromium and nickel plating are directly related to the tensile residual stress in the plated layer. Barklie and Davies [356] and, more recently, Almen [358], have demonstrated that the fatigue strength of nickel plated specimens can be increased if the tensile residual stress is

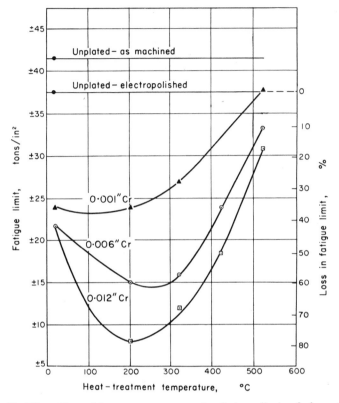

FIG. 99. The effect of heat-treatment on the fatigue limit of chromium plated steel for three thicknesses of chromium (En 25 steel, DPH 400). (Williams and Hammond [359])

reduced by varying the plating process and their results are included in Table 44. The fatigue strength of chromium plated pieces can be appreciably modified by subsequent heat-treatment and this is illustrated in Fig. 99. Heat-treatment at 200–300°C results in further reductions in fatigue strength, but improvements are obtained for temperatures above about 400°C. This behaviour was shown to correspond closely with the residual stress in the deposited layer; heat-treatment at 200–300°C increased the residual tensile stress, while at temperatures above 440°C a residual compressive stress was induced. Similar results were obtained by Logan [355] on a chrome–molybdenum steel, SAE X 4130. Heat-treatment after

TABLE 43. THE EFFECT OF CHROMIUM PLATING ON THE FATIGUE STRENGTH OF STEEL

| Steel | Tensile strength tons/in² | Chromium deposit | | Fatigue test conditions | Fatigue strength unplated tons/in² | Fatigue strength plated tons/in² | Change of fatigue strength due to plating % | Investigator | Ref. |
|---|---|---|---|---|---|---|---|---|---|
| | | Type | Thickness in. | | | | | | |
| 0·3% C steel | 40 | | 0·005 | R.B. | 15·8 | 16·1 | +2 | Kuun | 354 |
| SAE X4130, normalized (0·3% C 1% Cr) | | | 0·0001–0·009 | R.B. | 20 | 18 | −12 (Av. 10 results) | Logan | 355 |
| SAE X4130, quenched and tempered | | | 0·0001–0·017 | | 42 | 26 | −39 (Av. 14 results) | | |
| SAE 6130, quenched and tempered (0·3% C 1% Cr, 0·2% V) | | | 0·0001–0·009 | | 37 | 25 | −32 (Av. 10 results) | | |
| SAE 4130 | 83 | Standard Standard | 0·001 0·010 | | 36·4 | 27 28·4 | −26 −23 | Sinnott | 353 |
| | | CR110 (proprietary solution) | 0·001 0·010 | | | 33·6 33 | −8 −9 | | |

| Material | | Standard | | R.B. | | | | | |
|---|---|---|---|---|---|---|---|---|---|
| En 25 2·3–2·8% Ni 0·5–0·8% Cr 0·4–0·7% Mo | 80 | Standard | 0·0001 0·0003 0·0005 0·001 0·006 0·012 0·001 0·006 0·012 | | 37·5 | 28 27 27 24 21·6 21·6 20·6 21·6 21·1 | −25 −28 −28 −36 −42 −42 −26 −22 −23 | Williams and Hammond | 353 |
| | 60 | | | | 27·8 | | | | |
| SAE 4140 | 97 | CR 110 (proprietary solution) | 0·00006 0·00012 0·0003 0·010 | | 48·7 | 32·4 32·4 33·5 32·8 | −33 −33 −31 −32 | Stareck and others | 353 |
| S 11, 3% Ni Cr steel | 63 | | 0·0015 0·010 | Bending | 35·5 | 17·7 17·7 | −50 −50 | Frith | 310 |
| S 82, 4% Ni Cr steel, carburized | 71 | | 0·005 | | 43·5 | 19·2 | −56 | | |
| DTD 306, 3% Cr Mo steel, nitrided | 61 | | 0·002 | | 46·2 | 38·4 | −17 | | |

o

TABLE 44. THE EFFECT OF NICKEL PLATING ON THE FATIGUE STRENGTH OF STEEL

| Steel | Tensile strength tons/in² | Nickel deposit | | | Fatigue test conditions | Fatigue strength unplated tons/in² | Fatigue strength plated tons/in² | Change of fatigue strength due to plating % | Investigator | Ref. |
|---|---|---|---|---|---|---|---|---|---|---|
| | | Type | Thickness in. | Internal stress tons/in² | | | | | | |
| 0·09% C steel | | — | — | High | R.B. | 15·2 | 10·2 | -33 | Barklie and Davies | 356 |
| | | | 0·0005 | Low | | | 14·2 | -7 | | |
| 0·14% C steel | | | 0·0035 | | | 16 | 15·5 | -3 | | |
| | | | | | | | 9 | -44 | | |
| Armco iron | 20 | — | 0·004 | | Bending | 13·2 | 14·4 | +9 | Frith | 310 |
| S11, 3% Ni Cr steel | 64 | | 0·0015 | | | 35·2 | 21·8 | -38 | | |
| | | | 0·015 | | | | 15 | -57 | | |
| SAE 4330 (Ni Cr Mo steel) | | Soft plate Watts process | 0·0004 | | | 35·2 | 24·1 | -32 | Moore | 357 |
| | | Hard-plate process | 0·0004 | | | | 24·1 | -32 | | |
| | | Hard-plate process | 0·003 | | | | 19·7 | -44 | | |
| | | Soft-plate Watts process | 0·001 | | | | 19·7 | -44 | | |

| Material | | Bath | Thickness (in) | Stress | Hardness | | ± | Investigator | Ref |
|---|---|---|---|---|---|---|---|---|---|
| BS 5005/401, 3% Ni | 43·3 | Watts | 0·001 | 18·5 | 24·5 | 19·7 | −20 | Hothersall and Gardam | 353 |
| | | | 0·005 | | | 14·7 | −40 | | |
| | | | 0·005 (lapped) | | | | | | |
| | | Bright A | 0·001 | nil | | 18·7 | −24 | | |
| | | | 0·005 | | | 27·6 | +12 | | |
| | | | 0·005 | | | 18·4 | −24 | | |
| S65, 3% Ni 1% Cr | 72·5 | Watts | 0·001 (lapped) | 12 | Av. 34 | 26·2 | +7 | | |
| | | | 0·005 | 12 | | 29·5 | −14 | | |
| | | | 0·001 | slightly compressive | | 19·0 | −44 | | |
| | | Bright A | 0·001 | slightly compressive | | 23 | −28 | | |
| | | | 0·001 (lapped) | | | 33 | +3 | | |
| | | | 0·005 | −3·3 | | 26·5 | −21 | | |
| | | Shot-peened before plating | | | 21 R.B. | 8·5 | −60 | Almen | 358 |
| | | Shot-peened after plating | | | | 18·3 | −13 | | |
| | | | | | | 24·5 | +17 | | |

TABLE 45. THE EFFECT OF ZINC COATINGS ON THE FATIGUE STRENGTH OF STEEL (Love [120])

| Material | Tensile strength tons/in² | Testing conditions | Fatigue strength unplated tons/in² | Change of fatigue strength due to | | Investigator |
|---|---|---|---|---|---|---|
| | | | | Electroplating % | Hot-dip galvanizing % | |
| 0·02% C steel | 20 | R.B. | 12·1 | +2 | −4 | Swanger and France |
| 0·45% C steel annealed | 36 | R.B. | 16·1 | | −25 | |
| 0·45% C steel quenched | 54 | R.B. | 35·8 | | −42 | |
| 0·45% C steel tempered | 46 | R.B. | 20·8 | +5 | −14 | |
| 0·72% C steel annealed | 41 | R.B. | 15·6 | 0 | −13 | |
| 0·72% C steel quenched | 79 | R.B. | 55·6 | | −40 | |
| 0·72% C steel tempered | 75 | R.B. | 42·0 | +11 | −42 | |
| 0·5% C steel normalized | 43 | R.B. 0·275 in. dia. | 16·4 | −2 | −10 | Sopwith and Gough |
| 0·5% C steel as drawn | 65 | R.B. About 0·1 in. dia. | 24·5 | 0 | +1 | |
| Various wire steels | 76–85 98–112 | R.B. | 28–32 29–33 | | −21 to −28 −15 to −20 | Watt |

chromium plating at a temperature not less than 400–450°C can therefore be recommended provided that the resulting softening of the chromium deposit can be tolerated and that the mechanical properties of the steel will not be affected [359]. Unlike chromium, low temperature baking of nickel deposits applied to medium- and high-strength steel has little effect on the fatigue strength.

The fatigue strength of nickel- and chromium-plated steel can be increased by nitriding, by shot-peening or by surface rolling. The effect of shot-peening on nickel-plated specimens was investigated by Almen and his results are quoted in Table 44. Shot-peening before plating considerably increased the fatigue strength but an even greater improvement was obtained by shot-peening after plating. More recent investigations have confirmed that shot-peening produced similar improvements in the plated fatigue strength of high strength steels. Light grinding of peened and un-peened surfaces, carried out either before or after plating, has no significant effect on the fatigue strength [353].

It has been suggested that the reduction in fatigue strength resulting from electroplating may be partly attributed to the effect on the steel of the hydrogen absorbed during the plating process, but it has been shown that occlusion of hydrogen has little effect on fatigue strength [360] and also that the fatigue strengths of specimens from which the nickel or chromium plating has been removed, are equal or almost equal to the initial unplated fatigue strength [120].

The fatigue behaviour of nickel- and chromium-plated steels can be explained in general terms as follows. When the base metal is weaker than the plated layer, the fatigue strength is dependent almost entirely on the base metal and is not significantly influenced by the plating; this is illustrated by the results for chromium-plated 0·3% C steel in Table 43 and for nickel-plated Armco iron in Table 44. For higher strength steels, the fatigue strength is dependent predominantly on the strength of the plated layer. This is evident from the close relation between the fatigue strength and the internal stress in the plated layer and from the observation that, for a given heat treatment, the fatigue strength of chromium-plated steel is approximately independent of the strength of the steel [353]. This behaviour might be expected, for once a fatigue crack is formed in the deposited layer, the stress concentration at the end of the crack may be sufficient to propagate it through the underlying metal. On the other hand, the resistance of the base metal to crack propagation can sometimes influence the fatigue strength, as is shown by the beneficial effect of nitriding and mechanical surface treatments before plating.

Table 45 shows that zinc electroplating, unlike nickel and chromium, usually results in a slight improvement in fatigue strength, although hot-dip galvanizing is detrimental. A limited amount of data exists on the effect of other non-ferrous coatings on the fatigue strength of steel. Love [120] reports from various sources that electroplated lead and cadmium and sprayed aluminium have little effect; in two cases electroplated copper reduced the bending fatigue strength by 12% and electroplated tin markedly reduced the repeated load strength of some coiled springs. Some recent results, however, have shown that cadmium plating may reduce the fatigue strength of very high strength steels [671]. To lessen the risk of a reduced fatigue strength, a treatment to introduce residual compressive stress in the surface layers before plating was recommended and a heat treatment after plating to prevent embrittlement. Metal spraying can result in appreciable reductions in fatigue strength, probably as a result of the roughening treatment used before spraying. It has been shown recently, however, that satisfactory adhesion can be obtained by spraying a thin layer of molybdenum on to a shot blasted surface and in this condition the reduction in fatigue strength for various steels was less than 10% [361]. Phosphate coatings which improve resistance to fretting corrosion, cause slight reduction in the normal fatigue strength [120, 310].

*Surface coatings on non-ferrous metals.*—There is much less information available on the effect of surface coatings on the fatigue strength of non-ferrous metals than there is for steel. The effect of nickel and chromium plate on aluminium alloys are variable; under some conditions little reduction in fatigue strength has been found [310], while in others marked reductions have been observed [353]. A coating of high purity aluminium (alclad), applied to aluminium alloys to improve their corrosion resistance, reduces the fatigue strength of laboratory specimens appreciably (see Table 7) but it has little effect on the fatigue strength of joints. Anodising treatments, producing an oxide coating for protection against corrosion and abrasion, usually have little effect on the fatigue strength of aluminium alloys [362], although a reduction of 50% has been reported for an aluminium–copper alloy [363]. A significant reduction in fatigue strength as a result of anodising has also been found for a magnesium alloy (see Table 51, page 224).

## CHAPTER VII

# CORROSION FATIGUE AND
# FRETTING CORROSION

### Corrosion fatigue

CORROSIVE action on the surface of a metal may cause a general roughening of the surface and the formation of pits or crevices at certain points and this can result in a considerable loss in fatigue strength if the metal is subsequently subjected to fluctuating stresses. Much greater reductions in fatigue strength result, however, from the combined effect of both corrosion and fluctuating stresses acting together than from either factor acting separately and the term corrosion fatigue is used to describe this behaviour. It is difficult to define corrosion fatigue precisely because corrosion can proceed in any oxidizing environment. Normal fatigue in air might therefore be regarded, strictly, as corrosion fatigue and it has been demonstrated that the fatigue strength of a number of metals can be increased if the supply of air to the surface is restricted. For practical purposes, however, corrosion fatigue may be regarded as the effect of fluctuating stresses in a corrosive environment other than air. The process has been shown to be an electro-chemical one and, as discussed later, this accounts for its highly damaging effect. Reviews of corrosion fatigue behaviour have been written by Gough in 1932 [364], and more recently by Gilbert [365], Gould [366] and Evans [367]; Gilbert gives an extensive bibliography. Corrosion fatigue is a process quite distinct from stress corrosion cracking, which results from a steady stress acting in a corrosive environment. Stress corrosion occurs only in certain metals, generally after an incorrect heat-treatment [367], while most, if not all, metals are susceptible to corrosion fatigue.

Corrosion fatigue accounts for a wide variety of failures in service, including, for example, marine propeller shafts, boiler and superheater tubes, turbine and pump components, and pipes carrying corrosive liquids. Corrosion fatigue failures differ from normal fatigue failures in a number of ways. Firstly, the surface is often discoloured by the corrosion process, although this is not an essential characteristic. The amount of surface corrosion observed depends on the material and the corrosive medium and is usually greater in service failures than in laboratory failures because of the shorter duration of most laboratory tests. Ordinary steels show slight

205

surface rusting when tested in fresh water and more pronounced rusting in salt water, but stainless steels and nitrided steels often show no obvious signs of rusting even though the fatigue strength has been reduced considerably by subjection to salt spray.

Another distinguishing feature of corrosion fatigue is the appearance of the fatigue cracks. There are usually many more cracks present than in a normal fatigue failure; this is because the electro-chemical attack is reduced as the crack grows; consequently the rate of crack propagation is reduced, allowing time for further cracks to form. Photographs of typical service fractures are shown in Figs. 100 and 101. Figure 100 shows a specimen cut from a water-wall side box of a water-tube boiler, the external surface of which had been chilled intermittently by wet fuel coming into contact with it. The individual cracks are widened at the surface by corrosion that has occurred after their initiation. The width decreases below the surface, ending in a fine crack which is similar to a normal fatigue crack and is usually transcrystalline. A photomicrograph of a corrosion fatigue crack showing these features is illustrated in Fig. 102. Corrosion fatigue cracks are easily distinguished from stress corrosion cracks, which show many branches and are usually intercrystalline. In shafts subjected to torsional stresses, the direction of corrosion fatigue cracks is at 45° to the axis, on planes normal to the maximum principal stresses and this leads to the characteristic criss-cross appearance and serrated fracture illustrated in

FIG. 100. Typical corrosion fatigue cracks. (Cottell [1])

FIG. 101. Corrosion fatigue fracture in tailshaft resulting from sea water penetrating rubber sleeve between two liners. (Bunyan [368])

Fig. 101. In this respect the behaviour differs from that of torsional fatigue failures in air, where the cracks usually propagate in the directions of maximum shear stress. However, cracks normal to the principal stresses do occur in air if stress concentrations are present and the corrosion fatigue behaviour can be explained by the stress raising effect of the corrosion pits.

Comparisons of the results of fatigue tests carried out in corrosive environments, with those carried out in air, show that the detrimental effect of corrosion increases with the duration of the test. S–N curves obtained from corrosion fatigue tests show much less tendency to become horizontal and even in a relatively mild corrosive liquid like fresh water it is doubtful whether any metals show a distinct fatigue limit. In a strong corrosive medium, the downward slope of the S–N curve can be very marked, and this is illustrated in Fig. 103 by the results of Gough and Sopwith [369] on various materials tested in a salt spray. It is clearly necessary always to quote the corrosion fatigue strengths for a given endurance and not to use the term corrosion fatigue limit. It is also found that the corrosion fatigue strength is dependent on the frequency of the stress cycle and this

should therefore also be quoted. For the data in Fig. 103 both direct stress
and bending fatigue tests were carried out at about 2200 cycles per minute.

### Influence of Prior Corrosion on Fatigue Strength

The effect of corrosion in the absence of stress on the subsequent fatigue
behaviour in air has been thoroughly investigated by McAdam. He carried
out tests on a wide range of steels and some aluminium alloys in which

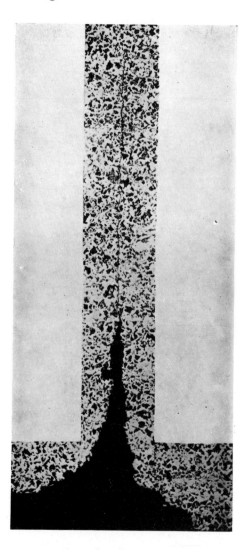

Fig. 102. Corrosion pit and fatigue crack in water-cooled piston rod.
(H. J. Gough [364])

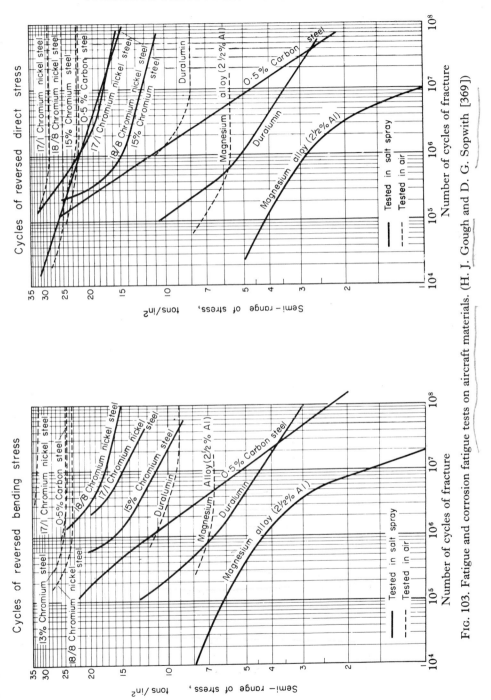

FIG. 103. Fatigue and corrosion fatigue tests on aircraft materials. (H. J. Gough and D. G. Sopwith [369])

specimens were corroded in fresh water for varying times, then dried and oiled and subjected to fatigue tests. The prior corrosion reduced the fatigue strength, the reduction increasing with the time of immersion in water, but the *S–N* curve for a given immersion time was similar in shape to the curve in air; thus, the curves for steel became horizontal and showed a fatigue limit. The detrimental effect of the prior corrosion increased with the tensile strength of the metal and McAdam and Clyne [295] showed that the results could be conveniently summarized by plotting the reduction in fatigue limit against the tensile strength for various corrosion times, as shown in Fig. 104. They attributed the loss in fatigue strength primarily to the stress concentration effect of the corrosion pits formed, because the general loss in section from corrosion was negligible, and they showed that curves similar in shape to those in Fig. 104 were obtained from tests on

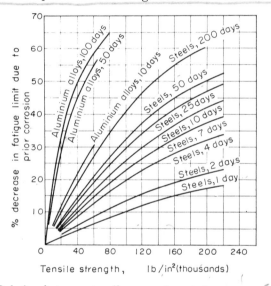

Fig. 104. Relation between tensile strength and the percentage decrease in fatigue limit of steels and aluminium alloys due to stressless corrosion. (D. J. McAdam and R. W. Clyne [295])

specimens with mechanical notches. In later work McAdam attempted to correlate the behaviour with the form, size and distribution of the corrosion pits [370].

### The Resistance of Metals to Corrosion Fatigue

The resistance of metals to corrosion fatigue is determined by carrying out fatigue tests in normal fatigue machines on specimens maintained in a corrosive environment. A number of different methods have been used for applying the corroding liquid including complete immersion, a flow or spray of liquid directed at the specimen or a tape or wick saturated with the liquid to maintain a film on the specimen surface. The corrosion fatigue strength is considerably influenced by the method of application, because the corrosion rate depends on the supply of oxygen; thus, for example, a spray of liquid is much more damaging than complete immersion. As a result it is obviously not possible to quote a single value for the corrosion fatigue strength of a metal, nor is it usually possible to make quantitative comparisons of the results of different investigators. However, a number of investigators have determined the corrosion fatigue resistance of a wide range of metals for a particular set of test conditions and it is therefore possible to make some generalizations about the influence of chemical composition and heat treatment.

The most important conclusion to be drawn from the data available is that resistance to corrosion fatigue depends primarily on resistance to corrosion. This is evident from a most comprehensive series of experiments carried out by McAdam, the results of which were reviewed by Gough [364]. McAdam carried out rotating bending fatigue tests, both in air and with a stream of fresh water directed at the specimen, for a wide range of ferrous and non-ferrous metals. The results of his tests on steels are summarized in Fig. 105, where the fatigue strengths in air and in water are plotted against the tensile strength. The results in air show the usual behaviour, the fatigue limit being approximately proportional to the tensile strength. For the results in water, however, the fatigue strength of the carbon steels and low alloy steels is almost independent of the tensile strength. All the results on carbon steels, covering a range of carbon content from 0·03 to 1·09%, both annealed and hardened and tempered, showed corrosion fatigue strengths between $\pm 6$ and $\pm 11$ tons/in². For the low alloy steels, with tensile strengths ranging from 40 to 112 tons/in², the range was $\pm 5\frac{1}{2}$ to $\pm 13\frac{1}{2}$ tons/in². For both carbon and low alloy steels the corrosion fatigue strength was usually higher in the annealed condition than hardened and tempered. The corrosion resistant steels, containing 5% or more of chromium, showed much greater resistance to corrosion fatigue and, as shown in Fig. 105, the corrosion fatigue strength was approximately proportional to the tensile strength.

Some other corrosion fatigue data for ferrous metals from various sources have been collected in Table 46. It can be seen from these results that salt water is much more harmful than fresh water. The fatigue strength of carbon steels is only about 2 tons/in² at $10^8$ cycles in the presence of salt water and the fatigue strength of corrosion resistant steels is seriously reduced. The tests made by Wescott were carried out with the specimens completely immersed in brine, so that the supply of oxygen was restricted, and under these conditions the reductions in fatigue strength are not so

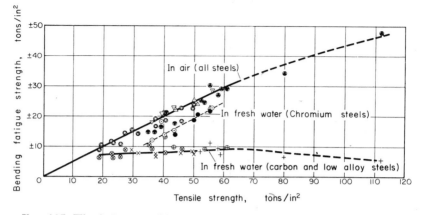

FIG. 105. The influence of heat-treatment and chemical composition on the corrosion fatigue strength of steels. (McAdam [371], Gough [364])

Rotating bending fatigue strength
(20 × 10⁶ *cycles*, 1450 *cycles per min*)

|  | Heat-treated material tested in air | Annealed material tested in air | Heat-treated material tested in fresh water | Annealed material tested in fresh water |
|---|---|---|---|---|
| Carbon Steels | ◓ | ◓ | × | ⊗ |
| Low Alloy Steels | ◓ | ◓ | + | ⊕ |
| Chromium Steels | △ | ▽ | ● | ⊙ |

serious. Unlike the results of McAdam's tests in fresh water, Wescott's results show that low alloy steels are considerably more resistant than carbon steels. The effect of steam on the fatigue strength of steels is illustrated in Table 47 by the results of an investigation by Fuller [376]. The effect of prior corrosion was examined by tests on specimens which were heated for a week in an atmosphere of wet steam and air and subsequently tested either in air or in steam. The results of these tests showed that, as with corrosion in water, the effect of prior corrosion is small compared with the damage caused by combined corrosion and fluctuating stresses. The high resistance to corrosion fatigue shown by nitrided steels is also illustrated by Fuller's results in Table 47. Martin and Smith [377] investigated the effect of liquid metal environments and showed that the fatigue strengths of mild steel and of stainless steel at 300°C were little affected by liquid tin and liquid sodium respectively.

A collection of corrosion fatigue data on non-ferrous metals is given in Table 48. McAdam's results [378] illustrate the high resistance of copper and copper alloys to corrosion fatigue even in cold-worked alloys, which are susceptible to stress corrosion. The results for a series of copper–nickel alloys show that the damaging effect of corrosion increases as the

TABLE 46. CORROSION FATIGUE DATA FOR FERROUS METALS

| Material | Heat treatment | Tensile strength tons/in² | Type of fatigue stress | Frequency of stress cycles/min | Corrosive medium | Endurance basis for corrosion fatigue tests | Fatigue limit in air tons/in² | Corrosion fatigue strength tons/in² | Corrosion fatigue strength ÷ Air fatigue strength | Ref. |
|---|---|---|---|---|---|---|---|---|---|---|
| Mild steel 18/8/1 Cr, Ni, W steel | Normalized Annealed | | R.B. | | River Tees water drip feed | 10⁸ | 17·0 17·6 | [2] 11·1 | 0·12 0·63 | Inglis and Lake [372] |
| 0·21% C steel | Annealed | 31·8 | R.B. T | 1300 1500 | Sea water | 10⁸ | 14·3 9·0 | 1·9 2·5 | 0·13 0·28 | Hara [373] |
| 12·5% Cr steel / 18/8 stainless / 18·5% Cr steel / 0·48% C steel, Cd plated | Annealed | 65 84 50 72 | T | 360 | Fresh water | 25 × 10⁶ | 16·3 12·3 15·6 12·9 | 8·0 5·3 12·3 3·3 | 0·49 0·44 0·79 0·26 | Haven [374] |
| C steel SAE 1035 (0·32–0·38% C) / C steel SAE 1050 (0·48–0·55% C) | | 39 / 42 | R.B. | 1750 | (1) 6·8% salt solution (2) 6·8% salt solution sat. with H₂S specimens completely immersed | 10⁷ | 18·1 / 14·1 | (1) 11·0 (2) 4·7 (1) 8·9 (2) 4·9 | 0·61 0·26 0·63 0·35 | Wescott [375] |
| C steel SAE 1050 | Water quenched and drawn | 58 | | | | | 26·9 | (1) 11·3 (2) 6·2 | 0·42 0·23 | |
| Alloy steel SAE 4130 (0·8–1·1% Cr, 0·15–0·25% Mo) | Water quenched and drawn | 57 | | | | | 31·3 | (1) 12·0 (2) 6·3 | 0·38 0·20 | |
| Alloy steel SAE 9260 (0·55–0·65% C, 1·8–2·2% Si) | Normalized | 64 | | | | | 32·2 | (1) 11·1 (2) 6·6 | 0·35 0·20 | |
| 5% Cr steel | Oil quenched and drawn | 58 | | | | | 33·0 | (1) 23·6 (2) 6·9 | 0·71 0·21 | |
| Wrought iron | | 21 | | | | | 13·6 | (1) 8·7 (2) 7·3 | 0·64 0·54 | |

Corrosion fatigue data for steels given protective treatments are given in Table 50
R.B. = Rotating bending
T = Torsion

TABLE 47. THE EFFECT OF STEAM ON THE FATIGUE STRENGTH OF STEELS (Fuller [376])

Rotating bending tests at 2200 cycles/min.
Fatigue strengths based on $50 \times 10^6$ cycles

Fatigue strength, tons/in²

| Material | Tensile strength tons/in² | In air | Under jet of steam in air | In steam at pressure and temperature given | | |
|---|---|---|---|---|---|---|
| | | | | 0 lbs/in² 100°C | 60 lbs/in² 149°C | 220 lbs/in² 371°C |
| 3·5% Ni steel | 47 | 20·5 | 10·5 | | 16 | 15·5 |
| 3·5% Ni steel | 53 | 26 | 10·5 | 26 | 24 | 23·5 |
| 3·5% Ni steel, Cr plated | | | 18·5 | | 20·5 | |
| 12·5% Cr stainless iron | 45 | 27 | 14·5 | 24 | 24·5 | 24 |
| 0·36% C 1·5% Cr 1·2% Al nitriding steel, not nitrided | 55 | 33 | | | 28·5 | 22·5 |
| 0·36% C 1·5% Cr 1·2% Al nitriding steel, nitrided | | 40·5 | 32·5 | | 31 | 26 |

copper content is decreased. Gcugh and Sopwith [379] have also demonstrated the high resistance of copper alloys by tests on a number of bronzes carried out in a salt spray. A corrosion fatigue strength of $17 \cdot 4$ tons/in² at $5 \times 10^7$ cycles, obtained by them for a beryllium bronze, was higher than they had previously found for stainless steels or any other materials under similar testing conditions. Later tests by Sopwith [380] showed that, as for steels, no improvement in the corrosion fatigue resistance of bronzes was obtained by heat treatment. Higher corrosion fatigue strengths can be obtained now with titanium alloys. For example, Inglis [384] quotes a result obtained with commercially pure titanium showing a higher fatigue strength in a 3% salt solution than in air. Further results in Table 48 show that the fatigue strength of aluminium alloys can be considerably reduced by corrosion and the fatigue strength of magnesium alloys reduced to very low values indeed.

*Effect of the Nature, Concentration and Temperature of the Corrosive Environment*

Most of the data quoted refer to corrosion fatigue tests in fresh or salt water, but tests have been carried out in a number of other environments. In general the effect of a corrosive solution on resistance to fatigue is closely related to its effect on stressless corrosion. The detrimental effect increases with the concentration of the solution but a limit may be reached because the solubility of air decreases with increasing concentration of the solution and oxygen is usually necessary for the corrosion fatigue process [366]. Few attempts have been made to compare directly the effects of different corrosive environments, although McAdam included tests on four different waters in his investigations. He found there was little difference between hard and soft fresh water, but a river water containing some salt was usually more detrimental (see Table 48).

Many components and structures operate out of doors and are therefore subject to atmospheric corrosion from continuous exposure to the weather. There is no doubt that this must affect their resistance to fatigue, but there is almost no experimental evidence to show to what extent the fatigue strength is reduced. One attempt has been made to determine the effect of atmospheric corrosion on the fatigue strength of aluminium alloys by conducting intermittent fatigue tests out of doors, so that the specimens were exposed to the weather for several months during the course of the tests [385]. By comparison with similar tests conducted indoors, the atmospheric effects reduced the average lives of the specimens by about 3 times for the alloys 7075–T6 and 2024–T3 in the bare condition, about $1\frac{1}{2}$ times for alclad 7075–T6 and had no significant effect on alclad 2024–T3. Some Russian results have been quoted [386], which show that the fatigue strength of a quenched and tempered carbon steel was reduced by nearly 50% by testing in moist air containing $0 \cdot 27\%$ $SO_2$.

P

TABLE 48. CORROSION FATIGUE DATA FOR NON-FERROUS METALS

| Material | Heat treatment | Tensile strength tons/in² | Type of fatigue stress | Frequency of stress cycles/min | Corrosive medium | Endurance basis for fatigue tests | Fatigue strength in air tons/in² | Corrosion fatigue strength tons/in² | Corrosion fatigue strength / Air fatigue strength | Ref. |
|---|---|---|---|---|---|---|---|---|---|---|
| Aluminium | Annealed | 5·6 | R.B. | 1450 | (1) Fresh water<br>(2) River water with saline content about $\frac{3}{8}$ that of sea water | $2 \times 10^7$ | 2·7 | (2) 1·1 | 0·41 | McAdam [378] |
| Aluminium | Half hard | 7·1 | | | | | 3·2 | (1) —<br>(2) 1·6 | —<br>0·50 | |
| Aluminium | Hard | 9·1 | | | | | 4·7 | (1) 2·7<br>(2) 2·2 | 0·57<br>0·47 | |
| Duralumin | Annealed | 14·9 | | | | | 7·8 | (1) 3·6<br>(2) 3·3 | 0·46<br>0·42 | |
| Duralumin | Heat treated | 30·9 | | | | | 8·0 | (1) 4·5<br>(2) 3·8 | 0·56<br>0·47 | |
| Electrolytic copper, hot rolled | Annealed | 13·9 | | | | | 4·5 | (1) 4·7 | 1·04 | |
| Electrolytic copper, cold worked | Tempered | 20·8 | | | | | 7·6 | (2) 7·8<br>(1) 7·8 | 1·03<br>1·03 | |
| 78% copper 21% nickel, cold worked | Annealed | 21·1 | | | | | 8·0 | (2) 8·5<br>(1) 8·5 | 1·06<br>1·06 | |
| 78% copper 21% nickel, cold worked | Tempered | 27·8 | | | | | 11·6 | (1) 10·7<br>(2) 11·6 | 0·92<br>1·0 | |
| 48% copper 48% nickel, cold rolled | | 38·2 | | | | | 17·0 | (1) 13·0<br>(2) 14·7 | 0·76<br>0·86 | |
| Monel 67% Ni 30% Cu, cold rolled | Annealed | 36·5 | | | | | 16·1 | (1) 12·0<br>(2) 13·0 | 0·75<br>0·81 | |
| Monel 67% Ni 30% Cu, cold rolled | Tempered | 56·7 | | | | | 23·6 | (1) 13·8<br>(2) 15·6 | 0·58<br>0·66 | |
| Nickel, cold rolled | Annealed | 34·6 | | | | | 15·2 | (1) 11·2<br>(2) 10·3 | 0·74<br>0·68 | |
| Nickel, cold rolled | Tempered | 58·7 | | | | | 23·2 | (1) 13·4<br>(2) 12·0 | 0·58<br>0·52 | |
| 62% copper 37% zinc, cold drawn | Annealed | 23·7 | | | | | 10·0 | (1) 8·5 | —<br>0·85 | |
| 62% copper 37% zinc, cold drawn | Tempered | 37·5 | | | | | 10·7 | (2) 8·0<br>(1) 8·0 | 0·75<br>0·75 | |
| Duralumin | As rolled | 28·2 | R.B.<br>Ax. | 2200 | 3% Salt spray | $5 \times 10^7$ | 9·2<br>6·7-9 | 3·4<br>2·6 | 0·37<br>0·33 | Gough and Sopwith [369] |
| Magnesium 2·5% Al alloy | As rolled | 16·4 | R.B.<br>Ax. | | | $10^7$ | 6·7<br>5·2-6 | (1·0)<br>(1·0) | 0·15<br>0·18 | |
| Phosphor bronze 4·2% tin | Rolled and drawn normalized<br>Extruded and drawn | 27·6<br>35·7 | R.B. | 2200 | 3% Salt spray | $5 \times 10^7$ | 9·8 | 11·7 | 1·19 | Gough and Sopwith [379] |
| Aluminium bronze 8·9% Al 1·4% Zn | Extruded and drawn | | | | | | 14·3 | 9·8 | 0·68 | |
| Beryllium bronze 2·2% Be | As forged | 41·8 | | | | | 16·3 | 17·4 | 1·07 | |
| Superston bronze 9·7% Al 5·0% Ni 5·4% Fe | As forged | 51·7 | | | | | 22·7 | 14·6 | 0·64 | |

| Material | Condition | | Test | Cycles | Environment | $N$ | | | | Reference |
|---|---|---|---|---|---|---|---|---|---|---|
| Aluminium bronze 9·3% Al | Quenched | 36·8 | R.B. | 2200 | 3% Salt spray | $5 \times 10^7$ | 11·4 | 8·7 | 0·76 | Sopwith [380] |
| Aluminium bronze 9·3% Al | Quenched and reheated | 32·8 | | | | | 9·9 | 7·8 | 0·79 | |
| Beryllium bronze 2·2% Be | Solution-treated | 32·2 | | | | | 17·4 | 13·6 | 0·78 | |
| Beryllium bronze 2·2% Be | Fully heat-treated | 81·2 | | | | | 19·4 | 15·9 | 0·82 | |
| *Sand-cast copper alloys:* | | | | | | | | | | |
| High tensile brass | As cast | | R.B. | 3000 | 3% Salt spray | $100 \times 10^6$ | | | | J. Stone & Co., London |
| 50% alpha phase | | 32·4 | | | | | 12 | 6·3 | 0·52 | |
| 30% alpha phase | | 36·8 | | | | | 10 | 5·5 | 0·53 | |
| 15% alpha phase | | 38·2 | | | | | 8·8 | 5·5 | 0·62 | |
| 5% alpha phase | | 39·1 | | | | | 6·4 | 4·3 | 0·67 | |
| 60% Cu 34% Zn | | 40·8 | | | | | 9·2 | 6·4 | 0·70 | |
| Superston 40, 8% Al 12% Mn | | 44·1 | | | | | 16·5 | 9 | 0·54 | |
| Superston 60, 8% Al 12% Mn | | 52·2 | | | | | 13·2 | 8·5 | 0·64 | |
| *Manganese bronzes:* | | | | | | | | | | |
| Parsons manganese bronze | | 33/35 | R.B. | | Salt spray | $25 \times 10^6$ in air | 11·6 | 7·5 | 0·65 | Manganese, Brass and Bronze Co., Ipswich |
| Immadium II | | 34/38 | | | | $50 \times 10^6$ in salt spray | 13·7 | 9·2 | 0·67 | |
| Immadium V | | 40/44 | | | | | 10·7 | 10·5 | 0·98 | |
| Immadium VI | | 45/50 | | | | $10^8$ | 13·0 | 8·0 | 0·61 | |
| 80% copper 10% Al 5% Ni 5% Fe | | 45/55 | | | | | 20·9 | 10·8 | 0·51 | |
| *Aluminium–zinc–magnesium alloys:* | | | | | | | | | | |
| | Solution treated | 17·5 | R.B. | | 3% salt solution liquid film | $10^7$ | 9 | 4·5 | 0·50 | Stubbington and Forsyth [381] |
| | Fully heat-treated | 31·1 | | | | | 12·5 | 5 | 0·40 | |
| DTD 683 | Overaged | 27·3 | | | | | 11 | 5 | 0·45 | |
| *Wrought aluminium alloys:* | | | | | | | | | | |
| Al 3% Mg | Heat treated | | R.B. | 5000 | 3% Salt spray | $20 \times 10^6$ | 8·2 | 3·2 | 0·38 | Sterner-Rainer [382] and Jung-Konig |
| Al 7% Mg | Heat treated | | | 5000 | | | (7) | 3·2 | (0·45) | |
| Al Cu Mg | Heat treated | | | 5000 | | | (11·4) | 5·4 | (0·47) | |
| *Magnesium alloys:* | | | | | | | | | | |
| Mg–Al–Zn AZG | | | | | Tap water | $20 \times 10^6$ | 5·1 | 2·5 | 0·49 | Beck [145] |
| Mg–Al–Mn AM 537 | | | | | Tap water | | 5·0 | 3·4 | 0·68 | |
| Mg–Al–Zn AZ 855 | | | | | Tap water | | 9·5 | 3·5 | 0·37 | |
| Mg–Al–Mn AM 503 | | | | | 3% salt water | | 3·6 | 1·3 | 0·36 | |
| Mg–Al–Mn AZ M | | | | | 3% salt water | | 9·9 | (0·8) | (0·08) | |
| Pure lead | | | R.B. | 1785 | 38% sulphuric acid, drip feed | $40 \times 10^6$ | 0·19 | 0 | 0 | Mack [383] |
| Tellurium lead, 0·05% Te 0·06% Cu | | | | | | | 0·27 | 0·18 | 0·67 | |
| Antimonial lead, 1% Sb | | | | | | | 0·38 | 0·33 | 0·86 | |
| Storage battery lead, 9·4% Sb 0·4% Sn | | | | | | | 0·91 | 0·83 | 0·90 | |

R.B. = Rotating bending
Ax. = Axial stress

Corrosive attack increases with temperature, but again the effect may be limited by the decrease of the solubility of the air with increase in the temperature of the corrosive solution. Fuller's tests in steam, for example, quoted in Table 47, showed that the supply of oxygen was the most important factor; a jet of steam in air was considerably more damaging than immersion in steam at 371°C. Experiments at different temperatures between 15 and 90°C have shown that the fatigue strengths of steels in the presence of salt water are little affected by the temperature. The corrosion fatigue strength usually falls slightly as the temperature is increased, but Cornet and Golan [387] found the reverse effect, which they attributed to the kind of pits developed; these became shallower and more evenly distributed with increasing temperature.

*Effect of Stress Conditions on Corrosion Fatigue Resistance*

In air, fatigue strengths in bending are usually higher than in direct stress. Under corrosion fatigue conditions direct comparisons are limited, but Gough and Sopwith [369] have given results for six materials. These are reproduced in Fig. 103 and show that two of the materials had a significantly higher corrosion fatigue strength in direct stress than in bending. A similar effect was observed by Gould [366] on mild steel and was attributed by him to a higher rate of electrochemical attack in bending as a consequence of the smaller number of anodic regions subjected to the maximum tensile stress at any given time. Gough and Sopwith [388] also investigated the effect of superimposed static tensile stresses on the corrosion fatigue strength of the six materials mentioned above. They found that the effect of variation in the mean stress, on the fatigue strength in salt spray was similar to the effect in air. Few direct comparisons have been made between corrosion fatigue strengths in bending and torsion. Hara's results on mild steel (Table 46) and Dolan's results on an alloy steel (Table 49) show that corrosion has a considerably greater effect on the bending fatigue strength than on the torsional fatigue strength and results on cast iron (Table 49) show, on average, a similar but smaller effect. This behaviour might be expected because fatigue cracks propagate from corrosion pits and the stress concentration factor for a given notch is greater in bending than in torsion.

Only a few investigations have been made of the corrosion fatigue resistance of specimens containing mechanical notches. Dolan [389] carried out tests on an alloy steel both in bending and in torsion, and Collins and Smith [390] carried out similar tests on four cast irons. Their results are summarized in Table 49, and these illustrate clearly that the combined effects of a mechanical notch and corrosion can reduce the fatigue strength still further than either factor acting independently. Indeed, for some of the results the strength reduction factor, resulting from corrosion fatigue tests

TABLE 49. CORROSION FATIGUE STRENGTH OF NOTCHED AND UNNOTCHED SPECIMENS OF CR NI STEEL SAE 3140 (Dolan [389]) AND CAST IRONS (Collins and Smith [390])

| Material and heat treatment | Type of stress | Type of specimen | Minimum diameter of specimen in. | Radius of hole or fillet in. | Tensile strength tons/in² | Frequency of stress cycle/min | Endurance basis for fatigue strengths | Fatigue strength tons/in² | | Strength reduction factor $K_f$ | | |
|---|---|---|---|---|---|---|---|---|---|---|---|---|
| | | | | | | | | In air | In stream of tap water | Mechanical notch alone | Corrosion alone | Corrosion and mechanical notch |
| *SAE 3140* (1·1–1·4% Ni 0·55–0·75% Cr) Hot rolled | T | Unnotched | 0·32 | | 51 | 1400 | 10⁷ | 19·6 | 14·5 | 2·0 | 1·35 | 3·3 |
| | | Hole | 0·4 | 0·04 | | | | 9·8 | 6·0 | | | |
| | R.B. | Unnotched | 0·3 | | 57 | | | 28·6 | 15·2 | 2·06 | 1·88 | 4·0 |
| | | Hole | 0·4 | 0·04 | | | | 13·8 | 7·1 | | | |
| Quenched and tempered | T | Unnotched | 0·28 | | 72 | | | 25·0 | 14·5 | 1·87 | 1·73 | 2·8 |
| | | Hole | 0·38 | 0·036 | | | | 13·4 | 8·9 | | | |
| | R.B. | Unnotched | 0·3 | | 74 | | | 40·2 | 5·8 | 2·90 | 6·9 | 10·0 |
| | | Hole | 0·4 | 0·04 | | | | 13·8 | 4·0 | | | |
| Slightly alloyed ordinary grey cast iron | T | Unnotched | 0·3 | | 9·9 | 1750 | 5 × 10⁷ | 4·9 | 3·5 | 1·36 | 1·40 | 1·36 |
| | | Hole | 0·4 | 0·04 | | | | 3·6 | 3·6 | | | |
| | R.B. | Unnotched | | | | 1450 | | 4·0 | 3·1 | 1·11 | 1·29 | 1·82 |
| | | Hole | | | | | | 3·6 | 2·2 | | | |
| Ni Mo cast iron | T | Unnotched | | | 23·8 | 1750 | | 9·8 | 5·4 | 1·38 | 1·81 | 2·7 |
| | | Hole | | | | | | 7·1 | 3·6 | | | |
| | R.B. | Unnotched | | | | 1450 | | 9·4 | 3·6 | 1·52 | 2·6 | 4·3 |
| | | Hole | | | | | | 6·2 | 2·2 | | | |
| Slightly alloyed Ni Cr Cu inoculated cast iron | T | Unnotched | | | 20·5 | 1750 | | 7·6 | 8·2 | 1·19 | 0·93 | 1·14 |
| | | Hole | | | | | | 6·4 | 6·7 | | | |
| | R.B. | Unnotched | | | | 1450 | | 9·0 | 7·1 | 1·18 | 1·27 | 1·34 |
| | | Hole | | | | | | 7·6 | 6·7 | | | |
| Austenitic high Ni Cu Cr cast iron | T | Unnotched | | | 14·1 | 1750 | | 5·3 | 2·7 | 1·18 | 1·97 | 1·97 |
| | | Hole | | | | | | 4·5 | 2·7 | | | |
| | R.B. | Unnotched | | | | 1450 | | 5·3 | 2·7 | 1·71 | 1·97 | 2·9 |
| | | Hole | | | | | | 3·1 | 1·8 | | | |

T = torsion
R.B. = rotating bending

on notched specimens, is roughly equal to the product of the strength reduction factors for a mechanical notch alone and for corrosion alone.

The effect of the frequency of the stress cycle on resistance to corrosion fatigue was investigated by McAdam by two-stage tests [364]. In the first stage, specimens were subjected to a stream of water for varying times while undergoing fatigue tests at various frequencies. In the second stage, the fatigue strength of the corroded specimens was determined in air. To illustrate the effect of stress, time and frequency in the first stage of the tests, McAdam compared the conditions required to reduce the fatigue strength in the second stage by 15%. He found that a number of carbon steels and low-alloy steels behaved in a very similar manner and the results for all of them could be represented approximately by the relations shown in Fig. 106A. These show that for a given frequency, there is an exponential relation between the stress and the time, which may be expressed by the relation:

$$R = CS^n \tag{36}$$

where $R$ represents the rate of damage (i.e. the rate at which the first-stage treatment reduces the subsequent fatigue strength), $S$ is the alternating stress and $C$ and $n$ are constants. The results in Fig. 106a have been re-plotted in Fig. 106B on the basis of the number of cycles instead of the time in the first stage. The lines at different frequencies are more closely spaced in the second figure, which shows that under the particular testing conditions the damage was dependent primarily on the number of cycles and only to a small extent on the frequency.

The direct effect of frequency on the corrosion fatigue strength of carbon steels has been investigated by Endo and Miyao [391] by means of bending fatigue tests in air, in tap water and in salt water. They showed that if the frequency was decreased, the number of cycles to fracture was reduced, but the time to fracture was increased. There was a tendency, however, for the curves at different frequencies to converge at long endurances when plotted on a stress–log time to fracture basis, in other words, failure tended to become dependent predominantly on the time.

### Protection against Corrosion Fatigue

Metals can be protected from corrosion fatigue either by surface treatment or by the addition of inhibitors to the corrosive medium. Some experimental results showing the effect of a variety of surface treatments are given in Tables 50 and 51 for steels and non-ferrous metals respectively.

Some degree of protection against corrosion fatigue can be obtained by mechanical surface treatments, such as surface rolling and shot-peening [399], and nitriding is particularly effective; this has been demonstrated by many investigators and some typical results are included in Table 50.

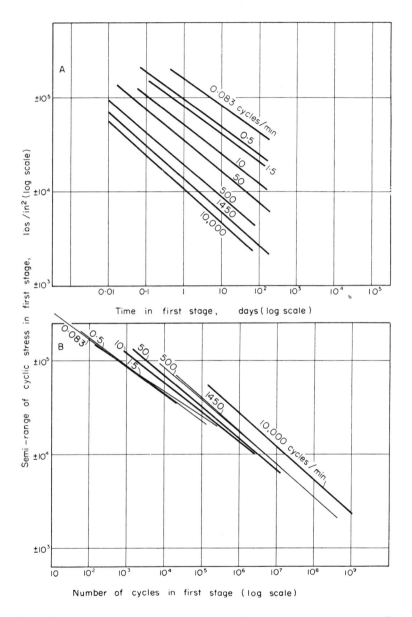

FIG. 106. Relationship between stress and time at various constant cyclic frequencies under a stream of tap water required to reduce the subsequent fatigue strength of carbon steels and low-alloy steels by 15%. (McAdam, Gough [364])

TABLE 50. THE EFFECT OF SURFACE TREATMENTS ON THE CORROSION FATIGUE STRENGTH OF STEELS

All fatigue tests in rotating bending

| Material | Tensile strength tons/in² | Surface treatment | Approximate thickness of protective layer in. | Frequency of stress cycles/min | Corrosive medium | Endurance basis for fatigue strength | Fatigue strength tons/in² | | Corrosion fatigue strength tons/in² | | Source | Ref. |
|---|---|---|---|---|---|---|---|---|---|---|---|---|
| | | | | | | | Untreated | Treated | Untreated | Treated | | |
| 0·5% C cold drawn steel: as drawn normalized | 64·6 43·1 | Enamel | | 2200 | 3% salt spray | $2 \times 10^7$ | 24·5 16·4 | 22·8 17·2 | 3·5 4·0 | 10·8 11·2 | Sopwith and Gough | 392 |
| as drawn normalized | | Galvanizing | 0·0019 | | | | | 24·7 14·8 | | 23·2 16·6 | | |
| as drawn normalized | | Sherardizing | 0·0005 | | | | | 22·8 14·8 | | 24·5 15·2 | | |
| as drawn normalized | | Electrolytic zinc plating | 0·00056 | | | | | 24·4 16·1 | | 21·4 14·7 | | |
| as drawn normalized | | Electrolytic cadmium plating | 0·00052 | | | | | 22·8 15·2 | | 18·9 13·7 | | |
| as drawn normalized | | Electrolytic cadmium plating +enamel | 0·0005 | | | | | 23·2 15·8 | | 17·7 13·5 | | |
| as drawn normalized | | Electrolytic cadmium plating +oil | 0·0005 | | | | | 21·8 15·8 | | 15·0 13·4 | | |
| as drawn normalized | | Phosphate treatment +enamel | | | | | | 22·8 17·8 | | 10·7 12·9 | | |
| as drawn | | Aluminium spray | 0·002 | | | | | 25·8 | | 19·5 | | |

| Material | Treatment | | | Environment | Cycles | | 25.2 | | 24.1 | Author | Ref |
|---|---|---|---|---|---|---|---|---|---|---|---|
| Mild steel 25 (as drawn) | Aluminium spray +enamel | 0.002 | | | | | | | | Cazaud | 116 |
| | Hot dipped soft solder | 0.0004 | | Fresh water drip feed | $10^8$ | 14 | 16.5 | 7 | 9 | | |
| | Hot dipped cadmium coating | 0.0008 | | | | | 14.5 | | 11 | | |
| | Electroplated nickel | 0.008 | | | | | 10 | | 10 | | |
| | Electroplated chromium | 0.008 | | | | | 14.5 | | 14.5 | | |
| Mild steel 26.2 | Surface rolling | | | Fresh water | | 16.5 | 18.5 | 6.5 | 9.5 | Thum and Ochs | 116 |
| Medium carbon steel | Surface rolling | 0.02 | | Fresh water | $2 \times 10^6$ | 18.5 | 23 | <10 | 19 | Foppl | 116 |
| Nitralloy 1.6% Cr 0.9% Al 0.3% Mo steel | Nitriding | | | River water drip feed | $10^8$ | 33 | 37 | <5 | 25 | Inglis and Lake | 372 |
| SAE 6120 0.7–0.9% Cr 0.1% V steel 55 | Nitriding | | 1450 | Stream of tap water | $10^8$ | | 47 | | 38 | Dolan and Benninger | 393 |
| 0.47% C steel 47 | Galvanizing Sherardizing Zinc plating Cadmium plating | | | Fresh water | $2 \times 10^7$ | 27 | | 9 | 19.5 19.5 22 20.5 | Harvey | 394 |
| 0.38% C steel | Bright zinc plating | 0.0005 0.001 | | Complete immersion in oil well brine saturated with hydrogen sulphide | $10^7$ | 25.2 | | 5.4 | 8.8 10.2 8.5 8.9 | Wescott | 395 |
| | Ductile zinc plating | 0.0005 0.001 | | | | | | | | | |
| SAE 4620 1.65–2% Ni 0.2–0.3% Mo steel | Nickel plating | 0.005 | | | | 23.4 | 17.9 | 10.0 | 15.6 | | |
| 0.4% C 0.2% Cu steel | Zinc plating | 0.0023 | | | | 18.3 | | 4.9 | 11.2 | | |

TABLE 51. THE EFFECT OF SURFACE TREATMENTS ON THE CORROSION FATIGUE STRENGTH OF NON-FERROUS METALS

All fatigue tests in bending

| Material | Tensile strength tons/in² | Surface treatment | Approximate thickness of protective layer in. | Frequency of stress cycles/min | Corrosive medium | Endurance basis for fatigue tests | Fatigue strength in air tons/in² | | Corrosion fatigue strength tons/in² | | Corrosion fatigue strength—treated ÷ Fatigue strength in air—untreated % | Refs. |
|---|---|---|---|---|---|---|---|---|---|---|---|---|
| | | | | | | | Untreated | Treated | Untreated | Treated | | |
| Duralumin | 24–27 | Anodizing | | 2000 | 3% salt spray | 50 × 10⁶ | 9·0 | 11·0 | 3·0 | 9·5 | 105 | Gerard and Sutton [396] |
| | | Anodizing + synthetic resin varnish (stoved) | | | | | | | | 5·7 | 63 | |
| | | Synthetic resin varnish only (stoved) | | | | | | | | 6·4 | 71 | |
| | | Zinc plating | 0·0005 | | | | | | | 2·5 | 28 | |
| | | Cadmium plating | | | | | | | | 4·8 | 53 | |
| | | Aluminium spraying | 0·003 | | | | | | | | | |
| Aluminium alloy (0·61% Mg, 0·94% Si) | | Anodizing + hot water sealing | | 5000 | (1) Tap water | 10⁸ | 8·0 | 7 | (1) 4 (2) 2 | (1) 7 (2) 6 | 87 75 | Inglis and Larke [397] |
| | | Anodizing + sealing in Pot. Dichromate | | | (2) 3% salt solution | | | 7 | | (1) 6 (2) 6·5 | 75 81 | |
| | | Painting | | | | | | 8·5 | | (1) — (2) 8·5 | 106 | |
| Magnesium alloy (3% Al, 1% Zn) | | Anodizing | | | Salt spray | 10⁷ | 5·9 | 4·1 | | 4·5 | 76 | Bennett [398] |

Surface coatings can afford protection in two ways; firstly, they can prevent access of the corrosive agent to the base metal and secondly, if the coating is anodic to the base metal, they can restrict the electro-chemical attack. If corrosion fatigue is to be avoided solely by preventing access of the corrosive agent, the coating must be completely continuous and non-porous, but anodic coatings can give protection even when they are discontinuous. Because it is difficult, in practice, to avoid all discontinuities in the coating, it is usually found that anodic coatings give better protection. Thus, for example, zinc, which is anodic to steel, gives good protection, but a coating of copper, which is cathodic to steel, may actually reduce the resistance to corrosion fatigue [400]. The superiority of a zinc coating has been demonstrated by Royez and Pomey [401] and also by the results of a comprehensive series of tests carried out by Forsman and Lundin [402], some of which are summarized in Fig. 107. For aluminium alloys, Gerard and Sutton [396] showed that zinc plating increased the resistance to corrosion fatigue in a salt spray but cadmium plating did not (see Table 51). Non-metallic surface coatings can also be used to give protection against corrosion fatigue. For light alloys anodizing is effective, particularly when followed by a coat of varnish, and Inglis and Larke [397] obtained complete protection against salt water with paint, applied in accordance with a carefully specified schedule. It has also been claimed that epoxy resin films give complete protection to aluminium alloys against a 3% salt spray [403]. Inhibitors give protection by forming an adherent corrosion resistant chemical film on the metal surface. The inhibitors most widely investigated for use with steels are the chromates and dichromates, and sodium carbonate and emulsifying oils have been used [365, 367].

## The Influence of Oxygen on Fatigue Strength

In his review of corrosion fatigue in 1932, Gough [364] showed that there was considerable evidence of the importance of oxygen in the atmosphere on fatigue behaviour. A number of experimenters had shown that fatigue strengths were not greatly affected by corrosive environment if the supply of oxygen was restricted. For example, Lehmann had found that complete immersion of steel specimens in distilled or salt water had little effect on the fatigue strength and Binnie had demonstrated that the detrimental effect of salt water dripping on to steel specimens was much reduced in an atmosphere of pure hydrogen. Other investigators had obtained higher fatigue strengths in corrosive environments than in air. This result was obtained by McAdam on copper tested in fresh water, and also by Haigh and Jones on lead alloys immersed in acetic acid, where the evolution of hydrogen restricted the supply of oxygen to the specimens.

From these results it appeared that normal fatigue tests in air might be

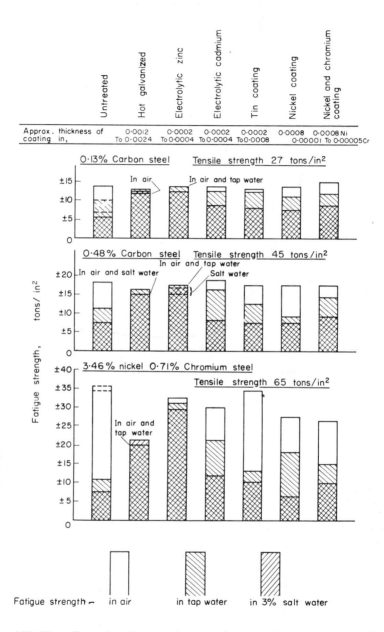

FIG. 107. The effect of surface coatings on the corrosion fatigue strength of steels. (Forsman and Lundin [402])

*Rotating bending tests at 3,000 cycles per min. Fatigue strengths based on 15 million cycles.*

influenced by the presence of oxygen in the atmosphere, and Gough and Sopwith [404, 405] demonstrated that this was so by carrying out fatigue tests in a partial vacuum at a pressure of less than $10^{-3}$ mm of mercury. The difference between fatigue strengths in air and in vacuo was markedly dependent on the material. There was little or no effect on steels, an aluminium alloy and a magnesium alloy, but the fatigue strengths in vacuo were 14% higher than in air for annealed copper, 26% higher for annealed 70:30 brass and more than double for lead. In later experiments [406] an attempt was made to determine the separate effects of oxygen and water vapour. For copper, the results showed clearly that the reduced fatigue strength in air depended on the presence of both oxygen and water vapour, but the tests on brass were inconclusive. More recently, Wadsworth and Hutchings [407] have carried out fatigue tests at a range of pressures down to about $10^{-5}$ mm of mercury; they found that for pure copper the endurance was related exponentially to the pressure and the fatigue strength ($10^7$ cycles) at the lowest pressure was about 30% higher than in air. There was a smaller effect for aluminium and no effect for gold. Cracks were observed at an early stage in the fatigue life and the authors considered that the effect of the atmosphere is to increase the rate of crack propagation.

### The Mechanism of Corrosion Fatigue

The first stage in the corrosion fatigue process is the formation of rounded cavities on the surface, similar to those occurring from corrosion in the absence of stress. This is followed by the progression of narrow corrosion pits, or cracks, extending from the bottom of the cavities downwards into the metal. The rate of propagation of these pits tends to decrease as they grow, thus allowing time for the growth of further pits before fracture occurs as a result of a normal fatigue crack propagating from the bottom of one of the pits (see Fig. 102).

As corrosive attack in the absence of stress often occurs preferentially at the grain boundaries, considerable attention has been paid to the paths of cracks in corrosion fatigue. It has been found, however, that corrosion fatigue cracks are predominantly transcrystalline. The principal exceptions to this behaviour are lead, in which fatigue cracks follow the grain boundaries in air, as well as in corrosive environments, and in some aluminium alloys where corrosion fatigue failures are sometimes partially intercrystalline [381]. It is possible that corrosion fatigue cracks may be initiated at grain boundaries though this is certainly not an essential requirement, because corrosion fatigue cracks have been observed wholly within one grain [364] and corrosion fatigue failures have been demonstrated in single crystals [408].

It is well established that corrosion fatigue is an electrochemical process.

Certain regions of the surface of the metal are anodic to other regions as a result of irregularities in the surface or to local differences in the accessibility of oxygen. The surface therefore consists of a large number of cells in which metal ions are passing into solution at the anodes. This type of corrosion is dangerous for two reasons; firstly the corrosion products are formed in the corrosive solution so that there is no possibility of the reaction being stifled and secondly, the attack is confined to the anodic regions and this can be severe if the anodic area is much smaller than the cathodic area. The concentrated attack in certain regions, which is typical of corrosion fatigue, affords evidence that the process is electrochemical. In addition, it has been shown that corrosion fatigue can be delayed or prevented by cathodic protection from contact with a less noble metal and the beneficial effect of inhibitors is well known. Further evidence was supplied by Evans and Simnad [409] who showed that the process could be delayed by the application of an e.m.f.

In the same paper these authors suggested that the accelerated effect of corrosion caused by alternating stresses could be attributed to the following four factors, which they described in electrochemical terms:

1. The distortion or obliteration of the crystalline structure of the metal which thus becomes less stable and more reactive. This would give a bodily shift of the anodic potential in the "base metal" direction.

2. The rupture of protective films, giving a reduced anodic polarization.

3. The removal of corrosion products which would otherwise slow down the attack, giving a reduced resistance of the electrolyte path between cathodes and anodes.

4. The improvement in the supply of oxygen, giving a reduced cathodic polarization.

They showed experimentally that the last three of these factors were involved in the corrosion fatigue of mild steel. In later experiments Whitwham and Evans [410] showed that prior fatigue stressing in the absence of corrosion had little effect on the subsequent corrosion fatigue resistance, showing that the first factor is not of major importance. On the other hand, the removal of the corrosive environment at a comparatively early stage of the test does not significantly increase the total life and may actually reduce it [409, 665]. It was shown that this was because fatigue cracks were formed at an early stage and most of the life was associated with crack propagation.

Probably the two principal reasons why the conjoint effect of corrosion and fatigue are so much more damaging than either acting separately are, firstly, that the formation of protective films, which generally slow down the rate of corrosion in the absence of stress, are continually being broken by fatigue stressing and, secondly, that the stress concentrations introduced by the corrosion pits considerably reduce the fatigue strength.

$Fe_2O_3$

## Fretting corrosion

If two solid surfaces in contact are subjected to a repeated relative movement of small amplitude, some damage to the surfaces may occur and this is known as fretting corrosion. Its presence is usually recognized by the corrosion products formed, which consist of finely divided oxide particles. In steel this is iron oxide $Fe_2O_3$, which is a reddish-brown colour and is sometimes referred to as "cocoa", while in magnesium and aluminium alloys the finely divided oxide particles appear black. The appearance of oxide particles is usually accompanied by localized pitting of the surfaces in the fretted region and this can result in serious reductions in fatigue strengths. The mechanism of fretting corrosion is not yet fully understood and this is reflected by the number of alternative terms used to describe the same process, for example friction oxidation, wear oxidation, chafing and false brinelling. The process is a form of mechanical wear which can occur without corrosion, but which can be greatly aggravated if corrosion occurs simultaneously [411].

Fretting corrosion is most often found in components which are clamped together and are not intended to undergo relative movement, such as bolted and riveted joints and hubs press-fitted on to shafts, but it can also occur between surfaces which are intended to act as bearings, such as ball races, control mechanisms and machine slides, as a result of vibration when the parts are not operating. As an example of this, fretting sometimes develops in the bearings of road vehicles during their transport by rail. Under these circumstances fretting may cause loss of fit or seizure in addition to increasing the susceptibility to fatigue failure. Fretting and its influence on fatigue strength have been reviewed recently by Teed [658].

Many service fatigue fractures originate in regions of fretting corrosion and one of the fractures illustrated in Chapter I (Fig. 4) occurred in this way. A further example, quoted by Fenner, Wright and Mann [412] is illustrated in Fig. 108. This shows part of a large machined mild steel plate, $61\frac{1}{2}$ in. by 24 in., $2\frac{3}{8}$ in. thick which acted as the spring of a machine for vibrating heavy loads and in service was subjected to alternating bending with a double amplitude of 0·12 in. A number of fatigue failures had occurred in these plates, the cracks originating in the region of the holes, where a steel cross member was bolted to the plate. Areas of fretting corrosion were evident on the surfaces of the plate and the cracks had usually propagated from these areas and not from the holes. The maximum stress in the plate, neglecting the stress concentration round the hole, was estimated to be about 3·5 tons/in². Since the plain bending fatigue limit of the steel would probably have been greater than 10 tons/in² the fatigue strength was therefore reduced by a factor of about 3. Other examples of fatigue failures resulting from fretting corrosion were discussed in the same paper and for these the fatigue strength reduction factors ranged from 2·5 to

FIG. 108. Fretted surface of mild steel spring plate, with cracks. (Fenner, Wright and Mann [412])

about 20. The whole of the reductions in fatigue strength need not be attributed entirely to fretting corrosion, because the fatigue strength must also be influenced by the stress concentrations at the changes in section of the clamped assemblies, and by the clamping pressures, but there is no doubt that the fretting contributes considerably to the result.

### The Effect of Material and Heat Treatment

The susceptibility of different metals to fretting corrosion has usually been assessed either by visual observation or by a measure of the weight loss, and in only a few experiments has the effect of fretting on the fatigue strength been determined. Judged by visual observation and weight loss methods, soft materials are generally more susceptible to fretting corrosion than hard materials and stainless steels are particularly susceptible. McDowell [413] compared the behaviour of a great many combinations of metals by visual observation and his summary of the results is shown in Table 52. A number of cast irons have been compared by Wright [414] by measurement of the volume of damaged material and he showed that the damage was inversely related to the hardness.

Such observations, however, do not necessarily indicate the susceptibility of materials to fatigue failure as a result of fretting corrosion, and in

TABLE 52. RESISTANCE TO ACTION OF FRETTING CORROSION (McDowell [413])

| Poor | Average | Good |
|------|---------|------|
| Aluminium on cast iron | Cast iron on cast iron | Laminated plastic on gold plate |
| Aluminium on stainless steel | Copper on cast iron | Hard tool steel on tool steel |
| Magnesium on cast iron | Brass on cast iron | Cold rolled steel on cold rolled steel |
| Cast iron on chrome plate | Zinc on cast iron | Cast iron on cast iron with phosphate coating |
| Laminated plastic on cast iron | Cast iron on silver plate | Cast iron on cast iron with coating of rubber cement |
| Bakelite on cast iron | Cast iron on copper plate | Cast iron on cast iron with coating of tungsten sulphide |
| Hard tool steel on stainless | Cast iron on amalgamated copper plate | Cast iron on cast iron with rubber gasket |
| Chrome plate on chrome plate | Cast iron on cast iron with rough surface | Cast iron on cast iron with Molykote lubricant |
| Cast iron on tin plate | Magnesium on copper plate | Cast iron on stainless with Molykote lubricant |
| Cast iron on cast iron with coating of shellac | Zirconium on zirconium | |
| Gold plate on gold plate | | |

Q

fact the results of fatigue experiments have shown that the fatigue strengths of hard materials are usually reduced to a greater extent by fretting corrosion than are soft materials. This conclusion is drawn mainly from the results of tests by Sachs and Stefan [415] on a wide range of metals. The tests were made in a rotating beam machine in which the specimen was clamped tightly in oil-hardened 0·4% C steel grips, so that fretting corrosion, leading to fatigue failure, occurred beneath the grips. Under these conditions the fatigue strength for most of the materials was higher in the annealed condition than cold-worked or age-hardened, and cast materials were less susceptible than forged; some of the results are given in Table 53.

Materials are often more resistant to corrosion fatigue when in the annealed condition and a similar behaviour under fretting corrosion suggests that a similar process may be involved. On the other hand, the fatigue strength under fretting corrosion conditions is influenced by the stress concentration at the clamps and the greater susceptibility of harder materials may result from their greater notch sensitivity.

*Factors Influencing Fretting Corrosion*

One of the characteristic features of fretting is the small amplitude of relative motion required to damage contacting surfaces, amplitudes of the order of 0·0001 in. often being sufficient. It was shown by Tomlinson [416] that if slip occurs, even to the extent of $10^{-6}$ in., fretting will result. The damage increases with the amount of slip, but an upper limit may be reached when the movement is sufficient to allow the oxidation particles to escape. The damage increases with the load or pressure applied and becomes more widely distributed over the surfaces, unless the pressure is sufficiently high to prevent slip, for then fretting will be avoided altogether. In contrast to corrosion or corrosion fatigue behaviour, damage as a result of fretting corrosion is greatest in dry conditions and decreases as the humidity increases [417]. Damage also increases as the temperature is reduced. Other factors such as surface finish and the frequency of vibration may be important, but the evidence is contradictory. Fenner and Field [418] found that the aluminium alloy L65 was more susceptible to fatigue failure as a result of fretting when a static stress was superimposed. With pads of the same material clamped to the specimens with a pressure of $\frac{1}{4}$ ton/in², the fatigue strength ($20 \times 10^6$ cycles) was reduced from $12·5 \pm 8·3$ to $12·5 \pm 1·5$ tons/in².

One important example of fatigue failure in service, which is aggravated by fretting corrosion, occurs in shafts with press-fitted assemblies and the effect of some of the factors mentioned above have been investigated, principally by Horger, on large diameter shafts with press-fitted wheels [419–421]. He found that the resistance to fatigue was not greatly influenced by the chemical composition or heat-treatment of the steel, but

Table 53. Fretting fatigue strengths of various metals (Sachs and Stefan [415])

Rotating bending fatigue tests at 3500 cycles/min

| Material | Condition | Tensile strength tons/in² | Hardness Rockwell B | Normal fatigue strength (10⁷ cycles) tons/in² | Fretting fatigue strength (10⁷ cycles) tons/in² |
|---|---|---|---|---|---|
| 0·35% C steel | Annealed | 47 | 65 | | 8·5 |
| | Cold worked | | 95 | | 9·5 |
| | Normalized | | 75 | | 9 |
| 18% Cr 9% Ni Stainless steel | Annealed | 47·8 | 89 | | 12·5 |
| | Cold worked | 77·8 | | | 10·5 |
| 19% Cr 11% Ni Stainless steel | Annealed | | 77 | | 11 |
| | Cold worked | | 95 | | 6 |
| Aluminium Bronze (4% Al 7% Zn) | Annealed | 34 | 77 | | 6·5 |
| | Cold worked | 48 | 94 | | 6 |
| Duralumin (4% Cu) | Annealed | 11·6 | 61 | | 4·5 |
| | Aged 1 hr at 175°C | | 56 | | 4 |
| | Water-quenched from 500°C | | | | 4 |
| 0·24% C steel | Forged and normalized | 36 | | 18 | 9 |
| | Cast and normalized | 34 | | 15 | 11 |
| Aluminium alloy (4·5% Cu) | Forged and heat-treated | 24·5 | | | 4·5 |
| Aluminium alloy (4% Cu) | Sand cast and heat-treated | 14 | | 3·5 | 3 |
| Aluminium alloy (4·5% Cu) | Chill cast and heat-treated | 16 | | 5·5 | 4·5 |

a considerable improvement could be obtained by inducing a compressive residual stress in the surface of the shaft, either by quenching or by surface rolling (see Table 74). Among other factors investigated by Horger were the influence of a water spray, of lubrication with molybdenum disulphide or with white lead and linseed oil and of a phosphate coating. None of these had a significant effect on the fatigue strength but some improvement was obtained by chromium plating. An improvement was also obtained by modifying the design of the assembly and some of the results are quoted in Chapter IX (see page 307).

A comprehensive investigation of the effect of fretting corrosion on a titanium alloy has been carried out by Liu, Corten and Sinclair [422] by means of reversed bending fatigue tests on specimens gripped at one end between pads of various materials. The results, some of which are quoted in Table 54, showed that gripping with soft materials did not damage the specimen surface and had little effect on the fatigue strength, but gripping with hard materials produced fretting corrosion and reduced the fatigue strength usually from 3 to 5 times. There was a slight reduction in fatigue strength with increase in clamping pressure and both shot-peening and coating with Teflon proved beneficial.

### Methods of Preventing or Reducing Fretting Corrosion

The most suitable method for combatting fretting corrosion will depend on the application and each condition must be considered on its merits. For applications where no relative movement is intended it may be possible to prevent slip occurring and hence to avoid fretting corrosion entirely. This may be achieved by increasing the pressure or by increasing the coefficient of friction, but if slip is not prevented by these means the damage may be increased. The coefficient of friction may be increased by electroplating with such metals as cadmium, copper, tin, silver or gold, but if slip still occurs the plated layers are rapidly worn away and do not prevent damage. An alternative method of preventing slip is to introduce an elastic material, for example, rubber, between the contacting surfaces in order to absorb the relative movement elastically.

If it is not possible to prevent slip, then it may be better to reduce the coefficient of friction. Scarlett [423] has experimented with many different greases and found that the loss of weight from fretting could be considerably reduced by the use of some of them. Lubrication with oils or greases is not always effective, however, probably because with the small relative movements which can produce fretting, they do not prevent metal-to-metal contact. Greater success has been achieved for steels with a phosphate coating impregnated with a lubricant and for light alloys with impregnated anodized coatings. Fretting can also be reduced with solid lubricants such as a bonded layer of molybdenum disulphide and with plastic coatings

TABLE 54. Fretting fatigue strength of titanium alloy RC130B (Liu, Corten and Sinclair [422])
Titanium 4% Al 4% Mn alloy, tensile strength 72 tons/in², hardness DPN 354

| Gripping material | Hardness of gripping pads D.P.N. | Gripping pressure p.s.i. | Fretting fatigue strength (5 × 10⁷ cycles) tons/in² | |
|---|---|---|---|---|
| None | — | | 40 | Conventional fatigue test |
| Magnesium | 39 | 15,000 | 38 | |
| Aluminium (1100–F) | 41 | 15,000 | 38 | |
| Aluminium (2011–T8) | 126 | 15,000 | 36 | |
| Copper | 96 | 15,000 | 32 | |
| 70/30 brass | 117 | 15,000 | 13·5 | |
| Aluminium (7075–T6) | 194 | 15,000 | 17 | |
| Aluminium (7075–T6) | 194 | 15,000 | 24·5 | Shot-peened |
| Titanium RC 130B | 354 | 15,000 | 16 | |
| Steel SAE 4340 | 397 | 4,000 | 12·5 | |
| | 397 | 22,000 | 9·5 | |
| | 397 | 60,000 | 8 | |
| | 595 | 40,000 | 8·5 | |
| | 397 | 40,000 | 10 | |
| | 238 | 40,000 | 9·5 | |
| | 238 | 40,000 | 9·5 | Argon atmosphere |
| | 238 | 40,000 | 21·5 | Shot-peened |
| | 238 | 15,000 | 23 | Teflon coated |
| | 238 | 15,000 | 22·5 | Oxidized |

such as polytetrafluoroethylene (P.T.F.E. or Teflon). The beneficial effect of shot-peening and of inducing surface compressive residual stresses by heat treatment or surface rolling is demonstrated by the results quoted in Tables 54 and 74. Wiegand [424] has shown that the fatigue strength of steel under fretting corrosion can be appreciably increased by nitriding.

Despite the number of methods which may be used to counteract fretting corrosion, there will always be many applications where it will not be possible to prevent its occurrence. In these circumstances the detrimental effect may often be reduced by modification in design.

### Mechanism of Fretting Corrosion

The mechanism of wear produced by the sliding in one direction of one surface along another is now fairly well understood. The two surfaces make contact at only a small number of high points and in these regions plastic flow and cold welding occurs. Friction and wear result from the breaking of the welds and a ploughing action through one surface by the high points in the other. In the early stages of fretting corrosion the damage that occurs is similar to the wear resulting from unidirectional sliding, and this is illustrated in Fig. 109 by an electron micrograph of a steel surface after only 250 cycles. As fretting proceeds, more wear particles are produced and owing to the small relative movement these cannot escape but build up between the two surfaces. It has been shown by electrical resistance measurements [412] that metal-to-metal contact ceases at an early stage, so that subsequent damage must result from the action of the wear particles rubbing against the surfaces.

A number of fretting corrosion experiments have been carried out in inert atmospheres in order to determine the role of corrosion or oxidation in the fretting process. These have shown that fretting still occurs in the absence of oxygen, metallic particles being produced from the fretting surfaces, but the rate of damage is usually much reduced. The presence of oxygen may accelerate the attack in two ways. Firstly, the oxide films on the surfaces may be continually broken up and removed by the wear process, thus exposing fresh metal surfaces which will oxidize rapidly and secondly, the oxide particles may act as abrasives and accelerate the wear process.

Some experiments carried out by Fenner and Field [418] provide evidence that the reduction in fatigue strength results predominantly from the first stage of fretting, involving the welding and fracture of metal-to-metal surfaces and not from the subsequent damage produced by oxide particles rubbing against the surfaces. As already mentioned, they showed that the fatigue strength of the aluminium alloy L65 was markedly reduced when pads of the same material were clamped to the specimens in order to induce fretting. However, when pads of a resin-bonded aluminium oxide were

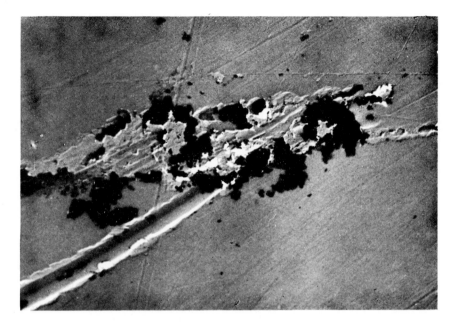

Fig. 109. Electron micrograph of fretting corrosion damage to steel surface after 250 oscillations in air. (Fenner, Wright and Mann [412])

used—the same as the oxide produced by metal-to-metal fretting of an aluminium alloy—the fatigue strength was only slightly reduced, even though the wear damage was much more severe than with metal pads. They showed further that the fatigue damage produced by fretting in the specimens with metal clamps was fully developed after about one-fifth of the total endurance, for the life was not affected if the clamps were removed at this stage. Examination of the specimens with an optical microscope showed that shallow cracks were formed at an early stage in the tests.

## CHAPTER VIII

# THE INFLUENCE OF TEMPERATURE ON FATIGUE STRENGTH

FOR most metals failure by fatigue can occur at any temperature below the melting point and the characteristic features of fatigue fractures, usually with little or no deformation, are apparent over the whole temperature range. The results of fatigue tests show a similar stress-endurance relation at all temperatures, although at high temperatures there is seldom a fatigue limit and the downward slope of the curve is usually steeper than at air temperature.

There is little call for information on the fatigue strength of metals at low temperatures, although the aircraft industry are concerned with fatigue behaviour down to −80°C and there are many chemical processes which operate at low temperatures. At high temperatures the limiting factor in design is usually static strength, but resistance to fatigue is an important consideration in engine design, particularly when static and alternating stresses are combined. In addition, many service failures occur by thermal fatigue, resulting from repeated thermal expansion and contraction.

## Fatigue at low temperatures

Almost without exception fatigue strengths of both plain and notched pieces are increased by a reduction of temperature. It is probably because of this that there are relatively few fatigue data at low temperatures, for it is possible to design for air temperature conditions and to feel confident that fatigue failures will not result from operation at lower temperatures.

An attempt has been made in Table 55 to summarize the information on fatigue strengths at low temperatures by averaging the available results for each class of material. Most of the results are based on $10^6$ cycles to fracture, because the tests at the lowest temperatures have not often been continued beyond this endurance. The variation from one alloy to another may be considerable so that the results in the table only indicate a general trend in fatigue behaviour at low temperatures. More detailed results are quoted in Table 83, and further data are quoted by Teed [425]. It can be seen from Table 55 that fatigue strengths are, in general, significantly higher at −40 and −78°C than at air temperature and appreciably higher at −186 to −196°C. The proportional increase in fatigue strength

TABLE 55. A COMPARISON OF FATIGUE STRENGTHS AT LOW TEMPERATURES
WITH FATIGUE STRENGTHS AT AIR TEMPERATURE

| Material | Average value of the ratio: Fatigue strength at low temperature / Fatigue strength at room temperature | | | Average value of the ratio: Notched fatigue strength at low temperature / Notched fatigue strength at room temperature | | Average value of the endurance ratio (unnotched): Fatigue strength / Tensile strength | | | |
|---|---|---|---|---|---|---|---|---|---|
| | −40°C | −78°C | −186 to −196°C | −78°C | −186 to −196°C | Air temperature | −40°C | −78°C | −186 to −196°C |
| Carbon steels | 1·20 (4) | 1·30 (6) | 2·57 (4) | 1·10 (6) | 1·47 (4) | 0·43 (10) | 0·47 (3) | 0·45 (6) | 0·67 (4) |
| Alloy steels | 1·06 (6) | 1·13 (36) | 1·61 (11) | 1·06 (29) | 1·23 (7) | 0·48 (47) | 0·51 (6) | 0·48 (37) | 0·58 (12) |
| Cast alloy steels | | 1·22 (3) | | 1·05 (3) | | 0·27 (3) | | 0·27 (3) | |
| Stainless steels. | 1·15 (5) | 1·21 (2) | 1·54 (2) | | | 0·52 (7) | 0·50 (5) | 0·57 (2) | 0·59 (2) |
| Aluminium alloys | 1·14 (16) | 1·16 (9) | 1·69 (3) | | 1·35 (2) | 0·42 (5) | | 0·46 (5) | 0·59 (3) |
| Titanium alloys | | 1·11 (2) | 1·40 (3) | 1·22 (2) | 1·41 (3) | 0·70 (3) | | 0·63 (2) | 0·54 (3) |

The figures in brackets are the number of determinations from which the averages were calculated with decrease in temperature is usually greater for soft materials than for hard ones and is particularly marked for mild steel. The tensile strength also increases with decrease in temperature but not usually to the same extent as the fatigue strength. It can be seen from the notched results quoted in Table 55 that the increase in fatigue strength at low temperatures is less when stress concentrations are present, in other words, metals are usually more notch sensitive at low temperatures. The effect of mean stress on fatigue strength has been investigated for steels at temperatures down to $-188°C$ [426, 427]. Plotting the $R-M$ diagrams shows that the behaviour for unnotched specimens is similar to that at air temperature, the results lying between the Goodman line and the Gerber parabola. Many of the results on notched specimens, however, were below the Goodman line. McCammon and Rosenberg [127] have shown that the fatigue strengths of a number of metals continue to increase with decreasing temperature at least down to $4°K$ ($-269°C$) (see Table 83). Iron and zinc were exceptions to this behaviour, but both are liable to brittle fracture and the tensile strength of each was also reduced at the lowest temperatures. Brittle fracture and its relation to fatigue is discussed in Chapter III, see page 67.

## Fatigue at high temperatures

At high temperatures the application of a static load to a metal produces a continuous deformation or creep, which may eventually lead to fracture if the load is maintained for a sufficient time [428, 680]. The creep rupture strength, which is the stress that a metal can withstand for a given time without breaking, decreases rapidly with increase in temperature to values which may be considerably lower than the fatigue strength. Consequently, the first requirement of metals at high temperatures is that they should withstand static loads and heat resistant alloys have been developed primarily to give high creep strengths. Fortunately, it is found that those alloys which possess good creep resistance are also resistant to fatigue, although the condition of an alloy giving the maximum creep strength is not necessarily the condition for maximum fatigue strength.

The relation between fatigue strength and temperature for a selection of materials used at high temperatures is shown in Fig. 110. The fatigue strengths are based on failure in about $10^7$ cycles and all the tests were made in bending. More precise data for the materials shown in Fig. 110 and for other materials, together with details of other mechanical properties are given in Table 84.

The fatigue strength of aluminium alloys is not much affected by temperature up to 100 or 150°C, but at higher temperatures it decreases quite rapidly, the alloys retaining little strength above 350°C. The high-strength aluminium alloys depend for their strength on precipitation-hardening

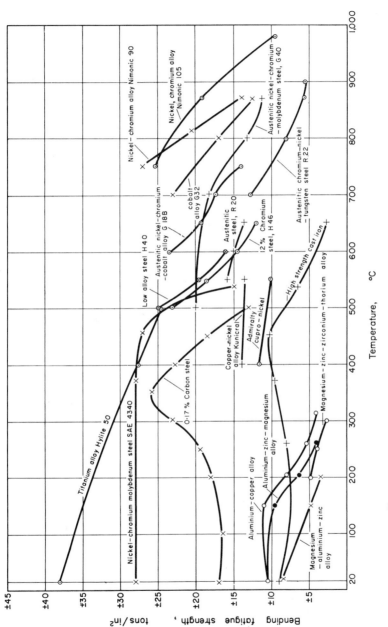

FIG. 110. The influence of temperature on the fatigue strength of metals.

and the benefit of this is lost when the temperature is high enough for precipitation to continue during service and lead to overageing. The best resistance to fatigue and to creep at high temperatures is therefore shown by those alloys which best resist overageing at the service temperature. The aluminium–zinc–magnesium alloys (such as DTD 683 or the American alloy 75S), which are normally solution-treated at about 465°C, and aged at about 130°C, are less resistant to high temperatures than the aluminium–copper alloys (such as DTD 364 or the American alloy 24S) which are normally solution-treated at about 510°C and aged at about 175°C. The high temperature properties of the aluminium–copper alloys can be improved by additions of magnesium and nickel, as in Y alloy, one of the first aluminium alloys developed. Aluminium–silicon alloys also show relatively good mechanical properties at high temperatures. For temperatures above about 300°C however, the creep and fatigue strength of all the conventional aluminium alloys is exceeded by Sintered Aluminium Powder (S.A.P.). This is a powder metallurgy product, made by compacting flakes of aluminium, coated with aluminium oxide; it obtains its strength from insoluble particles, which remain stable up to the melting point. The fatigue strengths of cast aluminium alloys are considerably below those of wrought alloys at air temperature, but the differences tend to disappear with increase in temperature.

The behaviour of magnesium alloys at high temperatures is similar to that of aluminium alloys; overageing can occur during service and result in reduced fatigue and creep strengths. The high strength magnesium–aluminium–zinc alloys lose their strength rapidly with increase in temperature and are less resistant, both to fatigue and creep above 200°C, than the magnesium–manganese alloys. A considerable improvement in the high temperature properties can be obtained by the addition of zirconium and of one of the rare earth elements, cerium or thorium. The fatigue strength of cast magnesium alloys is lower than for wrought alloys of similar compositions at all temperatures, although the creep strength is higher for cast alloys above about 200°C.

The strength of titanium alloys is comparable with that of alloy steels at temperatures up to 500°C, with the advantage of a density only a little more than half that of steel. It is, therefore, in the temperature range 250°C to 500°C that titanium alloys can be used to advantage for applications where the highest strength-to-weight ratio is required.

Carbon steels show an unusual fatigue behaviour at high temperature. From a minimum value at about 100°C, the fatigue strength increases with increase in temperature by as much as 40% to a maximum value at about 350°C, then, with further increase in temperature, decreases rapidly. The static tensile strength also shows an increase with increase in temperature, but of smaller magnitude, with a maximum strength at about 250°C. This behaviour is attributed to the strengthening effect of strain ageing (see page 344). Cast iron behaves in a similar manner, but the effect is smaller or absent in alloy steels.

Alloy steels for use at high temperatures have been developed primarily to withstand creep. For this purpose it is found that the most effective alloying element is molybdenum, and further improvement is achieved by small additions of chromium or vanadium. Alloys of this type retain appreciable fatigue strength up to 600°C. The highly alloyed ferritic steels containing more than 10% chromium, although weaker at low temperatures are more resistant than the low alloy steels above 600°C. The strengths of quenched and tempered alloy steels decrease rapidly as the service temperature approaches the tempering temperature. For service above 400° to 450°C, it is usually found that steels in the normalized, or normalized and tempered conditions have a superior creep resistance, although at lower temperatures they are inferior to quenched and tempered steels.

For temperatures above 600°C austenitic steels are superior to the ferritic steels both in mechanical properties and resistance to oxidation. The basis for the development of austenitic steels for use at high temperatures is an alloy containing 18–20% chromium and 8–12% nickel with a small addition of titanium or niobium to reduce the rate of precipitation of chromium carbide. An alloy of this type shows a fatigue strength of about 13 tons/in$^2$ at 650°C, while some of the more complex alloys that have been developed show about this strength at 750°C.

For use at temperatures above 750°C, iron alloys are replaced by nickel-base alloys, exemplified by the Nimonic series or by cobalt-base alloys which have been developed mostly in the United States. Nimonic 75, which is used, for example, in sheet form for gas turbine flame tubes, is basically an alloy of 80% nickel, 20% chromium stiffened by the precipitation of titanium carbide. The high-temperature strength has been progressively increased in Nimonic 80 and 80A (20% chromium with additions of titanium and aluminium), Nimonic 90 (20% chromium, 18% cobalt, titanium and aluminium) and Nimonic 105 (15% chromium, 20% cobalt, titanium, aluminium and molybdenum) [429]. Cobalt-base alloys are not easily forged and are more often used in the cast condition. The alloys used for high temperature applications usually contain about 25% chromium with additions of nickel and molybdenum or tungsten. Alloys for use at even higher temperatures are still in the experimental stage and may be based on chromium, molybdenum, tungsten or niobium or on ceramic materials or mixtures of ceramics and metals, known as cermets.

A comparison of fatigue strengths at high temperatures with other mechanical properties shows that, as at room temperature, the fatigue strength is quite closely related to the tensile strength, unless the temperature is so high that the tensile strength is appreciably affected by creep. For example, for the data available for wrought aluminium alloys, the endurance ratio is roughly independent of temperature up to 250°C; for failure in $10^7$ cycles the average value is about 0·35 and for $10^8$ cycles about 0·25. Above 300°C the endurance ratio increases rapidly, approaching 1 at 450°C.

Although the ratio of fatigue strength to creep rupture strength is markedly dependent on temperature, quite a close correlation between the two is obtained for some materials, simply by plotting the alternating fatigue strength against the creep rupture strength for failure in the same time and at the same temperature [430]. Figure 111 shows the relation for

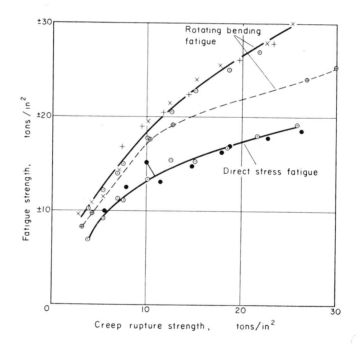

FIG. 111. Relation between fatigue strength and creep rupture strength of Nimonic alloys (Betteridge [429] and from data supplied by Henry Wiggin and Co. Ltd.).

●    Nimonic 80A
⊙    Nimonic 90
+    Nimonic 95
×    Nimonic 100
⊕    Nimonic 105

the Nimonic series of alloys for temperatures between 700 and 980°C and times to failure of 100, 300 and 1000 hr. The degree of agreement is sufficiently close for most of these alloys to permit the prediction of fatigue strength from the more extensive creep rupture results.

## Influence of Metallographic Structure

Strength at high temperatures is often obtained by precipitation-hardening. This is achieved by solution-treating a material at a temperature high enough for the hardening element to dissolve, quenching and then reheating, or ageing, at a temperature which will precipitate the hardening element in a finely divided form. Both the solution treatment and the ageing treatment have an important influence on the high temperature mechanical properties.

The solution treatment is important because it influences the grain-size. At moderate temperatures a fine grain-size gives a higher creep resistance than a coarse grain-size, but this is reversed at high temperatures, because the grain boundaries become weaker than the grains. This is shown by the appearance of fractured surfaces of materials which have failed by creep—fractures at moderate temperatures are transgranular, while fractures at high temperatures are intergranular. The fatigue strength is influenced in a similar manner by grain size, but the change from transgranular to intergranular fracture occurs at a considerably higher temperature in fatigue than in creep [431, 432]. Consequently, there is a range of temperature, which is often one that is important practically, when a coarse grain-size produces higher creep strength, but lower fatigue strength. In these circumstances it might be advantageous to vary the heat-treatment to suit the stress conditions. The influence of ageing treatment on high-temperature fatigue strengths has received little attention. There is evidence that fluctuating stresses accelerate ageing in aluminium alloys at air temperature and there may be a similar effect on other materials at high temperatures. If so, it is possible that better fatigue strengths would be achieved by under-ageing treatments.

The high-temperature fatigue strengths of castings are nearly always lower than those of forged alloys of similar composition. In this respect the fatigue behaviour differs from creep, for the creep strength of castings is often superior to forgings when the temperature is very high. One of the reasons for this is that the grain size is often greater in cast materials and if care is taken to produce fine-grained castings the fatigue strengths are improved. A disadvantage of cast material is the variability in the mechanical properties and this is most marked in fatigue. Harris and Child [433], for example, investigated this for the cast cobalt-base alloy G34 at 750°C and found a variation of about $\pm 15\%$ in creep rupture strength and about $\pm 30\%$ in fatigue strength.

*Influence of Corrosion*

An essential requirement of alloys for use at high temperatures is that they should show high resistance to oxidation, and it is usually found that heat-resisting alloys also show high resistance to corrosion fatigue. Most investigations of corrosion fatigue at high temperatures have been concerned with the effect of corrosive constituents in engine fuels. For example, it has been shown that the fatigue strength of Nimonic 80 at 800°C was unaffected by an atmosphere of sulphur dioxide [47], but its fatigue strength at 750°C was reduced by about 10% at 1000 hours by a coating of fuel ash containing vanadium salts [430]. A similar problem arising in internal combustion engines is the attack of valves and valve seatings by lead salts in the fuel. The fatigue resistance of austenitic steel valves in these circumstances can be improved by a coating of a nickel-base material [47].

*Fatigue under Fluctuating Stresses at High Temperatures*

At high temperatures, both the alternating stress and the static stress which a metal can withstand without breaking, decrease as the time of application of the stress increases. The relation between the static or creep rupture strength and the time can therefore be plotted on a stress-endurance curve in the same way as the relation between the fatigue strength and the number of cycles to failure. This is illustrated in Fig. 112 by some American results for the heat-resisting alloy N-155 at 815°C [185]; both the time and the number of cycles to failure are plotted on the abscissa. At 815°C the creep rupture strength of this material is lower than the alternating fatigue strength and it can be seen that the difference between the two becomes greater with increasing time. The results of fluctuating stress tests with an alternating stress superimposed on a static stress, are also shown in Fig. 112. The value of the maximum stress in the cycle is plotted, so that a direct comparison can be made with the fatigue and the creep rupture strengths; each curve represents a particular value of $R$, the ratio of the minimum stress in the cycle to the maximum stress.

The results in Fig. 112 also illustrate the steeper slope of the stress-endurance curves which is found at high temperatures and, in addition, a tendency for the slope to become steeper at long times. These features are of great practical importance, for such curves cannot be extrapolated to longer times with any degree of certainty. For this reason, tests at high temperatures, particularly static creep tests, must often be continued to very long times in order to determine satisfactorily the way in which a material will behave after long times in service.

As at air temperature, the fatigue strength of metals under fluctuating stresses at high temperatures can be represented by contours plotted on a graph of alternating stress against static stress. Each point on the contour

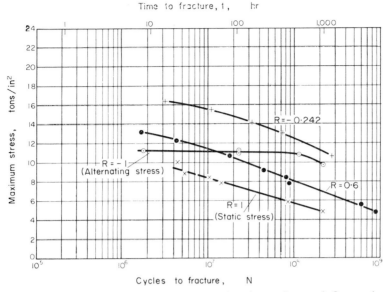

FIG. 112. *S–N* and *S–t* curves for static, alternating and fluctuating stresses for wrought N-155 alloy (20% chromium, 20% nickel, 20% cobalt, iron base) at 815°C (1500°F) [185].

represents a combination of static and alternating stress, ranging from the alternating fatigue strength to the creep rupture strength, causing failure in a given time. This is illustrated in Fig. 113 for Nimonic 80A, where contours are plotted for different endurances.

In order to compare the behaviour of different materials at various temperatures, it is more convenient to plot the results on a non-dimensional diagram, that is by plotting the ratio of the alternating stress to the fatigue strength, against the ratio of the mean stress to the creep rupture strength; each contour must then intercept the axes at unity. This method of plotting is used in Fig. 114 to compare the results of a number of creep-resistant alloys. It appears that the addition of an alternating stress up to 40% of the mean stress makes surprisingly little difference to the rupture strength and in some cases may increase it slightly. Such increases have been observed on a number of heat-resistant alloys, but the reason for it is uncertain. It has been suggested that the fluctuating stress accelerates constitutional changes in the alloy which result in an increase in hardness or that transcrystalline slip is produced by the fluctuating stress and relieves grain-boundary stress concentrations.

It can be seen from Fig. 114 that the modified Goodman law and Gerber's parabola drawn from the alternating fatigue strength to the creep rupture strength, generally gives an over-conservative estimate of the

R

strength under combined static and alternating stresses. It has been suggested that a circular arc on the non-dimensional diagram would be more appropriate [434] (this becomes an ellipse on the alternating stress–static stress diagram). This certainly gives closer agreement with the experimental results, although individual values show wide variations. An alternative empirical relation is to use the modified Goodman line, as used at

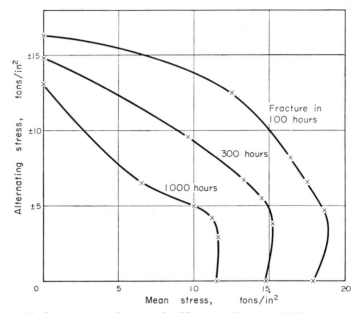

Fig. 113. Stress range diagram for Nimonic 80A at 750°C. (From data supplied by Henry Wiggin and Co. Ltd.).

air temperature, that is to say, a line drawn between the alternating fatigue strength and the *tensile strength*, but with the restriction that it does not apply if the static stress exceeds the creep rupture strength. This criterion cannot be represented on the non-dimensional diagram, but it is shown on the alternating stress–static stress diagram in Fig. 115, which gives the results of a number of investigators taking part in a co-operative research on the alloy N-155 [185]. The criterion cannot be used to predict fluctuating fatigue strengths accurately but it fits data at high temperatures as closely as the circular arc and is a better guide to fluctuating fatigue strengths at moderate temperatures. That this criterion fits the experimental data reasonably closely is an indication that in general there is little interaction between the creep and fatigue processes.

The appearance of fractures which have resulted from fluctuating stresses at high temperatures may be similar to creep fractures or to fatigue fractures or to a mixture of the two, depending on the relative magnitude of

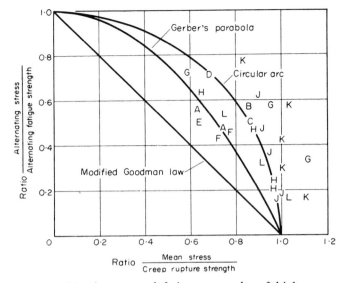

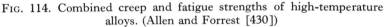

FIG. 114. Combined creep and fatigue strengths of high-temperature alloys. (Allen and Forrest [430])

*All results are based on an endurance of 300 hours.*

| | | | | | | |
|---|---|---|---|---|---|---|
| A | Rex 78 | 600 deg. C. | | G | Nimonic 80A | 700 deg. C. |
| B | Rex 78 | 650 deg. C. | | H | Nimonic 80A | 750 deg. C. |
| C | Rex 78 | 700 deg. C. | | J | N-155 | 649 deg. C. |
| D | Nimonic 80 | 600 deg. C. | | K | N-155 | 732 deg. C. |
| E | Nimonic 80 | 650 deg. C. | | L | N-155 | 815 deg. C. |
| F | Nimonic 80 | 700 deg. C. | | | | |

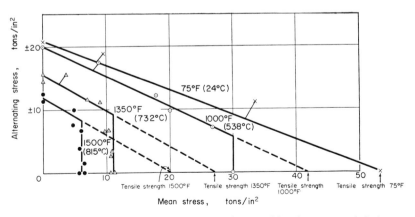

FIG. 115. Influence of temperature on the combined creep and fatigue strengths of wrought N-155 alloy at 500 hr. [185]

the static and alternating stresses. As would be expected, the amount of deformation in the region of the fracture is found to decrease as the ratio of alternating stress to mean stress increases.

It is not always sufficient to limit fluctuating stresses only to prevent fracture; for some applications it may be necessary to limit the creep deformation to a specified amount. The influence of a fluctuating stress on creep deformation may be represented graphically in similar ways to those used for fracture, which were shown in Figs. 113 to 115. One such diagram for the aluminium alloy RR59, is shown in Fig. 116 [435]. Experimental values of the creep occurring in 100 hours for various values of

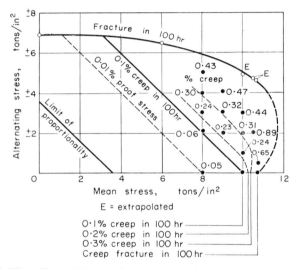

FIG. 116. The effect of fluctuating stress on the creep deformation of the aluminium alloy RR59 at 200°C. (Tapsell, Forrest and Tremain [435])

mean tensile plus alternating direct stress are plotted and from these, the contours for 0·2 and 0·3 per cent creep have been estimated. There is very little data of this sort available [659], so that it is usually necessary to estimate creep occurring under fluctuating stresses from static creep data. A conservative estimate may be obtained by assuming that the creep occurring under a fluctuating stress will not exceed that occurring from the steady application of the maximum stress in the cycle. This criterion is represented by a straight line drawn from the static stress for a specified creep strain to the same value of the alternating stress, and such a line is shown in Fig. 116. Attempts have been made to predict the creep occurring under fluctuating stresses on the simple assumption that for any instantaneous value of a varying stress, the creep rate will be the same as in a static creep test at that stress, at the same time from the beginning of the test [435, 436]. However, these attempts have not been sufficiently supported by experimental evidence to warrant their use in design. It is found, in general, that superimposing an alternating stress on a static stress may significantly increase the creep rate at moderate temperatures, but at higher temperatures the effect is smaller and the creep rate may even be decreased if the alternating stress is small [437].

The influence of stress concentrations and of frequency on materials subjected to fluctuating stresses is discussed later.

### Influence of the Frequency of the Stress Cycle

The data given so far in this chapter relate mostly to frequencies within the range 1000 to 10,000 cycles/min, at which fatigue testing machines usually operate. In practice the frequency varies between much wider limits, from the natural frequencies of vibration of turbine blades, to the slow fluctuations resulting from the daily alterations of operating conditions in power plant and chemical equipment. Fatigue failures can occur at any frequency between these extremes, yet little information is available on the influence of frequency at high temperatures.

At room temperature the frequency has little effect on the fatigue strength of most metals (except at very high frequencies), although a reduction in frequency may reduce slightly the number of cycles to failure at a given stress range. The effect usually becomes greater with increase in the temperature, so that failure tends towards dependence on the total time of application of the stress range instead of on the number of cycles. This behaviour probably arises because at low temperatures deformation occurs almost immediately a stress is applied, whereas at high temperatures deformation continues under stress.

In low melting-point metals, such as lead, which creep readily at room temperature, the effect of frequency is similar to that for other metals at higher temperatures. The behaviour of lead at room temperature has been studied by a number of investigators, because of the importance of very low frequency stress cycles in lead cables. Eckel [438] found that the effect of frequency on fatigue strength could be expressed by the equation:

$$\log l = \log b - m \log f, \qquad (37)$$

where $l$ is the time to failure, $f$ the frequency, and $b$ and $m$ are constants. If fatigue failure occurs after a certain number of cycles at all frequencies then $m = 1$, while if failure occurs after a certain time at all frequencies then $m = 0$. It is usually found that $m$ has a value between 0 and 1; Eckel's results for lead at 43°C and at frequencies between about 5 cycles/min and 1 cycle in 4 hr, show $m = 0.7$ and the data of Moore and Dollins [439] for lead at 23°C and at frequencies between 248 and 1 cycle/min give a value of about 0.55. Some results obtained by Gohn and

Ellis [440] for lead and lead alloys are shown in Fig. 117; for these results the value of $m$ depends on the strain range and varies from about 0·4 to 0·8. Similar results are quoted by McKeown [441]. For frequencies below about 1 cycle in 10 min, Gohn found that the number of cycles to failure was roughly constant for a given strain range.

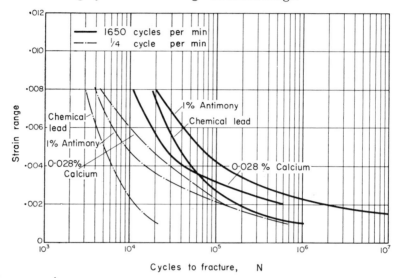

FIG. 117. Influence of frequency on the bending fatigue strength of lead and lead alloys at air temperature (29°C). (Gohn and Ellis [440]).

Direct stress fatigue tests on a 0·17% carbon steel have shown that the fatigue strength depends on the time to failure at 450°C [15]; the results are shown plotted on an $S$–$N$ curve in Fig. 118(a) and on an $S$–time curve in Fig. 118(b). On a time basis the results at the three different frequencies lie on one curve, so that $m = 0$. During these tests both the range of stress and the range of strain were measured and it appears that the behaviour may depend on the plastic strain occurring, for the results at the three frequencies lie close to a single line if the range of plastic strain is plotted against $N$ (Fig. 118(c)). In rotating bending for the same material and the same frequencies the value of $m$ was 0·5. The difference can be attributed to the influence of plastic deformation on the maximum stress in bending; more plastic deformation occurs at low frequencies and this diminishes the effect of frequency on fatigue strength.

In general, an increasing dependence of fatigue strength on total time, rather than on $N$, may be expected with increasing temperature, but the behaviour can be markedly influenced by metallurgical changes in the material. This can be illustrated by the results of fatigue tests on the same steel carried out at 2000 and at 10 cycles/min at temperatures up to 450°C (see Fig. 119). The metallurgical change in this instance is strain ageing (see page 344); at the lower frequency there is more time during the course of a stress cycle for ageing to occur, so that the maximum benefit is obtained at a lower temperature. As a result, the fatigue strength at temperatures between 200 and 300°C is considerably higher at 10 cycles/min than at 2000 cycles/min.

Under fluctuating stresses, the cyclic frequency affects both the life and the amount of creep which occurs. The results of fluctuating stress tests

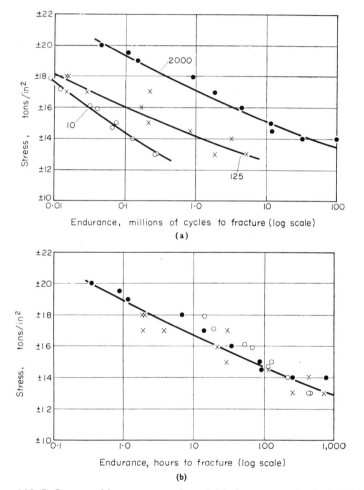

Endurance, millions of cycles to fracture (log scale)

(a)

Endurance, hours to fracture (log scale)

(b)

Fig. 118. Influence of frequency on the axial fatigue strength of a 0·17% C steel at 450°C: (Forrest and Tapsell [15]).

(a) Stress–endurance curves.

(b) Stress–time curve.

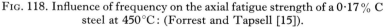

● 2000 cycles/min.    × 125 cycles/min.    ○ 10 cycles/min.

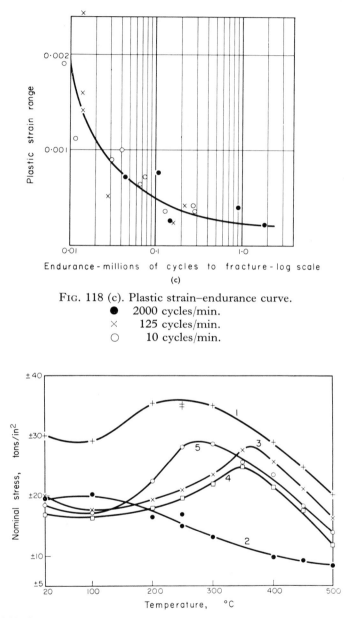

FIG. 118 (c). Plastic strain–endurance curve.

●    2000 cycles/min.

×    125 cycles/min.

○    10 cycles/min.

FIG. 119. Strength–temperature diagram for 0·17% C steel. (Forrest [442])

1, Tensile strength; 2, yield point (or 0·1% proof stress); 3, bending fatigue strength for 500,000 cycles at 2000 cycles/min; 4, bending fatigue strength for $10^8$ cycles at 2000 cycles/min; 5, bending fatigue strength for 500,000 cycles at 10 cycles/min.

carried out by Guarnieri [443] on several heat-resistant gas turbine alloys at frequencies between 10 and 15,000 cycles/min, show that the influence of frequency can be complex. He found that for a given static stress, the addition of an alternating stress increased the creeep rate and reduced the life at low and at high frequencies, but had the reverse effect at intermediate frequencies.

### The Effect of Stress Concentrations

In general, materials are less notch-sensitive in fatigue at high temperatures than at room temperature. The information available on notched fatigue strengths of magnesium and aluminium alloys has been summarized by Frith [146]. In general, the notch sensitivity is as great at 150°C as it is at air temperature, but there is a marked reduction at 200°C. Austenitic steels which are particularly insensitive to notches at air temperature become more notch sensitive at moderate temperatures of about 650°C, but above this temperature all the heat resistant alloys for which data are available show a decreasing notch sensitivity [184, 430]. The reduction in notched fatigue strengths for these alloys is quite small between 650°C (1200°F) and 815°C (1500°F). Cast iron remains insensitive to small notches at temperatures up to 600°C [444]. The notch sensitivity of low alloy steels increases with increase in temperature showing a maximum value between 300 and 400°C [177, 445]: this has been attributed to the inability of the steels to withstand repeated plastic deformation at these temperatures [445]. The steels become less notch sensitive with further increase in temperature.

The influence of notches on the strength of materials under fluctuating stresses can be shown on diagrams of alternating stress plotted against mean stress, similar to those used for unnotched results (see Figs. 113–115). The presence of a notch does not usually reduce the creep rupture strength of a material unless its ductility is low. There may be a slight reduction in creep rupture strength for a material that shows a reduction in area at fracture in an unnotched creep specimen of less than about 10%, but it is always much less than the reduction in fatigue strength cause by a notch. To estimate the notched fatigue strength of a material under fluctuating stresses at high temperatures, it is reasonable to assume that the mean stress component will not be affected by the notch and that the alternating stress component will be reduced by the strength reduction factor $K_f$ observed in alternating stress tests. This method will usually give a conservative estimate of the notched fatigue strength, although exceptions have been observed [446].

### The Effect of Surface Treatment

The effect of surface treatment, which can markedly affect the fatigue strength of hard alloys at air temperature, becomes less important with increase in temperature. There are probably a number of reasons for this; firstly, materials generally become less notch sensitive at high temperatures, so that the effect of small discontinuities on the surface is not so great; secondly, owing to oxidation, surface discontinuities are introduced irrespective of the initial surface condition and thirdly, residual stresses may be relieved by plastic flow [447]. The following results obtained by Jones and Wilkes [448] for the cobalt-base alloy S-816 illustrate the effect of residual stresses. They compared the notched fatigue strengths of specimens which had been ground in one pass (introducing surface residual tensile stress) with those which had been shot-peened (introducing surface residual compressive stress).

TABLE 56. INFLUENCE OF SURFACE TREATMENT ON NOTCHED FATIGUE STRENGTHS

Plane bending fatigue tests on 0·6 in. square section specimens with 60° V-notch 0·075 in. deep, 0·030 in. root radius. (Jones and Wilkes [448])

*Strength reduction factors:* $K_f$ ($10^8$ cycles; $K_t = 2·7$)

|  | Room temperature | 900–1100°F (482–593°C) | 1200°F (649°C) |
|---|---|---|---|
| Ground notch | 4·6 | 2·9 | 2·4 |
| Shot-peened | 1·3 | 1·5 | 1·9 |

It can be seen that the harmful effect of grinding and the beneficial effect of shot-peening tend to disappear at high temperatures. A similar effect has been observed on valve springs made from oil quenched and tempered steel wire [449]; shot-peening considerably improved the fatigue strength at air temperature, but the improvement had totally disappeared at 250°C. For service at high temperatures, shot-peening may even be deleterious, because recrystallization may occur during service as a result of the cold-work introduced by the peening [429].

### Thermal fatigue

The term thermal fatigue was first used to describe a type of failure which can occur in metals with a non-cubic atomic lattice when the temperature is fluctuated slowly with no external constraint applied to the material. Such failures are attributable to internal stresses set up by anisotropy of the thermal expansion. In metals such as zinc, cadmium, tin and uranium, slip lines and surface cracks are observed after repeated cycles of heating and cooling, but the more commonly used metals with a cubic atomic lattice do not fail in this way [450].

The use of the term thermal fatigue has subsequently been extended to cover failures caused by repeated thermally induced stresses, including those which result from temperature gradients and from constraints which prevent the free expansion of metal parts [681]. A high proportion of the fatigue failures in service at high temperatures occur in this way. It is a particularly serious problem, for example, in gas turbines, where high rates of change in temperature can occur in blades and flame tubes. It is also a problem in power stations where fatigue cracking may result from the wetting of heated metal surfaces [451], or from intermittent operation, for thermal stresses arise each time the plant is started and stopped. Failures commonly occur at welded joints, particularly at joints of dissimilar metals. The metal in the heat-affected zone close to a weld is liable to be brittle and there is usually some stress concentration at the edge of a weld. Failures at welded joints are discussed in detail by Thielsch [452] in a review of thermal fatigue. Thermal fatigue sometimes results in the formation of a network of fine cracks on the surface of a metal, known as craze cracking, heat checking or network or mosaic cracking [453]. This occurs quite often in industrial equipment such as ingot moulds, hot rolls and dies, where the surface of the metal is repeatedly heated and cooled. It is also found in steel railway wheels and in motor car brake drums as a result of the heating caused by application of the brakes and in cast-iron components in compression ignition engines [682]. Thermal fatigue may also, in the future, prove to be a problem in aircraft structures subjected to kinetic heating.

The ability of a metal to withstand failure by thermal fatigue is therefore important in many applications, but it is a property which is difficult to determine experimentally. The behaviour in service in influenced by a number of factors and it is difficult to reproduce equivalent conditions in the laboratory. Fluctuations in temperature during operation of high-temperature equipment will produce thermal stresses, but experience has shown that failure is generally more likely to result from the much larger expansions and contractions occurring when equipment is started and stopped. This has been convincingly demonstrated, for example, by full-scale tests on a gas-turbine engine [454.] By repeated starting and stopping of the engine, fatigue cracks were produced in the blades after 85 cycles using the nickel-base alloy M-252 and after 295 cycles with the cobalt-base alloy S-816. In contrast to this, no cracks were produced by running at full power for 360 hr, nor by rapid cycling between idling and rated speeds for 16 hr, although crack formation was accelerated when engine operation at rated speed and temperature was added to each start–stop cycle. These experiments provided a direct comparison of two materials under service conditions, but such tests are very expensive and most information of thermal fatigue resistance has been determined from tests in which a specimen or a component is subjected to controlled heating and cooling cycles until cracks are observed.

Northcott and Baron [453], for example, in an investigation of craze-cracking, used a wedge-shaped specimen one surface of which was repeatedly heated by induction, while the main mass was continuously water cooled. The temperature was cycled between 40°C and 800 to 1200°C so that the specimens, which were of steel, underwent a ferritic–austenitic and an austenitic–ferritic transformation during each cycle. Failure was defined by the growth of the longest crack to 0·02 in. and for most of the tests this occurred between 100 and 10,000 cycles. Several alloy steels, all containing 0·35% carbon, were tested and it was found that separate additions of manganese, nickel, chromium and molybdenum all increased the tendency to cracking, whereas vanadium (up to 0·3%), silicon and cobalt did not. In another series of steels containing 0·32% to 0·99% carbon and 0·6% manganese, the tendency to cracking increased with the carbon content. These results suggest that resistance to thermal fatigue is dependent on ductility rather than on tensile strength or fatigue strength, and this is supported by results of other similar investigations [455, 667]. On the other hand, the Nimonic series of alloys, 75, 80, 80A, 90, 100, which vary widely in ductility and creep resistance appear to show about equal resistance to thermal fatigue. This has been demonstrated by Lardge [456] by means of tests on sheet specimens containing a central hole, subjected to repeated slow heating and rapid cooling, and by Glenny and Taylor [457] with disc-shaped specimens which were subjected to rapid heating and cooling in fluidized beds. Some of the results of Glenny and Taylor are shown in Fig. 120. The criterion of failure was the detection of a crack with a binocular microscope at $\times 30$ to $\times 60$ magnification and each of the points on the curves represents the average endurance of 3 tests. Hunter [458] has compared the thermal fatigue resistance of a number of heat-resisting alloys by repeatedly heating specimens to temperatures between 1600 and 2000°F (871 and 1093°C) followed by air cooling. Failures were obtained between 200 and 20,000 cycles and, in general, cobalt-base alloys were more resistant than nickel or iron-base alloys, but the greatest resistance was shown by a 70% chromium 30% iron alloy. Muscatell and others [459], in tests involving the repeated heating and cooling of one edge of a triangular-shaped specimen also demonstrated the superiority of cobalt-base alloys. They tested a large number of heat-resistant alloys and found that wrought alloys were superior to cast alloys and that the larger the grain-size of the materials the lower was the resistance to thermal cracking. Two investigations on sheet metals [456, 460] have demonstrated the advantage of a high thermal conductivity, for in both, the maximum resistance was shown by copper coated with a heat-resistant material.

While such thermal fatigue tests as those described serve a useful purpose for particular applications, the data they provide cannot be applied generally to all thermal fatigue problems because the behaviour can be influenced to a great extent by the operating conditions. Some general guidance can be obtained, however, by considering individually the factors which determine thermal fatigue resistance. The most important of these are the coefficient of thermal expansion $a$, the thermal conductivity $k$ and the resistance of the material to alternating strain $\epsilon$.

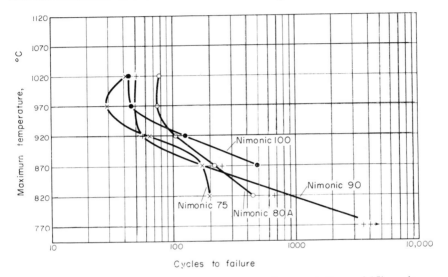

Fig. 120. Variation of thermal endurance of tapered discs of Nimonic alloys subjected to repeated heating and cooling cycles. (Glenny and Taylor [457])

The influence of thermal expansion is straightforward, for the thermal strains induced by a given distribution of temperature will be directly proportional to $a$. The effect of conductivity is not so simple. Under conditions of slow heating and cooling, where thermal strains are induced only by external constraints the conductivity will have no effect. Where thermal strains are induced by temperature gradients resulting from rapid rates of heating or cooling, on the other hand—and this is the more important practical problem—a high conductivity is generally beneficial because it reduces temperature gradients and hence the strains induced. However, if the rate of application of heat to a body is so high that its surface reaches the maximum temperature before any significant temperature change can occur in the bulk of the material, then the conductivity has little effect on the thermal strain induced in the surface.

For a given distribution of temperature in a material, the thermal expansion results in a given distribution of strain and the resistance of a material to thermal fatigue will therefore be directly related to its resistance to alternating strain $\epsilon$. It is necessary, here, to distinguish between strain and stress because thermal fatigue failures are usually produced in a small number of cycles so that appreciable repeated plastic deformation may occur. The following criteria can therefore be used as an indication of thermal fatigue resistance:

$$\frac{\epsilon}{a} \quad \text{or} \quad \frac{k\epsilon}{a},$$

the choice depending on the conditions. Manson [461] has discussed the influence of $k$ on the strain induced in a flat plate initially at uniform temperature, which is suddenly immersed in a medium of lower temperature. He showed that it depends on the value of Biot's modulus $\beta = ah/k$, where $a$ is half the thickness of the plate and $h$ is the heat transfer coefficient. The criterion $\epsilon/a$ is more appropriate for high values of $\beta$ (say $\beta > 10$) and $k\epsilon/a$ for low values (say $\beta < 1$).

The difficulty of applying the above criteria is that there is very little direct experimental evidence of the resistance of materials to alternating strain under conditions which lead to thermal fatigue, that is under varying temperature. One method for obtaining such data has been developed by Coffin [462]. This consists of a thin tubular specimen which is rigidly fixed at its ends and alternately heated by a high current and air cooled. The fluctuating temperature produces a fluctuating axial strain in the specimen and the test is continued until the specimen fractures. A number of different materials have now been tested by this method [463–468]. An attempt has been made recently to correlate the results of fluctuating temperature tests with constant temperature tests using a slow speed reversed bending machine [683]. It has been found, at least for two materials, that the resistance to alternating strain when the temperature is fluctuated in phase with the applied strain cycle is about the same as when the temperature is held constant at the maximum value all the time. This result is apparently obtained because the resistance of metals to small numbers of alternating strain cycles is markedly reduced at high temperatures and if it proves to be generally true it may be possible to assess thermal fatigue resistance by constant temperature tests carried out at the appropriate frequency.

The range of alternating strain that a material can withstand will be partly elastic and partly plastic. The elastic strain range is directly proportional to the fatigue strength for a given endurance and this is closely related to the tensile strength for low endurances, while Coffin has shown that the range of plastic strain is related to the ductility (see page 90). For low endurances of several hundred cycles or less, the range of plastic strain is greater than the range of elastic strain for ductile metals, while for long endurances of several thousands or more, the elastic strain range become predominant. In general, therefore, resistance to thermal fatigue will be dependent primarily on ductility for a small number of thermal stress applications and primarily on strength for a large number. This behaviour is illustrated to some extent in Fig. 120; an increasing number in the Nimonic series indicates in general, increasing strength and decreasing ductility.

The inter-relation of thermal stresses with other stresses has so far received little attention. Clauss and Freeman [466] have shown that in some circumstances prior thermal stressing can markedly reduce the creep rupture life of heat-resistant alloys and that prior creep deformation can markedly reduce the thermal fatigue life. Coffin [469] has shown that a small mean stress superimposed on a cyclic strain can result in very large deformations. No mention has been made of thermal fatigue in non-metals. The thermal fatigue resistance of ceramics is poor because of their brittleness and this is one of the reasons that has restricted their use.

Allowance for thermal stress in design has recently been discussed fully by Manson [672].

## CHAPTER IX

# THE FATIGUE STRENGTH OF JOINTS, COMPONENTS AND STRUCTURES

IN the preceding eight chapters emphasis has been placed on the fatigue strength of materials determined on small specimens tested under carefully controlled conditions. This method of testing is particularly suitable for comparing the resistance to fatigue of different materials and for investigating the effect of such factors as shape, stressing conditions, environment and temperature. The results of such tests, however, are usually inadequate for predicting the fatigue strength of engineering parts because of the difficulty of determining accurately the stress distribution in the part and also because of the unknown effects of such factors as size, residual stress and particularly fretting corrosion. Consequently, it is often necessary to carry out fatigue tests on actual joints and components, and even full-scale structures, in order to provide data that can be used quantitatively in design. Component fatigue testing also provides a useful means of determining the effect of design or fabrication changes and of detecting points of weakness more directly and often more quickly than could be achieved by stress analysis.

In structures subjected to fluctuating stresses, the joints between the individual components are often the weakest points because of the effects of stress concentration and fretting corrosion. To mitigate these effects is primarily a design problem and it is by attention to detail in design, more than any other factor, that the fatigue strength of joints may be improved. The non-uniform distribution of stress in a loaded joint results partly from true stress concentration which occurs at the changes in section and partly from load concentration which occurs because of the necessity of the load to flow round the contours of the joint. It is sometimes difficult to distinguish between the two, but both must be considered in design [277]. It is often found that the factors governing stress and load concentration are opposed, so that a change in design which reduces one increases the other. For example, if the fillet radius on a bolt head is increased, the stress concentration is reduced, but the bearing surface must be moved further from the axis of the bolt and this increases the bending moment and hence the load concentration.

## Screw threads

Threaded joints show good resistance to static loads, but owing to the high concentration of stress at the thread roots they are susceptible to fatigue failure when subjected to fluctuating loads. The fatigue strength is influenced by a number of factors, including the thread form, the material, the process of manufacture, the design and the method of assembly. These have been widely investigated and a number of reviews of the published work have been written [470–472]. Fretting corrosion sometimes occurs in screw threads, but this does not affect the fatigue strength because fatigue cracks propagate from the root of a thread away from the regions of fretting.

### Thread Form

The most thorough investigation of the effect of thread form has been made in connection with the development of "unified" screw threads for use in the USA, Britain and Canada [473, 474]. Fatigue tests were made in pulsating tension on double ended studs by the method shown in Fig. 121 to simulate the loading sustained by a nut and bolt in actual practice.

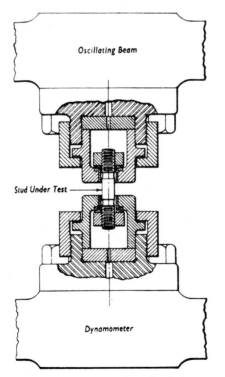

FIG. 121. Method of test for investigating the fatigue strength of screw threads. (Field [473])

S

TABLE 57. FATIGUE STRENGTHS OF UNIFIED (U.N. AND U.N.C.) B.S.F. AND B.S.W. SCREW THREADS (Field [473] Sopwith and Field [474]) See Fig. 121

| Diameter of stud in. | Threads per in. | Type of stud | | Method of production | Type of nut | | Range of fluctuating tensile stress at * Fatigue limit (10⁷ cycles) tons/in² | | | |
| | | Material | Tensile strength tons/in² | | Material | Tensile strength tons/in² | U.N. | B.S.F. | U.N.C. | B.S.W. |
|---|---|---|---|---|---|---|---|---|---|---|
| 3/8 | 20 | En 16T (1·3–1·8% Mn 0·2–0·35% Mo) | 60 | Ground | 3S1 (N) | 37 | 12·3 | 12·7† | | |
| | | En 16T (1·3–1·8% Mn 0·2–0·35% Mo) | 60 | Rolled | 3S1 (N) | 37 | 21·4 | <19·2 to 20·5 | | |
| | | 3S1 | 39 | Lathe cut | 3S1 (N) | 37 | 7·6† | 8·9† | | |
| | | 3S1 | 39 | Rolled | 3S1 (N) | 37 | 12·7 | 11·8 | | |
| 3/4 | 10 | En 16T | 63 | Ground | 3S1 (N) | 35–40 | | | 13·2 | 12·5 |
| | | En 16T | 63 | Rolled | 3S1 (N) | 35–40 | | | 27·9 | 22·3 |
| | | En 16T | 63 | Ground | En 17T (1·3–1·8% Mn 0·2–0·35% Mo) | 66 | | | 12·7 | |
| | | 3S1 | 39 | Lathe cut | 3S1 (N) | 35–40 | | | 7·6† | 7·1† |
| | | 3S1 | 39 | Ground | 3S1 (N) | 35–40 | | | 7·4 | |
| | | 3S1 | 39 | Rolled | 3S1 (N) | 35–40 | | | 15·4 | 12·5 |
| 2·52 (64 mm) | 6 mm pitch | 0·46% C steel | 34 | Ground | 0·14% C steel | 28 | 5·6‡ | | | |
| | 4 mm pitch | 0·46% C steel | 34 | Ground | 0·14% C steel | 28 | 5·0‡ | | | |

* Minimum stress of cycle 4·5 tons/in² for 3/8 in. and 3/4 in. bolts and 3 tons/in² for 2¼ in. bolts. All stresses are based on the minimum section at the root of the thread.

† Indicates uncertainty owing to scatter of results; in the worst cases this uncertainty amounts to ±1 ton/in².

‡ The apparent superiority of the finer thread derives mainly from its smaller core section. The ranges of the pulsating tensile *load* at the fatigue limit for the two threads were:

  6 mm pitch, 1·38 tons
  4 mm pitch, 1·35 tons.

In a preliminary investigation to determine the optimum form of thread it was shown that the geometric effect was slight, but there was a small increase in fatigue strength with increase in root radius. In a subsequent series of tests it was shown that the fatigue strength of the Unified thread (UN) was about the same as the British Standard Fine thread (BSF) and that the Unified Coarse thread (UNC) was somewhat stronger than the British Standard Whitworth (BSW); these results are summarized in Table 57. Previous investigations have shown that the Whitworth form is considerably better than the American standard form [475]. Among other factors investigated was the effect of "crossing" UN and BSW threads, i.e. assembling a nut of one form on a bolt of the other. This caused no loss in fatigue strength provided that soft nuts were used. Tests on both ground and rolled threads showed that drastic reduction of the depth of engagement of the threads, even to 25% of normal, caused no loss of fatigue strength, provided that the truncation was equally distributed between the stud and the nut. No appreciable difference was found between the fatigue strengths of the $\frac{3}{4}$ in. long 10 t.p.i. threads and the $\frac{3}{8}$ in. by 20 t.p.i. threads; the $2\frac{1}{2}$ in. diameter threads showed lower fatigue strengths and this was attributed partly to the lower tensile strength of the bolt material and partly to size effect.

*Type of Material*

As steels become more notch sensitive with increase in tensile strength, increasing the strength of the bolt material may not result in a similar increase of the fatigue strength of the bolt. Furthermore, a certain amount of ductility in a bolt may be desirable in order to accommodate strains arising from eccentric loading. A tensile strength of about 70 tons/in² has been recommended as an optimum value for plain and alloy medium carbon steels [471]. Nevertheless, much higher fatigue strengths can be achieved with high strength materials if particular care is taken in manufacture, as shown in Table 58.

It is inadvisable to carry out heat treatments on bolts after they have been threaded, as this may decarburize the surface and induce unfavourable residual stresses. The use of a soft nut on a higher strength bolt can have a beneficial effect on the fatigue strength (see Table 57) because plastic deformation of the nut tends to even out the load distribution in the bolt.

*Method of Manufacture*

The fatigue strengths of screw threads produced by rolling are considerably higher than those produced by cutting or grinding. This is illustrated in Table 57 and also in Table 59, which shows the results of fatigue tests carried out by Dinner and Felix [477] on 1 in. diameter threaded specimens of a steel with a tensile strength of 30 tons/in². The

TABLE 58. FATIGUE STRENGTH OF $\frac{1}{4}$ IN. DIAMETER BOLTS
WITH U.N.F. ROLLED THREADS, LOADED THROUGH A NUT
(Allsop and Fowler [476] G.K.N.)

| Material | Tensile strength tons/in² | Static strength of bolts lb | Range of fluctuating* tensile stress at an endurance of 10⁷ cycles tons/in² |
|---|---|---|---|
| 5% Cr. 1·5% Mo. 0·5% V. steel | 100/110 | 9420 | 46 |
| Titanium alloy (4% Al, 1·4% Mn.) | | 6250 | 28 |

$*\dfrac{\text{Minimum stress}}{\text{Maximum stress}}$,   $R = 0·1$.   The stresses are based on the minimum section at the root of the thread.

TABLE 59. THE EFFECT OF MANUFACTURING PROCESS ON THE FATIGUE STRENGTH OF SCREW THREADS
(Dinner and Felix [477])

| Process | Range of pulsating tensile stress at the fatigue limit, tons/in² | |
|---|---|---|
| | Loaded through a nut | Not loaded through a nut |
| Rolling | 12·7 | 18·5 |
| Cutting | 7·6 | 10·9 |
| Grinding | — | 11·7 |
| Milling | 7·6 | 12·1 |

lower results obtained, when the specimens were loaded through a nut, demonstrate the influence of load concentration. The beneficial effect of rolling can be attributed partly to residual compressive stresses induced in the threads, partly to the work hardening of the material and possibly also to the smoother surface finish produced. Subsequent heat treatment in order to increase the static strength should be avoided on rolled threads as the beneficial residual stresses may be lost. It has been shown by Almen [478] that the fatigue strength of a machined thread may be increased by a superficial rolling process. It has been reported that case-hardening is beneficial but there is some doubt whether its use is advisable for bolts, because of the loss in ductility [471].

*Effect of Tightening*

In order to avoid fatigue failure, a bolt should be tightened until it maintains a tensile load greater than the maximum load to which it will be subjected in service; in other words, it must be tightened sufficiently to ensure that the clamped parts always remain firmly in contact. Then, provided that the stiffness of the bolted members is high compared with the bolt stiffness, the fluctuating loads in the bolt will be quite small. This was demonstrated by Almen [478] who showed that the fatigue life of a bolted assembly increased markedly as the initial tension in the bolt was increased, and his results have been confirmed by similar tests carried out by Fisher, Cross and Norris [479]. They emphasized the importance of maintaining the initial tension which may be lost during service as a result of embedding or creep or from other causes. Almen maintained that adequate tightening was more important than the other factors affecting the fatigue strength of bolts and that its neglect contributed to many fatigue failures. The extent to which a bolt should be tightened will depend to some extent on the application, but in general it is beneficial to exceed the yield stress at the root of the thread as this will result in a favourable residual stress distribution, but the tension should not be so high that yielding occurs over the whole core section. The required degree of tightening can be obtained with a torque spanner, or by measurement of the bolt elongation or angular twist of the nut. A further important reason for maintaining adequate tightness in a bolted joint is that by decreasing the relative movement between the parts, the risk of failure of the clamped parts from fretting corrosion is reduced.

*Methods of Increasing the Fatigue Strength of a Threaded Joint*

The performance of a bolted joint may be improved either by reducing the stress and load concentrations in the bolt or by altering the stiffness of the bolt or of the clamped members. Fatigue failure in a bolt usually occurs at one of the three positions indicated in Fig. 122. These are at the change in section between the head and the shank, at the run-out of the thread and, most commonly, at the thread under the bearing face of the nut. The distribution of load along the length of the nut is not uniform owing to the strains set up in the bolt and nut under load [480, 481]. Sopwith [482] has shown that in a normal nut and bolt the maximum load concentration occurs at the bearing face of the nut and has a value between 2 and 4, depending on the thread form, the proportions of the members and the degree of lubrication.

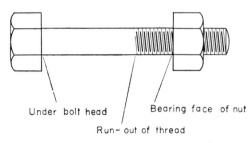

Under bolt head      Bearing face of nut

Run-out of thread

Fig. 122. Likely positions of fatigue failures in bolts.

A number of design modifications have been suggested for improving the load distribution. Wiegand [483] showed that the fatigue strength of a bolted joint could be improved 30% by introducing an annular groove at the base of the nut (see Fig. 123a) and 20% by tapering the thread of the nut slightly. The benefit of a tapered thread has been confirmed by Heywood [484], and he also showed that the fatigue strength could be improved by using a longer pitch for the nut thread than for the bolt or by using a nut with a convex or a concave face in conjunction with a suitably shaped washer. A more uniform distribution of load can also be achieved simply by using a nut with a lower modulus of elasticity than the bolt. Sopwith [482], for example, calculated that the stress concentration factor for one assembly could be reduced from 3·38 to 2·54 by substituting a duralumin nut for a steel nut on a steel bolt. Wiegand [483] obtained an improvement in the fatigue strength of steel bolts of 40% by using cast iron nuts, and Kaufmann and Janiche [485] an improvement between 35 and 60% with magnesium alloy nuts. Another simple method of distributing the load more uniformly is by locking two nuts together, and Cross and Norris [486] have reported an increase in fatigue strength of 50% by this means. Hetenyi [487] investigated the effect of design modifications on the stress distribution by means of photoelastic tests and showed that the stress concentration factor could be reduced from 3·85 for a conventional nut to 3·10 for a nut with tapered thread and to 3·00 for a nut with tapered lip (see Fig. 123b). A development of the tapered lip is the tension nut shown in Fig. 123c, which gives a more uniform load distribution because

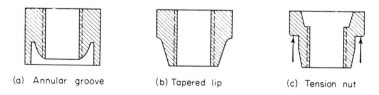

(a) Annular groove      (b) Tapered lip      (c) Tension nut

Fig. 123. Modified nut designs for improving load distribution.

both nut and bolt are stressed in tension. A similar loading condition occurs in studs and consequently a stud is more resistant to fatigue than a standard bolt and nut. The influence of design on the fatigue strength of studs has been investigated by Brown and McClimont [488] and their results are summarized in Table 60.

TABLE 60. FATIGUE STRENGTH OF STUDS
(Brown and McClimont [488])

| Type of stud | Fatigue strength ($10^7$ cycles) tons/in$^2$ |
|---|---|
| Relieving groove | $10\cdot3 \pm 7\cdot3$ |
| Recessed | $9 \pm 6$ |
| Collar | $8\cdot6 \pm 5\cdot6$ |
| Normal | $8\cdot1 \pm 5\cdot1$ |
| Bottoming | $7\cdot3 \pm 4\cdot3$ |
| 1 in. diameter lathe-cut bolts | $6 \pm 3$ |

Details of the studs are shown in Fig. 124.

The stress concentration at the run-out of the thread can be relieved considerably by reducing the diameter of the shank of the bolt and to gain the maximum benefit the shank diameter should be reduced below the diameter of the root of the thread; the resulting reduction in bolt stiffness is a further advantage. Alternatively a stress relieving groove can be used or the thread may be continued up to the bolt head. Apart from the danger of fatigue failure occurring at the run-out of the thread, the change in section there may intensify the stress concentration at the nut face. The nut should therefore never be run up to the end of the thread unless the shank is undercut below the thread.

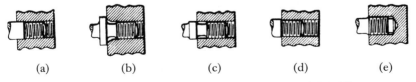

(a)            (b)            (c)            (d)            (e)

FIG. 124. Details of the studs tested by Brown and McClimont:
(a) recessed stud, (b) collar stud, (c) relieving groove stud, (d) normal stud,
(e) bottoming stud.

In a properly tightened bolted joint subjected to fluctuating load, the proportion of load fluctuation sustained by the bolt is equal to the ratio of the stiffness of the bolt to the stiffness of the joint. The danger of fatigue failure can therefore be reduced by reducing the stiffness of the bolt or by increasing the stiffness of the clamped parts. By these means a greater proportion of the fluctuating load is taken by the clamped parts, but because these are in compression they are unlikely to fail by fatigue. The use of a spring washer is beneficial because it reduces the effective stiffness of the bolt, but gaskets, on the other hand, are detrimental and should be as stiff as possible. The arrangement of the parts in a bolted assembly can also be important, as illustrated in Fig. 125, due to Almen [478].

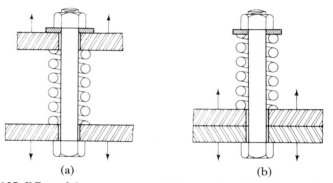

(a)                                    (b)

FIG. 125. Effect of the arrangement of the parts in a bolted assembly on its resistance to fatigue: (a) spring is part of abutments—bolt is weak; (b) spring is part of bolt—bolt is strong. (Almen [478])

High bending stresses can be induced in a bolt if it is not loaded axially and this probably accounts for a high proportion of bolt failures. Cottell [1] has claimed that if a fatigue crack in a bolt has progressed from one region, then it will usually be found that the nut or bolt head has not been bearing uniformly on the face beneath, resulting in non-axial loading.

### The Fatigue Strength of Lugs

Fatigue failures in service often originate at holes containing rivets, bolts or pins and this problem has received considerable attention recently, particularly with regard to aircraft structures. Lugs are the simplest type of pin joint and a number of fatigue experiments have been carried out on them. Many of the factors which affect their fatigue strength have not been investigated systematically, but Heywood [489] has attempted to correlate much of the available information and has suggested a simple design rule which may be used to estimate the fatigue strength of lugs. He considered only lugs with a small clearance between pin and hole; considerable increase in fatigue strength can be obtained using an interference fit and this is discussed later. Heywood noticed, firstly, that there appeared to be a pronounced size effect, the fatigue strength of large lugs being appreciably lower than that of small ones. Having allowed for this, the remaining differences between individual results were found to depend primarily on the value of the stress concentration factor $K_t$, based on the net area at the minimum section. He was therefore able to plot average $S$–$N$ curves for steel and aluminium alloys (see Fig. 126) giving the

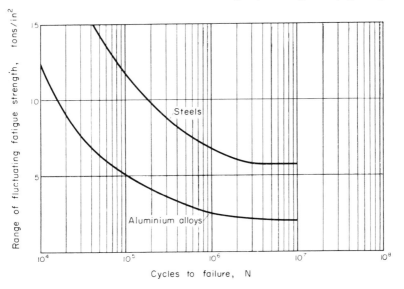

Fig. 126. Standard $S$–$N$ curves for lugs with 1 in. diameter hole and $K_t = 2.5$. (Heywood [489])

fluctuating fatigue strength for a "standard" lug with a 1 in. diameter hole and a value of $K_t$ of 2·5. The fatigue strength of a lug of any other size or shape is then given approximately by the relation:

$$\frac{S_a}{S_A} = \frac{2.5}{K_t}\left(\frac{2}{1+d}\right), \tag{38}$$

where $S_a$ is the range of fluctuating fatigue strength based on the fluctuating load divided by the cross sectional area at the hole, $d$ is the diameter of the hole in inches, and $S_A$ is the range of fluctuating fatigue strength of the standard lug. This relation should be regarded only as an approximate guide, although it yields values within $\pm 33\%$ of most of the data considered. These consisted of results for lugs with holes ranging from 0·2 to 2·8 in. diameter, for steels with tensile strengths mostly between 50 and 80 tons/in² and for heat-treated aluminium alloys with tensile strengths mostly between 32 and 38 tons/in². The fatigue strengths of both steel and aluminium alloy lugs were found to be approximately independent of the tensile strength. The tests were all made in fluctuating or pulsating tension and the effect of mean stress was neglected in the analysis. It has been shown subsequently, however, that increase in mean stress may reduce the fluctuating fatigue strength appreciably [490].

The direct relation between the fatigue strength and $K_t$ implicit in Heywood's relation illustrates the importance of design in improving the fatigue resistance of lugs. Values of $K_t$ for a wide range of lugs have been determined by Frocht [255] and some of his results are shown in Fig. 127. A reduction in $K_t$ can be achieved by increasing the distance from the

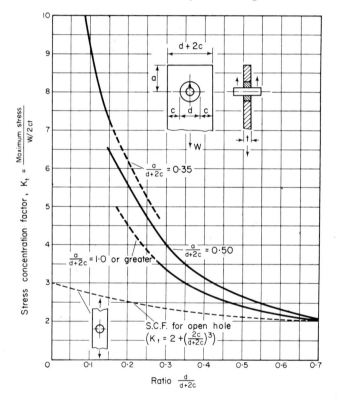

FIG. 127. Values of the theoretical stress concentration factor for lugs (after Frocht and Hill). (Heywood [489])

hole to the end of the lug or by increasing the ratio of the hole diameter to the lug width. Low [491] has demonstrated that the fatigue strength (based on the gross section) of L 65 aluminium alloy lugs of $2\frac{1}{4}$ in. width increases as the diameter of the pin is increased up to 1 in. It has also been shown that increasing the ratio of the thickness of the lug to the diameter of the hole reduces the fatigue strength and this has been attributed to non-uniform load distribution caused by bending of the pin [490].

An important result which is clearly demonstrated by Heywood's analysis is that the strength reduction factor $K_f$ for lugs, based on an endurance of $10^7$ cycles, has a remarkably high value of about 8, whereas $K_t$ is only about $2\frac{1}{2}$. The fatigue strengths are thus less than one third of the values which would be obtained by normal methods of computation, so that an approach similar to Heywood's appears to be essential for estimating the fatigue strength of lugs. The discrepancy can probably be attributed primarily to fretting between the pin and the bore of the lug.

The considerable improvement that can be obtained with an interference fit has been demonstrated by Low in tests on aluminium alloy lugs [491]. He found that with a 1 in. pin the optimum interference was about 0·007 in. and this increased the range of pulsating fatigue strength from about $1\frac{1}{2}$ to 9 tons/in²; similar results have been reported from other sources [490, 492]. The effect of interference is to increase the mean stress, but to decrease the stress range. This undoubtedly contributes to the improvement in performance, but the reduction in fretting corrosion may be equally important. Improvement in the fatigue strength of lugs can also be obtained by pre-stressing; this has been demonstrated by Heywood and his results are shown in Fig. 61.

### Riveted joints

Fatigue failures in riveted joints almost always occur through the plate or sheet, the fatigue cracks propagating from the rivet holes. Failure occurs in this way even in joints designed to fail statically by shear of the rivets because of the stress concentration in the plate or sheet at the edges of the holes. For steel, most of the information available on the fatigue strength of riveted joints has been obtained from fairly large-scale tests on steel plate, and some typical results are given in Table 61. For aluminium alloys a considerable number of fatigue tests have been made on riveted sheet because of its importance in aircraft structures [673] and some of these results are given in Table 62. The fatigue strengths quoted are based on the gross section of the sheet or plate, so that a direct comparison can be made of the load carrying capacity of riveted joints of different pitch or between riveted and welded or bonded joints. Details of the joints are included in the tables so that fatigue strengths on the net section can be calculated.

The most comprehensive series of fatigue tests on riveted joints in steel plate has been made by Wilson and Thomas [493]. They investigated the influence of a number of factors on the fatigue strength and some of their results are included in Table 61. The influence of the plate material was

TABLE 61. FATIGUE STRENGTH OF RIVETED AND BOLTED DOUBLE SHEAR BUTT JOINTS IN STEEL PLATE BASED ON $2 \times 10^6$ CYCLES

| Material | | Tensile strength of plate material tons/in² | Joint details | | | | | | Axial* fatigue strength tons/in² (on gross section) $2 \times 10^6$ cycles | Source | Ref. |
|---|---|---|---|---|---|---|---|---|---|---|---|
| Plate | Rivets or bolts | | No. of rivet or bolt rows | Spacing of rows in. | Rivet or bolt pitch in. | Rivet or bolt diameter in. | Plate width in. | Plate thickness in. | | | |
| | | | | *Riveted joints* | | | | | | | |
| C steel | C steel | 28·4 | 2 | 3 | 4¼ | 1 | 8¼ | ¾ | 0 to 8·8 | Wilson and Thomas | 493 |
| Si steel | C steel | 35·8 | 2 | 3 | 4¼ | 1 | 8¼ | ¾ | 0 to 8·7 | | |
| Ni steel | C steel | 44·2 | 2 | 3 | 4¼ | 1 | 8¼ | ¾ | 0 to 9·0 | | |
| Si steel | Mn steel | 35·8 | 2 | 3 | 4¼ | 1 | 8¼ | ¾ | 0 to 9·4 | | |
| C steel | C steel | | 3 | 3 | 4 | 1 | 6¾–7¼ | ¾ | ±6·3 | | |
| C steel | C steel | | 3 | 3 | 4 | 1 | 6¾–7¼ | ¾ | 0 to 9·1 | | |
| C steel | C steel | | 3 | 3 | 4 | 1 | 6¾–7¼ | ¾ | 9·3±3·1 | | |
| C steel | C steel | | 4 | 3 | 7 | 1 | 7 | ½ | 0 to 9·1 | | |
| C steel | C steel | | 2 | 3 | 4⅞ | 1 | 8⅛ | ½ | 0 to 8·4 | | |
| C steel | C steel | | 3 | 3 | 3⅝ | 1 | 10¼ | ½ | 0 to 8·5 | | |
| C steel | 0·3% C steel | 50·0 | 2 | 3½ | 3½ | 1 | 6½ | ½ | ±6 | Munse, Wright and Newmark | 494 |
| | | | | *Bolted joints* | | | | | | | |
| C steel | 0·3% C steel | 50·0 | 2 | 3½ | 3½ | 1 | 6½ | ½ | ±7·5 | | |

* The fatigue strengths quoted are based on a small number of tests and are determined by using the empirical relation

$$S = \frac{B}{N^{0 \cdot 1}}$$

where $N$ is the endurance at a stress $S$ and $B$ is a constant.

TABLE 62. FATIGUE STRENGTH OF RIVETED, BO

| Material | | | Type of joint | | | | |
|---|---|---|---|---|---|---|---|
| Sheet | Rivets or bolts | | No. of rivet or bolt rows | Spacing of rows in. | Rivet or bolt pitch in. | Type of rivet or bolt | |
| | | *Riveted joints* | | | | | |
| DTD 546B Alclad (Al Cu) artificially aged | DTD 327 | Double shear butt | 2 | $\frac{3}{4}$ | $\frac{3}{4}$ | Snap | |
| DTD 687A Alclad (Al Zn Mg) | DTD 327 | Double shear butt | 2 | $\frac{3}{4}$ | $\frac{3}{4}$ | Snap | |
| DTD 610B Alclad (Al Cu) naturally aged | DTD 327 | Double shear butt | 2 | $\frac{3}{4}$ | $\frac{3}{4}$ | Snap | |
| 24 S–T Alclad (Al Cu) | 17 S | Lap | 2 | 0·79 | 0·79 | Snap | |
| | | | 2 | 0·79 | 0·52 | Snap | |
| | | | 2 | 0·79 | 0·39 | Snap | |
| | | | 2 | 0·79 | 1·05 | Snap | |
| 75 S–T Alclad (Al Zn Mg) | | | 2 | 0·79 | 0·79 | Snap | |
| | | | 2 | 0·79 | 0·79 | Snap | |
| | | | 2 | 0·79 | 0·52 | Snap | |
| | | | 2 | 0·79 | 0·39 | Snap | |
| | | | 2 | 0·79 | 1·05 | Snap | |
| | | | 2 | 0·79 | 0·79 | Snap | |
| 24 S–T Alclad (Al Cu) | 17 S–T | Unnotched sheet | | No joint | | | |
| | | Lap* | 1 | | $\frac{1}{2}$ | Flush | |
| | | Lap | 2 | $\frac{1}{2}$ | $\frac{1}{2}$ | Flush | |
| | | Lap | 3 | $\frac{1}{2}$ | $\frac{1}{2}$ | Flush | |
| | | Lap with heavy stiffener 3 in. long, $\frac{1}{4}$ in. thick | 1 | | $\frac{1}{2}$ | Flush | |
| | | Single shear butt | 2 | | $\frac{1}{2}$ | Flush | |
| | | Double shear butt Multi-arc welded | 2 | | $\frac{1}{2}$ | Flush | |
| | | *Bolted joints* | | | | | |

| Diameter of rivet or bolt in. | Sheet width in. | Sheet thickness in. | Tensile strength of joint tons/in² based on gross section | Axial fatigue strength tons/in² based on gross section | | | | Source | Ref. |
|---|---|---|---|---|---|---|---|---|---|
| | | | | $10^4$ | $10^5$ | $10^6$ | $10^7$ | | |
| $\frac{3}{16}$ | 4·5 | 10 S.W.G. | 16·5 | | 2·7 $+$ 2·7 <br> 5·5 $+$ 2 | 1·7 $+$ 1·7 | | Kelsey and Spooner | 495 |
| $\frac{3}{16}$ | 4·5 | 10 S.W.G. | 17 | 5·3 $+$ 5·3 <br> 7·5 $+$ 4 | 2·1 $+$ 2·1 <br> 5 $+$ 1·8 | | | | |
| $\frac{3}{16}$ | 4·5 | 10 S.W.G. | 17 | 5·7 $+$ 5·7 | 3 $+$ 3 <br> 5·5 $+$ 2 | 1·5 $+$ 1·5 | 1·2 $+$ 1·2 | | |
| 0·12 | 6·3 | 0·031 | 18·0 | | 4·8 $+$ 3·7 | 4·8 $+$ 1·5 | 4·8 $+$ 1·0 | Hartman and Klaassen | 496 |
| 0·12 | 6·3 | 0·031 | 21·6 | | 4·4 $+$ 4·3 | 4·4 $+$ 1·9 | 4·4 $+$ 1·3 | | |
| 0·12 | 6·3 | 0·031 | 20·0 | | | 3·9 $+$ 2·1 | 3·9 $+$ 1·4 | | |
| 0·25 | 6·3 | 0·118 | 15·9 | | 4·4 $+$ 2·6 | 4·4 $+$ 1·0 | 4·4 $+$ 0·6 | | |
| 0·25 | 6·3 | 0·118 | 20·6 | | 3·9 $+$ 2·5 | 3·9 $+$ 1·0 | 3·9 $+$ 0·6 | | |
| 0·12 | 6·3 | 0·031 | 16·8 | | 4·8 $+$ 2·4 | 4·8 $+$ 1·1 | 4·8 $+$ 0·8 | | |
| 0·12 | 6·3 | 0·031 | 25·3 | | 4·4 $+$ 2·9 | 4·4 $+$ 1·5 | 4·4 $+$ 1·2 | | |
| 0·12 | 6·3 | 0·031 | 25·9 | | 3·9 $+$ 3·6 | 3·9 $+$ 1·7 | 3·9 $+$ 1·2 | | |
| 0·25 | 6·3 | 0·118 | 15·1 | | 4·4 $+$ 2·0 | 4·4 $+$ 0·9 | 4·4 $+$ 0·6 | | |
| 0·25 | 6·3 | 0·118 | 19·7 | | 3·9 $+$ 1·9 | 3·9 $+$ 0·9 | 3·9 $+$ 0·6 | | |
| | | | 30·2 | 20 $+$ 8·6 | 18 $+$ 8 | 11 $+$ 5 | 10 $+$ 4·3 | Russell, Jackson, Grover and Beaver | 497 |
| $\frac{1}{8}$ | 4·5 | 0·040 | 11·6 | 7 $+$ 3 | 4·3 $+$ 1·8 | 2·2 $+$ 0·8 | 1·9 $+$ 0·8 | | |
| $\frac{1}{8}$ | 4·5 | 0·040 | 20·8 | 12 $+$ 5·5 | 6·2 $+$ 2·7 | 3·4 $+$ 1·5 | | | |
| $\frac{1}{8}$ | 4·5 | 0·040 | 22·5 | 13 $+$ 5·5 | 7·3 $+$ 3·1 | 4·2 $+$ 1·8 | | | |
| $\frac{1}{8}$ | 4·5 | 0·040 | 11·2 | | 6·9 $+$ 3·0 | 4·7 $+$ 2·0 | 3·8 $+$ 1·6 | | |
| $\frac{1}{8}$ | 4·5 | 0·040 | 11·9 | | 6·6 $+$ 2·8 | 5·0 $+$ 2·2 | 4·3 $+$ 1·8 | | |
| $\frac{1}{8}$ | 4·5 | 0·040 | 17·5 | | 8·3 $+$ 3·6 | 6·0 $+$ 2·6 | | | |
| | 4·5 | 0·040 | 23·0 | 16 $+$ 7 | 13 $+$ 5·6 | 9·5 $+$ 4·1 | 9·0 $+$ 3·9 | | |

found to have little effect, the range of pulsating fatigue strength based on the gross section being between 8 and 10 tons/in² for all the steels tested. Changes in the joint design or using different methods of making the rivet holes also had little effect on the fatigue strength. The results of their tests to investigate mean stress show good agreement with the Goodman relation.

For aluminium alloys the effect of mean stress on the fatigue strength of riveted joints has been determined over only a relatively narrow range. Results obtained by Kelsey and Spooner, shown in Table 62, fit approximately the Goodman relation, but results obtained by Russell and others show little reduction in the range of fluctuating fatigue strength with

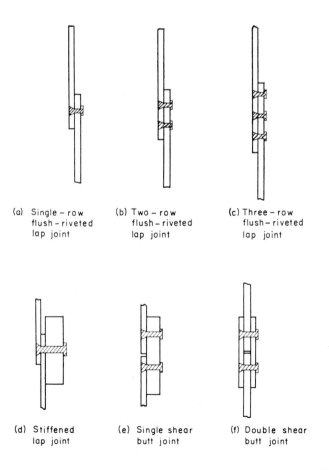

(a) Single – row      (b) Two – row      (c) Three – row
    flush – riveted        flush – riveted        flush – riveted
    lap joint             lap joint             lap  joint

(d) Stiffened      (e) Single shear      (f) Double shear
    lap joint             butt joint             butt joint

FIG. 128. Types of riveted joint tested by Russell and others [497].

increase in mean stress. Their results are shown in Fig. 129 and these illustrate the low fatigue strength of riveted joints compared with plain specimens.

The influence of design factors on the fatigue strength of riveted joints in aluminium alloy sheet has received considerable attention. The method of riveting has some effect and Grover, Gordon and Jackson [135] quote

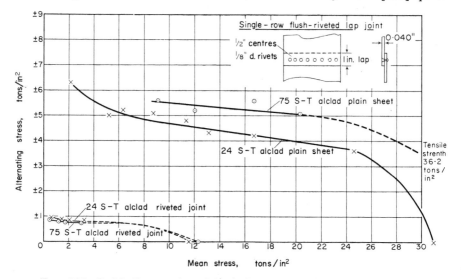

FIG. 129. *R–M* diagram for plain and riveted aluminium alloy sheet. (Russell, Jackson, Grover and Beaver [497])

All tests on 0·040 in. sheet. Plain specimens 1 in. wide. Stresses based on gross section.

the following order of decreasing fatigue strength, coin-dimpled holes, spin-dimpled holes, drilled holes, machine-countersunk holes. They also claim that brazier-head and round-head riveted joints are superior to joints with flush riveting, but Hartman [500] found no difference for long endurances. The fatigue strength increases with decrease in the rivet pitch; Hartman and Klaassen [496] recommend a rivet pitch to rivet diameter ratio of about 3, but the extent to which this ratio may be reduced to give the optimum condition does not appear to have been determined experimentally. The fatigue strength also increases with the number of rows of rivets and with the spacing between them [501]. A comparison of different joints from the results of Russell and others is shown in Table 62. Lap joints are improved by reinforcement, but are still inferior to butt joints. Some results are also included in Table 62 which show that redux-bonded joints may show better resistance to fatigue than riveted joints.

## Bolted joints

In many ways the fatigue behaviour of bolted joints is similar to that of riveted joints and the fatigue strength is influenced by the same factors. This is illustrated by some results included in Tables 61 and 62. By tightly clamping the bolts however, a considerable proportion of the load may be transmitted by friction between the plates and it is then possible to achieve higher fatigue strengths than in riveted joints. For example, Munse and others carried out tests on similar steel specimens fabricated with rivets and with bolts of high tensile steel and demonstrated that the fatigue strength of the bolted joints, properly assembled, was approximately 25% greater than the riveted joints (see Table 61). On thinner sections the effect is much more pronounced; for example, Fisher and Winkworth [502] achieved a four-fold increase in fatigue strength on 16 s.w.g. (0·064 in. thick) aluminium alloy sheet by tight clamping. The advantages to be gained by using an interference fit has been discussed in connection with lugs and is equally applicable to bolted joints.

The results of a large number of fatigue tests on aircraft wing structural joints have been correlated by Heywood [503]; these included extruded, rolled or forged aluminium alloy members, but excluded sheet material. He found that the range of fluctuating fatigue strength was little affected by mean stress or by the tensile strength or composition of the alloy, though the aluminium–copper alloys were slightly better than the aluminium–zinc–magnesium alloys. The detailed method of design was the predominating factor influencing the fatigue strength, the joints of best design withstanding about four times the fluctuating stress for a given endurance than those of worst design. A similar conclusion was reached by Hartmann and others [504] from the results of fatigue tests on a wide range of aircraft joints and some of their results are quoted in Table 63.

TABLE 63. FATIGUE STRENGTH OF ALUMINIUM ALLOY 75S–T6 BOLTED JOINTS
(Hartmann, Holt and Eaton [504])
Details of the joints are shown in Fig. 130.

| Type of joint | Fatigue life | |
|---|---|---|
| | at 16,000 ±5,330 lb | at 16,000 ±10,670 lb |
| Single shear,   Fig. 130 (a) | 42,000 | — |
| Double shear, Fig. 130 (b) | 3,427,000 | — |
| Plain scarf,     Fig. 130 (c) | 210,800 | 55,000 |
| Double scarf, Fig. 130 (d) | >26,000,000 | >418,000 |

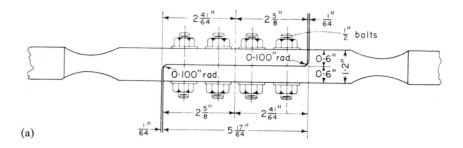

(a)

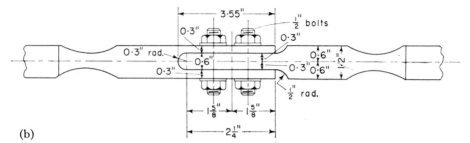

(b)

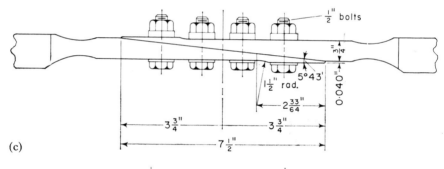

(c)

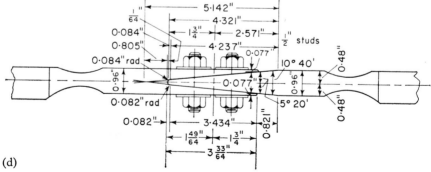

(d)

FIG. 130. Aluminium alloy bolted joints. (Hartmann, Holt and Eaton [504]):
(a) single shear joint, (b) double shear joint, (c) plain scarf joint, (d) double
scarf joint

Heywood pointed out that even for the best joints, the fatigue strength was only about one quarter that of polished specimens, so that further improvement should still be possible. In a later paper [505] he demonstrated how this might be achieved by a combination of tight clamping with very close spacing of the bolts. The results of his analysis are shown in Fig. 131.

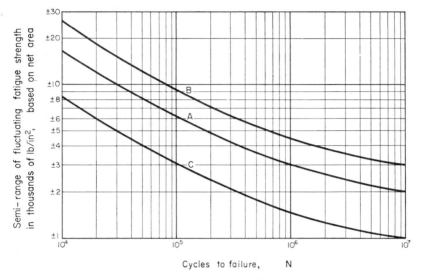

FIG. 131. Endurances of structural joints (aluminium alloy material—tensile loading). (Heywood [503])

Curve *A* is the mean of all results and Heywood derived the following equation relating the average value of the semi-range of fluctuating fatigue strength *S* to the endurance *N*:

$$S \text{ lb/in}^2 = 1500\left(1 + \frac{1000}{\sqrt{N}}\right), \qquad (39)$$

The equation is applicable for values of *S* below 10,000 lb/in². Curve *B* represents an upper limit of fatigue performance where special care has been taken in the design and manufacture, and curve *C* approaches the lower limit of fatigue performance where no special attention has been paid to fatigue.

The design of aircraft joints to withstand fatigue has been discussed by Stephenson [506] and Spaulding [507].

### Welded joints

There are a number of factors which may contribute to a reduction in the fatigue strength of a welded joint. The most important is the presence

T

of stress concentrations at geometrical discontinuities on the surface of the joint, but in addition, the weld metal is in a cast or partially worked condition, which may be inherently weaker than the parent metal, particularly if it contains internal defects. The material adjacent to the weld may be adversely affected by the welding process and residual tensile stresses may be present at the surface.

The static strength of a welded joint is often as great as that of the parent metal, because the weld reinforcement increases the section. The fatigue strength, on the other hand, cannot be increased by increasing the size of the weld nor by the addition of reinforcing straps, because failure will then occur at the transition between the joint and the parent metal as a result of the stress concentration introduced. The maximum resistance to fatigue is achieved, in fact, by reducing the discontinuity at the joint.

The resistance to fatigue of welded structures is at least equal to, and can be greatly superior to, that of riveted structures provided they are properly designed. There are some disadvantages of welded joints, however, which may result in low fatigue strengths if the structure is not well designed [508, 509]. Welded joints are much more rigid than riveted joints, because slip can occur in rivets and consequently the local static stresses do not relax to the same extent in a welded structure. The greater rigidity of welded joints also results in lower structural damping and this may lead to failures from resonant vibrations under some conditions. The continuity of a welded joint might be a further disadvantage, for once a fatigue crack has formed, it is likely to propagate more quickly than a crack in a riveted joint. There is evidence, however, that fatigue cracks usually spread slowly in welded structures, so that the detection and repair of fatigue damage can be undertaken during routine maintenance [510].

The fatigue behaviour of welded joints has received a great deal of attention and a considerable amount of fatigue testing has been carried out. Detailed reviews of the information available were written by Spraragen and Claussen in 1937 [511] and by Spraragen and Rosenthal in 1942 [512] and, more recently, articles have been written by Weck [508, 509] and by Whitman [513]. A conference on fatigue of welded structures was held at Cambridge in 1960 [510].

*Butt Welds*

Some typical values of the fatigue strength of transverse butt-welded joints in steel are quoted in Table 64. For structural mild steel a sound butt-welded joint has a fatigue strength of roughly two-thirds that of unwelded plate, but by machining the weld flush with the plate, it is possible to achieve a fatigue strength equal to that for black (unmachined) plate, although it is essential to have freedom from weld defects for this to be achieved [521]. In general, the fatigue strength is not much affected by the

**Fatigue strength tons/in²**

| Weld reinforcement on | | | | Weld reinforcement off | | | | | Source | Ref. |
| Alternating stress | | Pulsating tension range | | Alternating stress | | | Pulsating tension range | | | |
| $2 \times 10^6$ | $10^7$ | $10^5$ | $2 \times 10^6$ | $10^5$ | $2 \times 10^6$ | $10^7$ | $10^5$ | $2 \times 10^6$ | | |
|---|---|---|---|---|---|---|---|---|---|---|
| | | | 11·5 | | | | | 16 | Newman and Gurney | 514 |
| | | | 6·5 to 11 | | | | | 16 | | |
| ±5·2 to ±6·2 | | 11·5 to 16·9 | 7·6 to 10·6 | ±10·3 to ±12·5 | ±6·6 | | 14·9 to 24·2 | 11·8 to 13·0 | Univ. of Illinois | 515 |
| | | 14·4 17·4<br>17 to 28 | 9·0 11·8<br>10·7<br>8·7 to 16·3 | | | | | | Stallmeyer and Munse | 516 |
| | | | 6·3 to 9·0<br>6·3 to 9·0 | | | | | | de Leiris and Dutilleul | 517 |
| ±6·3<br>±7·1 | | 22<br>21·5<br>19·5<br>28·5 | 9·5<br>12·5<br>11·5<br>16·5 | ±19·5<br>±26 | ±12·5<br>±12 | | | | d'Orville Doty | 518 |
| | | | | ±28<br>±31<br>±27<br>±25 | ±16<br>±23<br>±13<br>±16 | | | | Grover, Bennett and Foley | 519 |
| | ±5·4<br>±6·9<br>±7·3<br>±11·1 | | | | | ±8·8<br>±9·8<br>±8·8<br>±10·9 | | | Unksov | 520 |

TABLE 64. THE FATIGUE STRENGTH OF TRANS

| Material | Tensile strength tons/in$^2$ | Size of plate in. | | Details of weld | Tensile strength of joint tons/in$^2$ weld reinforcement off | Type of fatigue stress* | |
|---|---|---|---|---|---|---|---|
| | | Width | Thickness | | | | $10^5$ |
| BS15 0·18% C steel | 28 | 2½ or 4 | ½ | Manual arc weld single V E319 electrodes both as-welded and stress relieved | | Ax | |
| | | | | Automatic weld-submerged arc stress relieved | | | |
| A.S.T.M. A-7 0·15–0·26% C steel | 24·3 to 28·2 | 5 | ¾ | Electrodes E6010 and E7016 | | Ax | ±7 to ±10 |
| Structural C steel A 242, 0·2% C, 1% Mn, 0·4% Cu, 0·6% Ni 0·3% silicon steel T-1 0·12% C, 0·75% Mn, 0·3% Cu, 0·8% Ni, 0·6% Cr | 27 34 36 47 | 4 | | | | Ax | |
| | 25 38 | 1·6 | ½ | Manual arc-weld | | Ax | |
| Ni, Cr, Mo, steel quenched and tempered | 47 | 3½ 3 3½ 3½ 3 3½ | ½ | Electrode E12015 Electrode E12015 shot-peened Electrode E9015 stress relieved Electrode E9015 shot-peened | | Ax B Ax Ax B Ax | ±15 ±22 |
| SAE 4130 (0·8–1·1% Cr, 0·15–0·25% Mo) | 54 86 | | ¼ machined to ⅛ | Flash: Normalized and tempered before welding Oil-quenched and tempered before welding Normalized and tempered after welding Oil-quenched and tempered after welding | 55 76 5] 77 | B | |
| 0·18% C steel | 31·5 | 2·95 | 1·97 | Electro-slag: As welded Stress relieved 2 hr at 650°C Normalized 1 hr at 920°C Hammer-peened | | B | |

*Ax = Axial stress
B = Plane bending

welding process; similar results are obtained with arc welding and gas welding, although higher fatigue strengths have been achieved with resistance welding on mild steel [512] and on alloy steels [509]. The fatigue strength is much more dependent on the shape of the joint and the quality of the weld.

Newman and Gurney [514] have demonstrated the importance of the reinforcement shape by comparing the fatigue strength of the joint with the angle $\theta$ between the plate surface and a tangent to the reinforcement bead at the edge of the weld (see Fig. 132). The values of fatigue strength

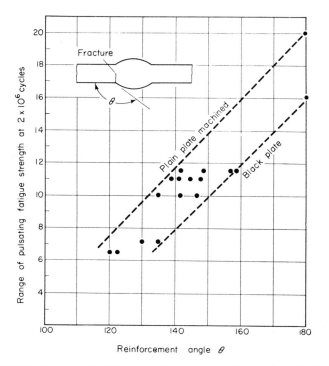

FIG. 132. Influence of reinforcement shape on fatigue strength of trans-verse butt welds. (Newman and Gurney [514])

shown correspond to $2 \times 10^6$ cycles of pulsating tension and were obtained from full penetration transverse butt welds in mild steel plate, free from significant internal defects. The variation is almost 2 to 1, from $11\frac{1}{2}$ tons/in² for the shape shown in Fig. 133a to $6\frac{1}{2}$ tons/in² for the shape shown in Fig. 133b. The latter value is about the lower limit of fatigue strength for sound welds made in accordance with good commercial practice. Permissible fluctuating stresses for butt welds in mild steel are quoted in B.S. 153 (1958) [522].

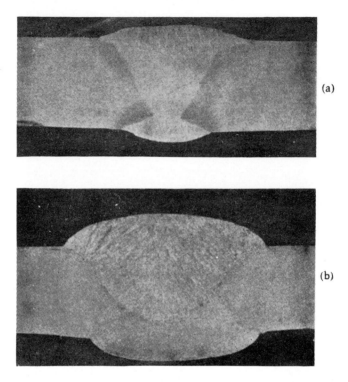

FIG. 133. Reinforcement shapes in butt welds: (a) high-strength joint,
(b) low-strength joint. (Newman and Gurney [514])

The effect of internal defects on mild steel welded joints has been reviewed recently [523]. It is generally agreed that a moderate degree of
porosity, slag or lack of fusion in a weld does not reduce the fatigue strength
of mild steel as much as surface defects. Stress raisers on the surface, such
as undercutting, or overlap at the edges of a weld are a more frequent
source of fatigue cracks. Serious reductions in fatigue strength can result,
however, from lack of penetration or from cracks either in the weld metal
or in the heat-affected zone. A quantitative investigation of the effect of
weld defects on fatigue strength has been undertaken by Newman [524].
He carried out a series of reversed bending fatigue tests on a number of
butt welds in 6 in. diameter pipe into which certain defects were deliberately introduced. The fatigue strength of plain pipes ($2 \times 10^6$ cycles)
was between $\pm 7 \cdot 5$ and $\pm 11$ tons/in$^2$ and that of sound welds with the
reinforcement left on, between $\pm 3$ and $\pm 6$ tons/in$^2$. (This range of values
is lower than those shown in Table 64 for mild steel, because for the pipe
the joints could only be welded from one side.) The introduction of
porosity, "tramline" slag, piping, gross defects or lack of fusion did not

reduce the fatigue strength further, but lack of penetration reduced the value to between $\pm 1$ and $\pm 1.5$ tons/in². de Leiris and Dutilleul [517] found that defects reduced the fatigue strength of arc-welded joints only if they were plainly visible in a radiograph, but transverse cracks seriously reduced the fatigue strength. It should be noted, however, that these results were obtained on joints with the weld reinforcement left on. If the weld is machined flush with the parent metal to remove the surface stress raisers, then the presence of internal defects is more likely to reduce the fatigue strength. Some investigators have found that stress-relieving treatments can improve the fatigue strength of butt-welded joints in structural steel, but it is generally agreed that the effect is small and may be masked by the influence of welding defects.

The use of welding in steel is confined primarily to mild steel, and there is much less information available of the fatigue strength of welded joints in high-tensile steels. The results that have been obtained have often been disappointing; although the fatigue strengths for short endurances or with high mean stresses have been appreciably higher than for mild steel, these materials usually show little or no advantage for long endurances [525] A number of reasons can be put forward to account for this behaviour. The high-tensile strength is often achieved by heat-treatment and the benefit of this may be lost in the weld metal and the heat-affected zone and, in addition, there is a greater likelihood of cracks being produced during welding in these materials because of their lower ductility. Furthermore, high-tensile steels are more notch sensitive and therefore suffer a greater reduction in fatigue strength from the presence of surface discontinuities and internal defects. (The results of fatigue tests by D'Orville Doty, quoted in Table 64, illustrate the considerable improvement in fatigue strength obtained in an alloy steel by machining off the weld reinforcement.) A further reason for their disappointing fatigue strength is that adverse residual stresses induced during welding are likely to be of greater magnitude in high-tensile steels, and are less likely to be reduced by subsequent stressing.

Some results that have been obtained of the fatigue strength of transverse butt welds in light alloys are shown in Table 65 and these illustrate a number of features similar to the results obtained for steel. The results of Hartmann, Holt and Eaton include a range of aluminium alloys and show that for endurances greater than a million cycles, welded joints of the high-strength alloy 14S–T6 are no more resistant to fatigue than the non-heat-treatable alloys. At low endurances, the fatigue strength was more closely related to the tensile strength of the joints and, indeed, up to 1000 cycles, the fatigue strength was almost equal to the tensile strength for all the materials tested. These authors found that machining off the weld reinforcement resulted in only a small improvement in fatigue strength

TABLE 65. THE FATIGUE STRENGTH OF

| Material | Tensile strength tons/in$^2$ | Size of plate, in. | | Details of weld | Reinforcement |
|---|---|---|---|---|---|
| | | Width | Thickness | | |
| Magnesium alloy HK31–H24 | | | $\frac{1}{8}$ | Shielded arc with HK31 welded rod | On<br>Off |
| Aluminium alloys:<br>HE 30 WP, 1·01% Si, 0·63% Mg, 0·57% Mn | 20·4 | $1\frac{1}{4}$ | $\frac{1}{4}$ | Argon arc from 1 and from 2 sides | On |
| | | | | Self-adjusting arc from 1 side | On |
| | | | | Self-adjusting arc from 2 sides | On and Off |
| NP 5/6, 4·2% Mg, 0·17% Si, as rolled | 21·7 | | | Metal arc from 1 side<br>Argon arc from 2 sides<br>Self-adjusting arc from 2 sides | On<br>On<br>On |
| NS 4 $\frac{1}{2}$H, 2·11% Mg, 0·11% Si, 0·31% Fe, 0·11% Mn, 0·027 %Cu | 15·9 | $3\frac{1}{2}$–4 | $\frac{1}{4}$ | Inert-gas metal-arc manually welded from both sides with NG 6 filler wire | On |
| NP 5/6 M, 4·36% Mg, 0·12% Si, 0·28% Fe 0·60% Mn 0·025% Cu | 19·75 | | | | |
| HP 30 WP, 0·65% Mg, 1·04% Si, 0·28% Fe 0·55% Mn 0·029% Cu | 21·25 | | | | |
| BA 28 NP 5/6 Al 4·6% Mg | | $\frac{3}{4}$ | $\frac{1}{4}$ | Inert-gas metal-arc | On<br>Off |
| 3S half hard<br>3S half hard | 9·5<br>9·5 | | $\frac{1}{16}$<br>$\frac{1}{8}$ | Gas<br>Gas and arc | On<br>On |
| 3S hot rolled | 10·2 | | $\frac{3}{8}$ | Arc | Off |
| 14S–T6 Alclad | 30 | 5 | $\frac{3}{8}$ | Arc with flux-coated metal electrode | On and Off |
| 61S–T6 (Al Mg Si) | 20 | | | Arc with flux-coated metal electrode | On and Off |
| 61S–T6 (Al Mg Si)<br>A54 S–H34<br>3S–F (pure Al) | <br>19<br>10 | | | Inert gas metal (Tungsten) and semi-automatic inert-gas metal-arc | On and Off |

TRANSVERSE BUTT WELDS IN LIGHT ALLOYS

| Tensile strength of joint tons/in² | Type of fatigue stress | Fatigue strength tons/in² | | | | | Source | Ref. |
|---|---|---|---|---|---|---|---|---|
| | | $10^4$ | $10^5$ | $10^6$ | $10^7$ | $10^8$ | | |
| | B | | | ±2·3 ±3·6 | ±1·7 ±3·4 | ±1·6 ±3·3 | Breen and Dwyer | 526 |
| 10·8 | Ax | | 8–10 | 4·5–7 | | | Newman | 527 |
| 14·4 | (Range of pulsating tension) | | 7–9 | 4·5–6 | | | | |
| | | | 9–11 | 6–8 | | | | |
| 12·0 | | | 6–7 | 3·5–5 | | | | |
| 19·6 | | | 9–11 | 6–8 | | | | |
| 19·4 | | | 8–10 | 4·5–6·5 | | | | |
| 13·1 | Ax | | 0±5·6 3±4 7±4 | 0±3·7 3±2·5 7±2·3 | 0±2·8 3±2 7±1·5 | 0±2·6 3±2 7±1·5 | Gunn and McLester | 528 |
| 18·7 | | | — 3±4·7 7±4·0 | 0±4·1 3±2·8 7±2·3 | 0±3·4 3±2·0 7±1·6 | 0±3·2 3±2·0 7±1·6 | | |
| 11·8 | | | — 3±5 7±4·5 | 0±4·0 3±3·1 7±2·5 | 0±3·0 3±2·1 7±1·5 | 0±2·4 3±1·9 7±1·4 | | |
| 18·4 | B | | ±5·4 | ±4·0 | ±3·7 | | Wood | 529 |
| 16·7 | | | ±8·1 | ±5·8 | ±5·5 | | | |
| 7·1 | B | | ±5·7 | ±4·2 | ±3·6 | ±3·1 | Templin and Holt | 530 |
| 6·9 | Ax (Range of pulsating tension) | | 2·3 | 1·2 | 1·2 | | | |
| 7·8–8·6 | Ax (Range of pulsating tension) | | 5·1 | 3·4 | 3·1 | | | |
| 15·2 | Ax (Range of pulsating tension) | 10·4–12·4 | 6·7–8·6 | 4·0–5·8 | 2·4–3·7 | | Hartmann, Holt and Eaton | 531 |
| 11·7 | | 5·8–9·9 | 2·9–7·1 | 2·2–4·6 | 2·1–3·5 | | | |
| | | 9·1–11·5 | 6·0–8·8 | 3·7–5·9 | 3·2–4·4 | | | |
| 17·0 | | 11·0–14·0 | 6·3–8·9 | 3·7–5·8 | 3·2–5·0 | | | |
| 7·8 | | 7·1–8·3 | 4·5–6·5 | 2·9–4·6 | 2·9–4·4 | | | |

TABLE 66. THE FATIGUE STRENGTH OF BUTT-WELDED AND FILLET-WELDED JOINTS IN ASTM-A7 STRUCTURAL STEEL (*Welding Handbook* [532])

Details of the fillet-welded joints are shown in Fig. 134

| Type of joint | Fatigue strength tons/in² | | | |
| --- | --- | --- | --- | --- |
| | Alternating stress | | Pulsating tension range | |
| | $10^5$ | $2 \times 10^6$ | $10^5$ | $2 \times 10^6$ |
| *Flat-plate specimens with and without butt welds, **as-welded and with** reinforcement removed flush* | | | | |
| Plain plate | ±12·0 | ±7·8 | 21·3 | 14·2 |
| Transverse butt-welded joint (single V) as-welded | ±10·0 | ±6·6 | 15·6 | 10·3 |
| Transverse butt-welded joint (a) single V, (b) single U–reinforcement off | ±12·2 (b) | ±7·1 (b) | 16·7 (a) | 12·8 (a) |
| Longitudinal butt-welded joint (single V) as-welded | — | — | 17·7 | 11·6 |
| Longitudinal butt-welded joint (a) single V, (b) double V–reinforcement off | ±9·4 (b) | ±7·0 (b) | 21·0 (a) | 13·6 (a) |
| *Fillet welds of various arrangements in specimens designed for failure in the welds* | | | | |
| A. Fillet-welded lap joints—$\frac{5}{16}$ in. transverse welds. Failure in welds | ±7·2 | ±5·0 | 13·5 | 8·2+ |
| B. Fillet-welded lap joints—$\frac{5}{16}$ in. longitudinal welds. Failure in welds | ±6·8 | ±4·8 | 12·1 | 8·8 |
| C. Fillet-welded lap joints—$\frac{5}{16}$ in. transverse and longitudinal welds. Failure in welds | ±5·8 | ±4·0 | 12·7 | 9·1 |
| D. Tee joints—$\frac{5}{16}$ in. fillet welds. Failure in welds | ±5·9 | ±2·8 | 8·5 | 4·3 |

and the figures quoted in the table represent the scatter band for all the results. Newman [527], on the other hand, found that the fatigue strength of butt-welded aluminium alloys was primarily dependent on the stress concentration at the reinforcement and was little influence by the welding process.

*Fillet Welds*

Fillet-welded joints generally have a lower fatigue strength than butt-welded joints because of the stress concentration at the change in section where the weld joins the plate. For resistance to static stress it is possible by using a sufficient thickness and length of weld to produce a joint with a higher strength than the parent metal, but, as for butt welds, the fatigue strength cannot be improved in this way. The fatigue strength of fillet-welded joints is unaffected by the size of the welds within fairly wide limits, and no further increase in fatigue strength is obtained by increasing the throat thickness or the length of the weld beyond a certain minimum size [509].

A comparison of the fatigue strengths of butt-welded and fillet-welded joints in structural steel is made in Table 66 from results quoted in the *Welding Handbook* [532]. The comparatively low fatigue strength quoted

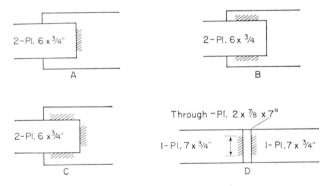

FIG. 134. Welded joints referred to in Table 66 (*Welding Handbook* [532]),

for the tee-joint is attributed to the fact that the welds were not carried across the full width of the connected plates. It may be noted that there is little reduction in the range of fatigue strength of fillet-welded joints with increase in mean stress. In general, no improvement is obtained in the fatigue strength of fillet-welded joints by using high-tensile steel.

Fillet welds that do not transmit load, but are used only for attaching stiffeners or brackets, may reduce the fatigue strength of a member as much as those transmitting load. As an illustration of this, de Leiris and

Dutilleul [517] showed that the two specimens in Fig. 135 had equal fatigue strengths.

The resistance of welded structures to fatigue depends to a large extent on the design, and the problems involved have been considered in some detail by Weck [508]. In transverse fillet welds the cracks most often propagate from the toe of the weld, and in longitudinal fillet welds, from

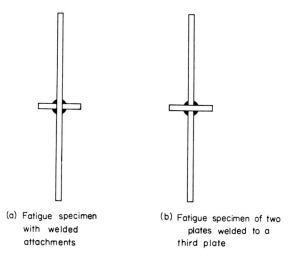

(a) Fatigue specimen          (b) Fatigue specimen of two
    with welded                   plates welded to a
    attachments                   third plate

FIG. 135. Fillet-welded specimens (de Leiris and Duttileul [517]).

the end of the weld. It is therefore possible to increase the fatigue strength by machining the fillet so that it blends smoothly into the plate; intersecting welds should be avoided. When possible, however, butt welds should be used instead of fillet welds. In plate structures, for example, it is better to use flange plates of variable thickness or width joined by butt welds, than to use fillet-welded cover plates.

This is illustrated in Table 67 by the results of Munse and Stallmeyer [533]. It may be noted that the shape of the cover plate has a considerable influence on the fatigue strength and any means used to make the change in cross-section of the beam more gradual is beneficial. A much higher fatigue strength is achieved, however, by butt-welding plates of different width or thickness. The larger plate should be tapered to the size of the smaller, as shown in Fig. 136, and even better results would probably be obtained by placing the weld some distance from the change in section. Cover plates should not be used to reinforce butt welds. Further sources of fatigue failures in welded structures, to which Weck [509] has drawn

TABLE 67. FATIGUE STRENGTHS OF BEAMS WITH VARIOUS CHANGES IN
FLANGE AREA (Munse and Stallmeyer [533])

| Description (see Fig. 136) | Range of pulsating tension fatigue strength tons/in² | |
|---|---|---|
| | $10^5$ cycles | $2 \times 10^6$ cycles |
| Partial-length cover plates, square ends with continuous weld all round (Type A) | 11·8 | 5·0 |
| Partial-length cover plates, tapered ends with continuous weld all round (Type B) | 14·7 | 5·1 |
| Partial-length cover plates, concave profile with continuous weld all round (Type C) | 13·7 | 6·5 |
| Partial-length cover plates, square ends with continuous weld along edges only (Type D) | 15·5 | 5·6 |
| Partial-length cover plates, tapered ends with continuous weld along edges only (Type F) | 16·3 | 6·1 |
| Partial-length cover plates, convex profile with continuous weld all round (Type G) | 12·9 | 5·2 |
| Butt-welded flange transition, tapered in width (Type J) | 15·6 | 8·7 |
| Butt-welded flange transition, tapered in thickness (Type K) | 15·4 | 8·3 |

attention, are stray flashes produced by accidentally touching the material with a welding electrode and tack welds used in preliminary assembly prior to welding. He recommends that tack welds should either be incorporated into the welded joints or placed in regions of the structure subjected only to low stresses.

Owing to the high stress concentration at fillet welds, the fatigue strength is considerably influenced by residual stress. Considerable benefit can therefore often be obtained by stress relieving treatments [534], and by applying local heating to induce favourable residual stresses, improvements as great as 150% have been obtained in the fatigue strength of mild steel fillet-welded joints [535].

*Spot Welds*

The behaviour of spot-welded joints when subjected to fluctuating

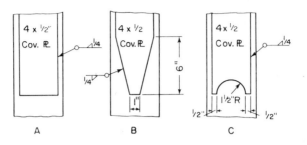

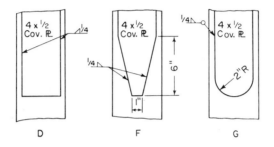

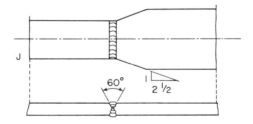

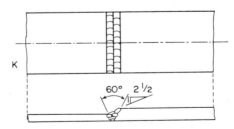

Fig. 136. Details of various types of cover plate. (Munse and Stallmeyer [533])

stresses is similar in many ways to that of riveted joints. The fatigue strength is influenced considerably by the quality of the welds, by the weld pattern and by the design of the joint and, as in riveted joints, the mode of failure by fatigue differs from that of static failure. Static failure occurs by shear of the weld spots or by pulling of the weld spots through the sheet, while fatigue failures usually occur through the sheet. A number of investigators have carried out fatigue tests on single lap spot-welded joints and typical values of the fatigue strength obtained for both steel and aluminium alloys are between 10 and 15% of the static strength [536]. In the range investigated it has been found that the fatigue strength increases with increasing size of spot, with the number of rows and with the number of spots in each row. Single lap joints are unsatisfactory because of the bending introduced and higher fatigue strengths can be obtained with double shear joints. Marked improvements in fatigue strength, as much as 300%, have been obtained by applying high pressure to the welded spots after welding [536] and this can be attributed primarily to the beneficial residual stresses introduced [537].

### Brazed Joints

The fatigue strength of brazed joints depends primarily on the quality of the joint and is little influenced by the parent metal; some values obtained for brazed butt joints are quoted in Table 68. For use at high temperatures, nickel–chromium alloy brazed joints have been developed which show high resistance to fatigue [540].

## The fatigue strength of components

### Plain Bearings

The majority of failures occurring in plain bearings are caused by fatigue and consequently considerable attention has been paid to the problem of improving their fatigue strength. It is essential, however, that bearing materials should have a low coefficient of friction and be sufficiently soft not to cause undue wear of the journal, and these factors tend to be incompatible with a high resistance to fatigue. Tin and lead-base alloys possess most of the attributes required of a bearing material and are satisfactory for many applications, but their fatigue strength is low and this renders them unsuitable for heavy duty. For heavier loads these materials have therefore been superseded by higher strength alloys such as copper–lead or aluminium–tin and the journals are then hardened to withstand the greater wear.

The stresses occurring in bearings in service are complex. The principal fluctuating stress is compressive, but tensile stresses may be induced in the longitudinal and circumferential directions and these may be responsible for fatigue cracking. Tensile stresses may also occur as a result of

TABLE 68. ROTATING BENDING FATIGUE STRENGTH OF BRAZED BUTT JOINTS

| Parent metal | Brazing metal | Tensile strength of joint tons/in² | Fatigue strength tons/in² | Source | Ref. |
|---|---|---|---|---|---|
| 2½% Ni ½% Mo steel | B–Ag 1 (45% Ag 15% Cu 16% Zn 24% Cd) | 13 | (10⁷ cycles) 5 | Hansel | 538 |
| | B–Ag3 (50% Ag 15·5% Cu 15·5% Zn 16% Cd 3% Ni) | 12–27 | 4 | | |
| | B–Cu (99·9% Cu) | 33 | 6 | | |
| 0·2% C steel (SAE 1020) | B–Ag 1 | 29 | (10⁸ cycles) 10 | Chatfield and Tour | 539 |
| Ni Mo steel (SAE 4140) | B–Ag 1 | 36–50 | 10 | | |
| Mild steel | 60% Cu 40% Zn | — | 8·5–10 | Doussin | 116 |

bending of the bearing liner or of the bearing itself, or from fluctuations in temperature. Quite large thermal stresses can be induced in bearing metals during casting and fluctuating thermal stresses will occur as a result of changes in temperature during service. These will be particularly severe where the coefficient of thermal expansion of the bearing and liner materials differ appreciably, as they do, for example, for lead or tin alloys on a steel liner. Furthermore, in tin, thermal stresses occur even when the metal is unconstrained as a result of the anisotropy of the thermal expansion [541] (see page 256). When fatigue occurs, a network of cracks is formed on the surface of the bearing. These cracks slowly propagate downwards and eventually, either at the junction of the bearing metal with the backing or before, they turn at right angles, so that the bearing breaks into a number of small pieces.

The performance of a bearing alloy cannot be assessed adequately simply from a determination of its fatigue strength on plain specimens, and a number of testing machines have therefore been designed for carrying out fatigue tests on actual bearings under conditions approximating to those in service [542, 543]. Table 69 shows some typical results from such tests quoted by Forrester [544], who commented that the conditions imposed by the testing machine were deliberately rather severe and, under more favourable conditions all the materials could carry higher fatigue loads than those indicated. In all the tests the lining material was bonded to a steel backing; the fatigue strengths are calculated from the maximum load on the projected area of the bearings.

A comparison of the fatigue performance of bearing alloys is discussed in more detail by Cuthbertson [542].

*Ball and Roller Bearings*

The loading conditions in ball and roller bearings are particularly severe because of the small contact area between the rolling elements and the raceways, and since the stresses induced are repeated with the passage of each element, fatigue is a common cause of failure. Steels with a high fatigue strength and resistance to wear are therefore required and 1% carbon $1\frac{1}{2}$% chromium steels have been specially developed for this purpose. Compressive stresses as high as 100 to 200 tons/in² may be induced at the contact area at the surface, but it has been shown [115, 545] that fatigue failures usually propagate from the region of maximum shear stress which occurs just below the surface; this leads to a characteristic type of failure known as spalling or flaking, in which small pieces of metal become detached from the bearing surface.

A number of fatigue machines for testing ball and roller bearings have been designed [545–547], because only in this way can the effects on fatigue life of such factors as lubrication, wear and abrasion be determined. A

TABLE 69. CHARACTERISTICS OF MATERIALS FOR FLUID-LUBRICATED BEARINGS
(Forrester [544])

| Lining material | Typical composition % | Thickness (×0.001 in.) | Fatigue strength p.s.i. | Wear rating | Seizure rating | Corrosion rating |
|---|---|---|---|---|---|---|
| Tin-base whitemetal | 7 Sb, 3 Cu, rem. Sn | 12 | 1900 | 1 | 1 | 1 |
|  |  | 4–7 | 2500 | 1 | 1 | 1 |
| Lead-base whitemetal | 1 Sn, 15 Sb, 1 As, rem. Pb | 12 | 1850 | 1* | 1 | 2 |
|  |  | 4–7 | 2400 | 1* | 1 | 2 |
| Intermediate whitemetal | 12 Sb, 3 Cu, 10 Pb, rem. Sn | 12 | † | 1 | 1 | 1 |
| Copper-lead | 30 Pb, 70 Cu | 12 | 3400 | 3 | 3 | 4 |
| Lead-bronze | 24 Pb, 4 Sn, 72 Cu | 12 | 5500 | 4 | 4 | 4 |
| Lead-tin overlay on copper-lead | 10 Sn, rem. Pb, on 30 Pb/70 Cu | 1·5 | 4100 | 1 | 1 | 2 |
| Lead-indium overlay on copper-lead | 50 In, rem. Pb | 1·5 | 4100 | 1 | 1 | 2 |
| Aluminium-tin | 20 Sn 1 Cu, rem. Al | 12 | 4600 | 2 | 2 | 1 |
| Aluminium-tin | 5–7 Sn, plus various hardeners | 12 | 5000 | 3–4 | 3–4 | 1 |

Wear rating. 1—least shaft wear; 4—most shaft wear

Seizure rating. 1—least tendency to seizure under conditions of oil starvation; 4—most tendency

Corrosion rating. 1—no attack; 4—marked attack by acidic oils

* The bearing wear of lead base is somewhat higher than tin base

† Not generally used for high alternating loads

feature of the tests carried out in these machines is the very wide scatter in the results obtained, which is often as high as a 50 to 1 variation in life at a given load. As a result of this, it is normal practice to carry out a large number of tests, at least 20 at each load, and to compare results on a basis such as the load resulting in 10% failures for a given life [548]. Much of this scatter can probably be attributed to the high scatter inherent in the very high strength steels used for rolling-contact bearings. It is found that the life of bearings can be increased by eliminating the more serious inclusions in the steel, but this does not result in a reduction of the scatter [115].

Extensive fatigue testing has been carried out on ball and roller bearings, particularly by Palmgren and from the results of these tests it has been found possible to devise empirical relations for predicting fatigue life. It has been well established that the life varies approximately inversely as the 3rd power of the load on the bearing. This behaviour persists up to endurances of at least $10^9$ cycles and there is no evidence of a fatigue limit [115]. Data are provided by the bearing manufacturers relating the fatigue life to the bearing load for various types of bearing.

### Gears

Most gear failures are caused either by breaking of the teeth at the roots as a result of repeated bending stresses or by pitting of the teeth at the contact surfaces. A fracture occurring at the root of a tooth is a normal fatigue failure, the crack usually propagating from the fillet where the stress is greatest. Such failures may result from the use of too small a fillet radius or, in surface-hardened gears, from a failure to continue the hardening into the root. Pitting of the teeth at the contact surfaces also results from fatigue and is similar to the failures occurring in ball and roller bearings. Investigations of both types of failure have been carried out by the Motor Industry Research Association and the results have been summarized by Love [345].

The bending fatigue strengths were determined by loading individual teeth at the tip in a hydraulic pulsator and the values of the bending fatigue limit quoted in Table 70 were calculated in the usual manner, considering the tooth as a simple cantilever beam and taking no account of stress concentration effects. The gears used for these tests were of 7 D.P. and $22\frac{1}{2}°$ pressure angle, with 34 teeth, 0·1185 in. addendum and 0·321 in. full depth. The case-hardened materials are appreciably more resistant than the through-hardened materials; for both, the addition of lead to improve the machinability has reduced the fatigue limit by about 30%. In subsequent tests, much lower fatigue strengths were obtained with induction-hardened gears but this was probably a result of incomplete hardening, because results have been obtained with induction hardening

U

Table 70. Bending fatigue limits for through-hardened and case-hardened gears (Love [345])

| Material | Treatment | Hardness V.P.N. (30 Kg load) | | Etched case depth, in. | Bending fatigue limit tons/in² |
|---|---|---|---|---|---|
| | | Surface | Core | | |
| En 24 1½% Ni Cr Mo steel | Oil-quenched from 840°C. (1544°F.). Tempered 1 hr at 230°C. (446°F.); water-quenched | 565 | — | — | 34 |
| En 24 Leaded | As for En 24 | 551 | — | — | 23 |
| En 30A 4¼% Ni Cr steel | Air-cooled from 820°C. (1508°F.). Tempered 1 hr at 180°C. (356°F.); water-quenched | 514 | — | — | 27 |
| En 36 3% Ni Cr steel | Carburized at 910°C. (1670°F.). Oil-quenched from 850°C. (1562°F.) and 780°C. (1436°F.). Tempered 1 hr at 180°C; water-quenched | 737 | 328 | 0·029 | 42 |
| En 39A 4¼% Ni Cr steel | As for En 36 | 718 | 410 | 0·031 | 52 |
| En 39A Leaded | As for En 36 | 752 | 420 | 0·032 | 37 (or less) |
| En 40C 3% Cr Mo V steel | Oil-quenched from 940°C. (1724°F.). Tempered 2 hr at 575°C. (1607°F.) and oil-quenched. Stabilized at 520°C. (968°F.) for 4 hr and air-cooled. Nitrided at 500°C. (932°F.) | 978 | 424 | 0·016 | 39 |

comparable to those with case-hardening. It was shown by further tests that grinding carburized tooth roots may be very harmful, but that improvements of 15–20% could be obtained by shot-peening. Extensive bending fatigue tests on gear teeth have been carried out in the United States and the application of the results to gear design has been described by Coleman [549].

Tests to determine the resistance to pitting were carried out at M.I.R.A. by running pairs of gears together. It was found necessary to use a reduced active face width with carburized gears to avoid tooth breakage by bending before the onset of pitting. A summary of the results is shown in Fig. 137.

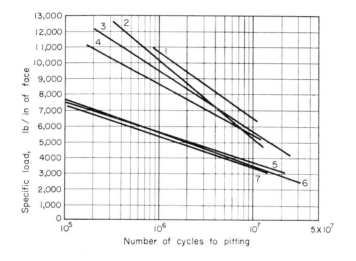

FIG. 137. Pitting fatigue curves for gears made from various steels.
(Love [345])

| 1. En 40C | 3% Cr Mo V Steel | 4. En 39A leaded |
| 2. En 36 | 3% Ni Cr Steel | 5. En 24    $1\frac{1}{2}$% Ni Cr Mo Steel |
| 3. En 39A | $4\frac{1}{4}$% Ni Cr Steel | 6. En 24 leaded |
| | | 7. En 30A   $4\frac{1}{4}$% Ni Cr Steel |

For material treatment see table 70

A number of investigators have used a contact roller test to simulate the conditions leading to pitting in gear teeth. This method has been criticized because of differences between the test conditions and those occurring in service, and Knowlton and Snyder [550] found that higher strengths were indicated by roller tests than from dynamometer tests on actual gears. Nevertheless, Gross [551] claimed that the results of such tests have correlated in a relative way with the behaviour of large gears and some of his results on $1\frac{1}{2}$ in. diameter rollers, quoted in Table 71, may therefore

TABLE 71. CONTACT ROLLER TEST DATA (Gross [551])

| Material | Treatment | Tensile strength tons/in² | Compressive load per inch length of roller to produce pitting in 10⁷ cycles, lb./in. |
|---|---|---|---|
| *Steels* | | | |
| 0·36% C steel SAE 1035 | As received | 36·2 | 95 |
| Ni Mo steel | As received | 45·6 | 290 |
| | Quenched and tempered at 800°F. | 83 | 515 |
| | Quenched and tempered at 600°F. | 96 | 1090 |
| | Quenched and tempered at 400°F. | 109 | 1480 |
| Cr Ni Mo V steel | Normalized and tempered | 60 | 265 |
| | Nitrided | | >4580 |
| Cr Ni steel NE–8615 | Carburized | | >4580 |
| *Non-ferrous metals* | | | |
| Wrought aluminium–copper alloy 14S–T6 | | 31 | 206 |
| Sand-cast aluminium–silicon alloy 356–T4 | | 12 | <57 |
| Sand-cast aluminium–silicon–copper alloy 319–T61 | | 18 | 91 |
| Copper–beryllium A.S.T.M. B.120 precipitation-hardened | | 67 min | 315 |
| Sand-cast magnesium–aluminium alloy aged | | 17·7 | 150 |
| *Non-metallic materials* | | | |
| *Type* | *Filler* | | |
| Nylon–FM1 | None | | 190 |
| Laminated phenolic | Cotton fabric | | 165 |
| Laminated phenolic | 10 oz cotton fabric | | 290 |

afford a useful comparison of the pitting resistance of some steels, non-ferrous metals and non-metallic materials.

### Springs

For many applications springs are subjected to fluctuating stresses and it is necessary to design them to withstand failure by fatigue. In coil springs, loaded either in tension or compression, the wire or rod is stressed in torsion and, if fatigue failures occur, the cracks are often initiated on the inner surface of a coil and propagate either longitudinally in the direction of maximum shear stress or diagonally in a direction perpendicular to the maximum tensile component of the stress. Coil springs are normally loaded only in one direction, either in tension or compression, but not both, and it is therefore possible to increase their yield strength and their resistance to fatigue by subjecting them to an overstrain in the direction in which they are to be used in service in order to induce beneficial residual stresses [552]. This process is known as scragging and, in compression springs, is usually carried out by loading the springs until they completely close.

A number of investigators have carried out fatigue tests on coil springs and each has developed a special fatigue testing machine to apply the large deflections required; some of the results obtained are quoted in Table 72. A guide to the design of helical compression springs to withstand fluctuating stresses is given in Ministry of Supply Design Data Sheets [557].

Overstraining and shot-peening may also be used to improve the fatigue resistance of other types of spring. Almen [558] quotes an example, where the fluctuating fatigue strength of a torsion bar spring was increased more than 20% by initial overstraining and further improvement was obtained by shot-peening, provided it was carried out before the overstraining. Leaf springs often show poor resistance to fatigue because they are used with decarburized surfaces and in addition, the rubbing together of the leaves may introduce the further hazard of fretting corrosion. Baldwin [559] quotes the fatigue strength of locomotive laminated steel springs with black decarburized surfaces as about $26 \pm 8\cdot5$ to $26 \pm 11\cdot5$ tons/in².

### Shafts

The resistance of shafts to fatigue is largely dependent on the severity of the stress concentrations occurring at changes in section, keyways, transverse holes or other discontinuities. The greatest proportion of failures probably occur at the changes in section and considerable improvement in the fatigue strength can often be obtained by increasing the fillet radius. Figure 138 shows the relation between the stress concentration factor $K_t$, the change in the shaft diameter and the fillet radius. The curves illustrate

TABLE 72. THE FATIGUE STRENGTH OF COIL SPRINGS

| Material | Heat treatment | Tensile strength tons/in² | Spring details | | | Spring treatment | Endurance | Fatigue strength tons/in² | Source | Ref. |
|---|---|---|---|---|---|---|---|---|---|---|
| | | | Wire or bar diameter in. | Mean coil diameter in. | No. of coils | | | | | |
| Silicon–manganese steel R.9357 Spec. STA 2(b) | Coiled 1000°C A.C. O.Q. 900°C T. 470°C | | 1·04 | 3·5 | 23½ | Scragged | Average life: 108,000 | 43·5±23·5 | Bardgett and Gartside | 553 |
| | Coiled 800/850°C A.C. O.Q. 900°C T. 470°C | | | | | Scragged | 76,000 | 43·5±23·5 | | |
| | Coiled 1000°C O.Q. 830/850°C T. 470°C | | | | | Scragged | 107,000 | 43·5±23·5 | | |
| | Coiled 1000°C O.Q. 830/850°C T. 470°C | | | | | Scragged, shot-peened and scragged | 170,000–270,000 | 43·5±23·5 | | |
| 0·85% C steel | Hardened from 850°C and tempered at 400°C | (DPH 460) | 1/32 | 2⅝ | 5 | None | Fatigue limit | 20±10<br>32±8·5<br>45±7·7<br>49±6·7 | Coates and Pope | 554 |
| 0·9% C steel | Hardened from 900°C and tempered at 400°C | (DPH 550) | 1/32 | 2⅝ | 6 | None<br>Scragged<br>Peened and scragged<br>Scragged and peened | 10⁶ | 28±11·1<br>28±13·1<br>28±15·9<br>28±19·7 | | |
| 0·65% C steel | Oil tempered and blued at 600°F | 103 | 0·135 | 1·115 | | Shot-peened | 2×10⁷ | 29·6±27·5 | Rickett and Mason | 555 |
| | Oil quenched and tempered at 735°F | 102 | | | | | | 29·2±27·0 | | |
| | Marquenched—Quenched in salt at 500°F, ½ min. Tempered 1 hr at 735°F | 102 | | | | | | 29·4±27·2 | | |
| | Austempered (in salt) at 650°F for 19 min | 100 | | | | | | 29·6±27·5 | | |
| 0·89% C steel music wire | Cold drawn | 164 | 0·039 | 0·39 | 4 | Scragged | 10⁶ | 31±24·5 (extrapolated) | Burnett | 556 |
| 0·89% C steel music wire | Cold drawn O.Q. 1600°F T. 800°F | 126 | | | | Scragged and peened<br>Scragged<br>Scragged and peened | | 45±38·5<br>35·5±29<br>40·5±34 | | |
| Vacuum-melted 0·88% C steel music wire | Cold drawn | 156 | | | | Scragged<br>Scragged and peened | | 33±26·5<br>44±37·5 | | |

clearly that $K_t$ is dependent to a much greater extent on the fillet radius than on the change in shaft diameter; even for a difference of only 1% between the diameters, the degree of stress concentration may be severe if the fillet radius is inadequate.

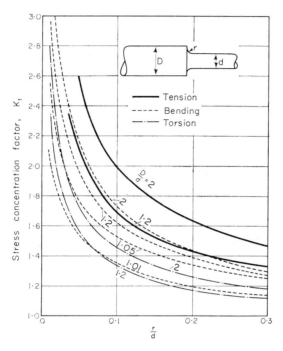

FIG. 138. Stress concentration factor $K_t$ for a shaft with a shoulder fillet in tension, in bending and in torsion. (Peterson [253])

$$\left\{ \text{For torsion, } K_t = \frac{\text{Max: shear stress with fillet}}{\text{Max: shear stress in shaft of uniform diameter } d} \right\}$$

The size effect cannot be neglected, for even in the absence of stress concentration a considerable reduction in fatigue strength is found for large shafts, as shown by the results quoted in Table 28 on page 139. The influence of size on the relation between $K_f$ and $K_t$ is also discussed in Chapter V. Some experimental results, quoted by Dorey and Smedley [288], showing the effect of fillet size on the torsional fatigue strength of large shafts are shown in Fig. 139. The shafts were forged from a medium carbon steel with a tensile strength between 28 and 32 tons/in². These tests were carried out to provide design data for the design of large marine diesel engine crankshafts.

For some applications there may not be room to use an adequate fillet radius and in these circumstances some alleviation of the stress concentration may be achieved by using two radii blended together or a streamlined fillet. Alternatively, a surface hardening process may be used (see Chapter VI); cold rolling is particularly beneficial and appreciable increases in fatigue strength can be obtained by shot-peening, though this is probably not so effective on large diameter shafts. Straightening shafts may reduce the fatigue strength by introducing unfavourable residual stresses and this process should therefore be followed by a stress-relieving treatment.

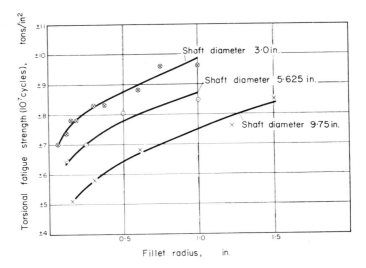

FIG. 139. The influence of fillet radius on the torsional fatigue strengths of large steel shafts. (Dorey and Smedley [288])

In the design of keyways or splines, as generous a root radius as possible should be provided in order to prevent torsional fatigue failures of the shaft. The resistance to fatigue from reversed bending stresses is considerably influenced by the end of the keyway and the advantage of using a sled-runner end is illustrated by the results of fatigue tests carried out by Peterson, see Table 73.

Gough [56] has investigated the effect of both torsional and bending stresses on the fatigue strength of splined shafts. The tests were made on a nickel–chrome–molybdenum steel of 65 tons/in² tensile strength using hollow shafts containing 6 splines of depth 0·0315 in. and root radius 0·0075 in. In torsion, for which $K_t$ was calculated to be 2·1, a value of $K_f = 2·0$ was obtained while in bending, for which $K_t = 1$, $K_f$ was found to be 1·04. The results of tests in combined bending and torsion, like those on other notched specimens, fitted approximately the ellipse arc relation (see page 112). It should be noted, however, that the fatigue strength of a

TABLE 73. THE EFFECT OF KEYWAYS ON THE FATIGUE STRENGTHS OF SHAFTS
(Details of the Keyways are shown in Fig. 140 (Peterson [560]))

| Material | Heat treatment | Tensile strength tons/in$^2$ | Bending fatigue strength tons/in$^2$ | | | | | |
| | | | No keyway | Based on gross section | | Based on net section | | |
| | | | | Sled runner | Profiled | Sled runner | Profiled | |
| Medium carbon steel | Normalized 825°C | 36 | 16·5 | 12·5 | 10·3 | 14·9 | 12·2 |
| Cr Ni steel | W.Q.875°C T.650°C | 46 | 25·9 | 16·1 | 12·5 | 19·1 | 14·9 |

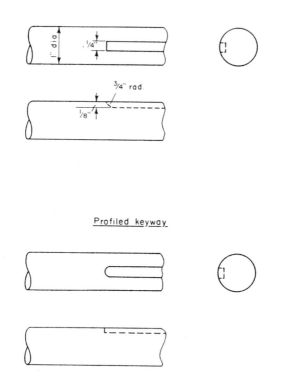

FIG. 140. Fatigue specimens with keyways. (Peterson [560])

shaft may be further reduced if the torque is transmitted through the splines or key, particularly if fretting corrosion occurs. Considerable improvements in fatigue strength can be obtained by surface hardening the root sections of splines and keyways.

Transverse holes are frequently required in shafts for lubrication. The stress concentration produced by a hole is usually much greater than at fillets in a well-designed shaft (see Fig. 141) and it is therefore important to avoid, if possible, placing holes in regions of high fluctuating stress. Sharp corners should be avoided and this can be conveniently achieved and combined with surface hardening by pressing a ball into the ends of the hole.

Particularly severe reductions in fatigue strength can occur where a member, such as a wheel or collar, is press- or shrunk-fit on to a shaft. This can be attributed either to the sharp change in section introduced or to fretting corrosion caused by the relative movement between the shaft and the fitted member. The problem has been investigated by Horger

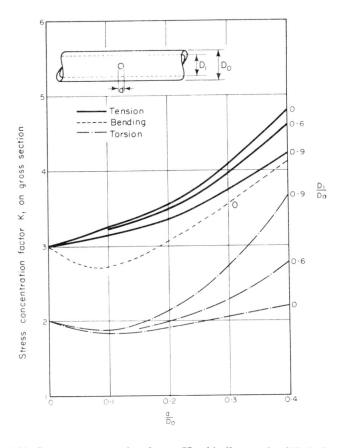

FIG. 141. Stress concentration factor $K_t$ of hollow and solid shafts, each with a transverse hole, in tension, in bending and in torsion. (Royal Aero. Soc. Fatigue Data Sheets [81] and Peterson [253])

$$\left( \text{For torsion, } K_t = \frac{\text{Max: shear stress with hole}}{\text{Max: shear stress without hole}} \right)$$

[419, 420] on large diameter shafts and some of his results are given in Table 74. It was found that fractures sometimes occurred after long endurances and the results are therefore based on an endurance of 85 million cycles. A further feature of these tests was the occurrence of non-propagating fatigue cracks (see page 146) in the fretted region of the shaft at the edge of the wheel, at stress ranges appreciably lower than the range required to cause complete fracture. It can be seen from the results that the resistance to fatigue is little affected by the tensile strength of the steel,

TABLE 74. FATIGUE STRENGTH OF PRESS-FITTED ASSEMBLIES
(Horger [419, 420])

Rotating bending fatigue tests on 9½ in. diameter steel shafts with press-fitted wheels 7 in. wide

| Chemical composition % | | | | | | Heat treatment | Yield strength tons/in² | Tensile strength tons/in² | Additional treatment | Number of shafts tested | Fatigue strength (85 × 10⁶ cycles) tons/in² | |
| --- | --- | --- | --- | --- | --- | --- | --- | --- | --- | --- | --- | --- |
| C | Mn | Ni | Cr | Mo | V | | | | | | For fracture | For initiation of cracks |
| 0·51 | 0·79 | | | | | Normalized and tempered | 22·4 | 40·7 | Waterquenched from 625°C | 15 | 5 | <2·2 |
| 0·51 | 0·79 | | | | | | | | Shot-peened | 3 | >8·5 | |
| 0·51 | 0·79 | | | | | | | | | 3 | 7 | |
| 0·51 | 0·79 | | | | | | | | Surface rolled | 10 | >10 | 3 |
| 0·47 | 0·85 | | | | 0·17 | | 27·0 | 46·0 | | 7 | 4 | 4 |
| 0·32 | 1·58 | | | | 0·19 | | 33·0 | 46·3 | | 9 | 4 | 3·5 |
| 0·24 | 0·89 | 2·95 | | | | | 29·4 | 39·0 | | 7 | 4 | 3·5 |
| 0·51 | 0·76 | | | | | Quenched and tempered | 36·2 | 55·8 | | 4 | 5·5 | |
| 0·51 | 0·76 | | | | | | | | | 6 | 8 | |
| 0·32 | 0·94 | 2·98 | | | | | 36·9 | 47·2 | Waterquenched from 537°C | 5 | 5 | 4 |
| 0·4 | 0·7 | 1·89 | 0·77 | 0·27 | | | 44·6 | 54·7 | | 4 | 5 | |
| 0·4 | 0·7 | 1·89 | 0·77 | 0·27 | | | 55·9 | 65·8 | | 5 | 5 | |

but that considerable improvement can be obtained by surface-hardening treatments. An improvement can also be obtained by a change in design, incorporating a raised wheel seat, as shown in Fig. 142 [419]. The upper curve shows the fatigue strength on the basis of the shaft not breaking completely after 85 million stress reversals and the lower curve gives the fatigue strength based on the initiation of fatigue cracks. The material was an 0·49% C steel with a tensile strength of 44 tons/in².

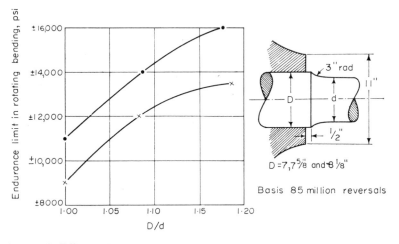

FIG. 142. Effect of height of raised wheel seat on endurance limit. (O. J. Horger [419])

Many full-scale fatigue tests have been carried out on crankshafts and some of the results obtained, both in bending and in torsion, are quoted in Table 75. A comparison of the results of tests on both forged and cast materials, using one design of crankshaft, shows that the fatigue strength, either in bending or torsion, is approximately proportional to the tensile strength. The low notch sensitivity in fatigue of cast iron is thus apparently of little benefit in crankshafts and this is probably because of their large size compared with notched laboratory specimens (see Chapter V). Direct evidence of the notch sensitivity of cast iron on large sizes is provided by the results of tests on cast crankshafts reported by Mills and Love [564]. These showed that although the fatigue strength was almost unaffected by the surface finish, an increase in fillet radius from 0·031 in. to 0·125 in. diameter increased the fatigue strength by 85%. The results obtained by Lehr and Ruef [274] on the crankshafts of large diesel engines, quoted in Table 75, illustrate the low fatigue strength of large size shafts. These authors found that the torsional fatigue strength of a scale model with

TABLE 75. THE FATIGUE STRENGTH OF CRANKSHAFTS

| Material | Tensile strength tons/in² | Crankshaft details | | | Nominal fatigue strength, tons/in² | | Source | Ref. |
|---|---|---|---|---|---|---|---|---|
| | | Crankpin diameter in. | Fillet radius in. | Web thickness in. | Bending, based on web section | Torsion, based on journal section | | |
| *Flake graphite cast irons:* | | | | | | | | |
| Low-alloy inoculated iron | 22 | 4 | 0·25 | 1·5 | 3·75 | | Love | 290 |
| Chrome–molybdenum alloy iron | 21 | | | | 3·4 | | | |
| Acicular iron | 24 | | | | 4·2 | | | |
| Low-carbon-alloy cast iron (or graphitic cast steel) | 36 | | | | 5·8 | | | |
| Magnesium-treated nodular cast iron, as-cast | 51 | | | | 5·0 | | | |
| Magnesium-treated nodular cast iron, quenched and tempered | 48 | | | | 4·7 | | | |
| *Cast alloy steels:* | | | | | | | | |
| 0·5% Ni, 1% Cr, 0·2% Mo | 65 | | | | 5·5 | | Williams and Brown | 561 |
| 0·5% Ni, 1% Cr, 0·2% Mo | 75 | | | | 6·3 | | | |
| 1·9% Ni, 0·9% Cr, 0·3% Mo | 82 | | | | 5·2 | | | |
| Forged 0·5% carbon steel | 47 | 2·68 | 0·157 | 0·868 | 8·9 | | | |
| Forged alloy steels: 3·7% Ni, 0·85% Cr | 58·5 | 2·68 | 0·157 | 0·868 | 10·3 | | | |
| 2·3% Ni, 0·37% Cr | 67·8 | 2·50 | 0·156 | 0·843 | 8·9 | | | |
| 3·4% Ni, 0·9% Cr, 0·5% Mo | 69·3 | 1·97 | 0·138 | 0·846 | 11·0 | | | |
| DTD 306, nitrided | | 1·97 | 0·138 | 0·846 | 13·5–17·5 | | | |
| Pearlitic iron | — | 1·89 | 0·079 | | 3·2 | 3·5 | Bandow | 562 |
| Blackheart malleable iron, flame hardened | — | | | | 4·1 | 3·8 | | |
| Forged steel | 53 | | | | 5·7 | 6·2–6·4 | | |
| Forged steel | 83 | | | | | 6·4–6·7 | | |
| Low-alloy cast iron | 40–45 | 2·36 | | | | 2·9 | Lurenbaum | 562 |
| High-alloy cast iron | 60–65 | | | | | 3·3 | | |
| High-carbon cast steel | 80 | | | | | 3·7 | | |
| Forged steel | | | | | | 4·4 | | |
| Forged steel | | | | | | 5·7 | | |
| Forged steel | | | | | | 8·4 | | |
| 0·35–0·4% C steel | 35–41 | 9·65 | 0·59 / 0·197 | | | 2·7 approx. 2·4 | Lehr and Ruef | 274 |
| X4340 A (Ni Cr Mo steel) quenched and tempered: | 66–75 approx. | 3 | 0·1875 | 1 | | | Gadd and Ochiltree | 563 |
| Not stress relieved | | | | | 11 | — | | |
| Stress relieved | | | | | 11·5 | 8·0 | | |
| Shot blasted | | | | | 14 | 8·9 | | |
| Nitrided | | | | | 18·5 | approx. 10·7 | | |

40 mm (1·58 in.) crankpin diameter was double that of the full-size crank-shaft having a crankpin of 245 mm (9·65 in.) diameter, the same material being used for both.

Gadd and others [565] have reported the results of fatigue tests on diesel crankshafts which had been hardened by surface rolling, by induction hardening extending into the fillets and by nitriding. A fair correlation was found between the fatigue strength and the surface hardness and it was claimed that the results were consistent with those obtained from engine tests; the highest fatigue strength was obtained with a nitrided surface. A technique for rolling crankshaft fillets has been developed by the Motor Industry Research Association and increases in fatigue strength of between 60 and 80% have been achieved both with cast and forged crankshafts [345].

The fatigue strength can be considerably influenced by changes in design. The most important factor in this respect is the fillet radius, which should be as large as possible, although undercutting the web to achieve this may not be beneficial [564]. Boring out the journals can improve the fatigue strength and in a series of tests, Mills and Love [564] obtained the maximum bending fatigue strength with a bore 0·4 of the journal diameter. Other factors such as the shape and size of the webs are also important, and their effect on fatigue strength has been discussed in detail by Love [562].

*Tubes Subjected to Fluctuating Internal Pressure*

The fatigue strengths of thin walled tubes subjected to fluctuating in-ternal pressure and axial load have been determined by a number of in-vestigators, and the results are summarized in Table 76. All the tests were made on tubes of 1 in. bore and 1·1 in. outside diameter. It can be seen that the results are dependent primarily on the range of maximum shear stress, and that on this basis the results of the internal pressure tests are in good agreement with those obtained in axial tension without internal pressure. The fatigue behaviour of thick cylinders subjected to fluctuating internal pressure has been investigated by Morrison and others [118] on cylinders of 1 in. bore with wall thicknesses ranging from 1/10 to 1 in. The results, which are summarized in Table 77, were also found to depend primarily on the range of maximum shear stress and they agree quite closely with the results obtained on thin tubes. Thus, for both series of tests the range of maximum shear stress is equal to about one-third of the tensile strength for steel and one-quarter of the tensile strength for aluminium alloy.

These relations might be used as an approximate design rule, but it should be pointed out that by comparison with the results of torsion fatigue tests on solid specimens, the fatigue strengths of the thick cylinders are only about half the values that would be expected (see Table 77), and

TABLE 76. FATIGUE STRENGTH OF THIN WALLED TUBES
(BASED ON FATIGUE LIMIT FOR MILD STEEL AND $2 \times 10^6$ CYCLES FOR THE ALUMINIUM ALLOY)

| Material | Tensile strength tons/in² | Range of hoop stress tons/in² | Range of longitudinal stress tons/in² | Range of maximum shear stress tons/in² | Source | Ref. |
|---|---|---|---|---|---|---|
| Mild steel SAE 1020 annealed | | —<br>3·5<br>9·5<br>15·5<br>16 | 18<br>17·5<br>18·5<br>8·0<br>16 | 9<br>9<br>10<br>8·5<br>9 | Morikawa and Griffis | 194 |
| Mild steel SAE 1020 annealed | 28 | 11·5<br>16·5<br>17·5<br>18·5 | —9<br>0·5<br>9·5<br>18 | 10<br>9<br>9·5<br>10 | Majors, Mills and MacGregor | 192 |
| Aluminium Alloy 14S–T4 | 28 | —<br>8<br>7<br>10<br>12<br>13·5 | 14<br>—8<br>13·5<br>4·5<br>0<br>13 | 7<br>8<br>7<br>5·5<br>6·5<br>7·5 | Bundy and Marin | 193 |

TABLE 77. THE STRENGTH OF THICK CYLINDERS SUBJECTED TO REPEATED INTERNAL PRESSURE (Morrison and others [118])

| Material | Tensile strength tons/in² | Torsion fatigue strength on solid specimens (shear) tons/in² | Range of pulsating fatigue strength ($10^7$ cycles) of thick cylinders (shear) tons/in² | | | | | |
|---|---|---|---|---|---|---|---|---|
| | | | k = 1·2 | 1·4 | 1·6 | 1·8 | 2·0 | 3·0 |
| Vibrac Ni Cr Mo steel | 56·2 | ±19·5 | 18·5 | 18·0 | 18·5 | 18·0 | 17·5 | 19·0 |
| Vibrac autofrettaged* | 56·2 | | | 23·5 | 20·5 | | 23·5 | |
| Vibrac | 66·4 | ±23·6 | | 23·5 | | 23·5 | | |
| Hykro Cr Mo steel | 53·8 | ±18·6 | | 18·5 | | | 19·0 | |
| Hykro nitrided bore | | | | | 29·0 | | | |
| 0·15% C steel | 25·5 | ±8·8 | | 8·0 | | | 8·5 | |
| 18% Cr 8% Ni Ti stainless steel | 38·3 | ±11·9 to ±14·2 | | 10·5 | | | 16·5 | |
| Aluminium-copper alloy DTD 364 | 32·6 | ±6·2 | | | | | 9·0 | |
| Titanium, commercially pure | 26·8 | ±10·2 | | 11·0 | | | 13·0 | |

Maximum shear stress (at bore) $= \dfrac{k^2 p}{(k^2 - 1)}$, where $p$ is the internal pressure

and $k = \dfrac{\text{Outer diameter}}{\text{Bore diameter}}$

* One application to the cylinders of a pressure sufficient to cause plastic flow in the bore layers.

Morrison has shown, at least for the Vibrac steel, that this may be partially attributed to the deleterious effect of the oil used to produce the pressure. Frost [677] has pointed out recently that this behaviour can be explained if the fatigue limit of a cylinder under pulsating pressure is determined by the critical stress required to propagate small surface microcracks. Cracks will propagate in a direction normal to the hoop stress, and the nominal stress causing the crack to open will be the sum of the hoop stress and the internal pressure in the crack. If $p$ = internal pressure and $k$ = ratio of outside-to-inside diameter of the cylinder, the hoop stress in the bore plus the internal pressure is:

$$p + \frac{p(1 + k^2)}{k^2 - 1} = \frac{2k^2p}{k^2 - 1} = 2 \times \text{maximum shear stress in bore.} \quad (40)$$

*Pipes and Piping Components*

Fatigue failures may occur in piping systems as a result of repeated thermal expansion, fluctuating internal pressure or vibration, or a combination of any of these factors. The fatigue behaviour of piping components has been investigated comprehensively by Markl [566, 567] and he has derived empirical relations for application of the results to design. He found that the results of many bending fatigue tests on straight and curved pipe and for various piping components fitted approximately the basic relation:

$$iSN^{0.2} = C, \quad (41)$$

where $i$ is the stress-intensification factor for a particular component (this is equivalent to the strength reduction factor $K_f$), $S$ is the nominal alternating stress computed from the elastic bending law $S = M/Z$, based on the section of the pipe and not the component, $N$ is the number of cycles to fracture and $C$ a constant. The equation is valid for values of $N$ between 100 and $10^6$ cycles. The results of tests on clamped pipe and on pipe with a butt-welded joint were used as a standard of comparison and these fit approximately equation 41 with $i = 1$. Values of $C$ and $i$ that have been determined experimentally are shown in Table 78. Most of the tests have been made on 4 in. pipes of standard weight. Equation 41 is valid for other components, provided the appropriate value of $h$ is used to determine $i$. The values quoted in the table are included in the American Standard Code for Pressure Piping ASA B.31. 1-1955, but they should be regarded only as an approximate guide to the fatigue behaviour and it should be noted that no allowance has been made for corrosion.

Similar tests have been carried out in Britain by Lane [568] on carbon steel pipe bends and the results show good agreement with those of Markl. The results of bending tests with a static internal pressure also showed good agreement when allowance was made for the effect of mean stress, but

TABLE 78. RECOMMENDED VALUES OF $C$ AND $i$ IN EQUATION (41)

| Material | Temperature | $C$<br>lb/in² |
|---|---|---|
| 0·15–0·29% C. steel<br><br>ASTM Spec. A 106, Grade B | Room temperature | 245,000 |
| Stainless steel ⎫<br>type 316 ⎭ | Room temperature<br>1050°F | 281,000<br>183,500 |

| Component | $i$ |
|---|---|
| Butt-welded straight pipe | 1 |
| Welding elbows, curved or mitre bends, or unreinforced ⎫<br>fabricated intersections of a thickness equal to that ⎬<br>of matching pipe for in-plane or out-of-plane bending ⎭ | $\dfrac{0\cdot9}{h^{2/3}}$ ; $\geqslant 1^{*}$ |
| Corrugated pipe | 2·5 |
| Bolted flange connection | 1·5 |
| Tapered transitions: 15° taper | 1·1 |
| 30° taper | 1·2 |
| 45° taper | 1·3 |

\* $h$ is the flexibility characteristic, defined as:

$$h = \frac{tR}{r^2} \qquad (42)$$

where $t$ is the pipe wall thickness, $R$ is the bend radius and $r$ is the mean pipe radius.

the results of fluctuating pressure tests showed a fatigue strength about 25% lower. In both bending tests and internal pressure tests the maximum tensile stress is in the transverse direction and fatigue cracks usually propagate longitudinally.

The possibility of failures resulting from repeated thermal stresses is also considered by Markl [567]. For most conditions the permissible expansion stresses are limited by the static and creep strength of the piping materials and this allows an adequate safety factor against thermal fatigue, but if the number of thermal cycles is to exceed 7000 (corresponding to 1 cycle per day for about 20 years), a further safety factor is recommended.

## Pressure Vessels

It has been customary practice in the past to base the design of pressure vessels on tensile strength, but recently, in considering an increase in design stresses, the possibility of fatigue failure has been recognized. It was realized that failure might occur at a pressure below the initial test pressure if the vessel were loaded and unloaded sufficiently often. For most practical applications the number of such loadings is very unlikely to exceed 100,000 and would often be no more than 1000 or 10,000. For such relatively short endurances steels can withstand a considerable repeated plastic strain, and it is the resistance of the material to repeated strain in the regions of stress concentration that determines the resistance of the vessel to fatigue failure. The resistance of steels to repeated strain is discussed in Chapter III, and it is shown that for endurances of 1000 to 10,000 cycles all steels show about the same result, indicating that there may be little advantage in specifying a high-strength steel for these conditions.

A comprehensive investigation of the resistance to fatigue of pressure vessel materials has been undertaken in the United States, including repeated strain tests on plain bar and notched plates and fluctuating pressure tests on model pressure vessels, and the results have been summarized by Kooistra [170]. The most severe discontinuity in the model pressure vessels was the nozzle attachment and compared with the results on plain bar, this reduced the strain range for a given endurance by a factor of about 4. In the absence of data on full-scale pressure vessels, it should be assumed that the strain range for a given endurance will be reduced by a factor equal to the maximum elastic stress concentration factor $K_t$.

## Lifting Gear Components

Gough, Cox and Sopwith [569] have discussed the design of lifting gear components and have quoted the results of fatigue tests on hooks and eye bolts which they carried out to determine the safe working loads and also as an experimental check on their stress analysis. The results obtained on hooks are shown in Table 79 and it can be seen that the fatigue strengths are above the specified safe working load, although the factor of safety for the sling hook is only 1·2. Nevertheless, the authors concluded that fatigue failures in service were unlikely from the relatively small number of stress applications to which these components are normally subjected. It is

TABLE 79. THE FATIGUE STRENGTH OF HOOKS
(Gough, Cox and Sopwith [569])

| Type of hook | Material | Safe working load tons | Breaking load in static tension tons | Pulsating range of load, tons: | | Estimated range of stress at fatigue limit tons/in² |
| | | | | For failure in $5 \times 10^5$ cycles | At fatigue limit | |
|---|---|---|---|---|---|---|
| Sling hook | Mild steel | 1·5 | | 2·4 | 1·8 | 15·1 |
| Liverpool | Mild steel | 1·5 | 13·4 and 11·9 | 3·9 | 3·3 | 19·6 |
| Liverpool | Wrought iron | 1·5 | 11·1 and 12·0 | 3·9 | 3·1 | 18·4 |

possible, however, with the introduction of lifting gear components of high-strength steels operating at higher working loads, that, as for pressure vessels, the possibility of fatigue failure will need to be reconsidered.

## Rails

Many of the fatigue failures occuring in railways, for example in springs and axles, are similar to those occurring in other branches of engineering and these have already been considered. Fatigue failure of rails, and also of tyres, however, is an important problem of particular concern only in railway engineering [559, 570, 571]. At one time, transverse fatigue failures starting from shatter cracks in the rail head were a common type of failure, particularly in the United States. The shatter cracks were caused by entrapped hydrogen and these have now been almost entirely eliminated by controlled cooling of the rails after rolling. Failure may also occur in the rail head or in the treads of the tyres by "shelling"; this is attributed to the high shearing stress just below the surface and is similar to the failures which occur in ball-bearings and gear teeth. Fatigue cracks often occur in the webs of the rail, particularly if the local conditions favour corrosion. If fish-plate joints are used, these cracks usually propagate from the bolt holes and considerable improvement in fatigue strength can be achieved by using fusion butt welds.

An investigation has been made recently of the fatigue strength of medium manganese rails with a tensile strength of about 50 tons/in² [669]. The alternating fatigue limit of plain new rail was about 10 tons/in² and this was reduced to about 7 or 8 tons/in² if the rail was first exposed in the track to wear and corrosion. These low values were attributed principally to the decarburized layer on the surface of the rails. For rails drilled with $1\frac{13}{16}$ in. diameter bolt holes, the range of stress at the fatigue limit under repeated bending, measured at the periphery of the hole, was 17 tons/in², but this value could be increased 50% by drilling the holes $\frac{3}{64}$ in. under size and pushing a hardened spherical-ended tool through to open them out to the correct diameter.

## The fatigue strength of structures

Fatigue testing complete structures is very costly and its use has therefore been restricted primarily to aircraft where it is essential to avoid serious fatigue failures in service. For other types of structure, where the consequences of fatigue are less serious a knowledge of the fatigue strength is, in effect, often obtained from operating experience in service. Fatigue is a fairly common source of failure in civil engineering structures even though the fluctuating loads occur relatively seldom and are often only a small proportion of the static loads. Most of these failures occur at riveted or welded joints and can often be attributed to poor detail design, usually aggravated by corrosion. Fortunately they do not often lead to complete collapse of the structure and the fractured parts can be repaired or replaced, if necessary with design modifications. In ships, fatigue is not likely to occur in the main structure, but it has been suggested that fatigue cracks could propagate from notches if precautions were not taken and these could be serious because they might lead to brittle fracture. In some circumstances simulated service tests are used to discover points of weakness in the structure. An example of this is the "pavé" track used by the Motor Industry Research Association for the accelerated testing of road vehicles. It has been found that behaviour on this track can be correlated with behaviour in service and satisfactory performance during a test run of 1000–2000 miles, at a speed of 25–30 m.p.h. is generally accepted as a suitable criterion [345].

The fatigue testing of aircraft structures is used for two purposes, firstly to provide general information of the behaviour of a complete structure under a variety of fatigue loading conditions and secondly, to determine the susceptibility to fatigue of a new design. The purpose of the latter is primarily to discover any points of weakness that have not been detected in preliminary component fatigue tests and to determine the crack propagation behaviour in order to ensure that catastrophic failure will not occur in service. To provide general information of the fatigue behaviour, use has been made of obsolete structures and sufficient tests have been carried out to enable some general conclusions to be drawn. For example, Fig. 143 shows an *S–N* curve compiled by the Royal Aeronautical Society

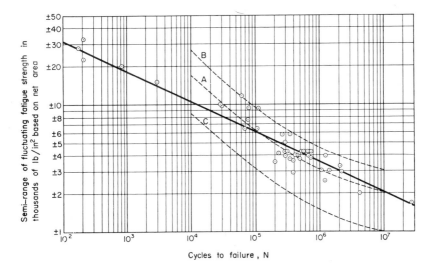

FIG. 143. Endurances for complete wings and tailplanes. (Royal Aero. Soc. Data Sheets [81])

from the results of fatigue tests on complete wings and tailplaines of a variety of British and American transport, fighter and training aircraft, constructed of medium and high strength aluminium alloys. These tests were carried out with a mean stress between 7000 and 19,000 lb/in², corresponding at least to the 1g level flight load or, for fighter and trainer aircraft, 25% of the ultimate static load: both mean and alternating stresses were calculated on the net area at the point of fracture. There is, inevitably an appreciable scatter in the results, because the detailed method of design has a predominant influence on fatigue life and the information is therefore considered suitable only for project design and preliminary fatigue analysis. The dotted curves B, A and C represent the results of fatigue tests on aluminium alloy structural joints and are taken from Fig. 131, and these show that there is quite a good correlation between the fatigue strengths of individual joints and the whole structure.

Another compilation, including some of the above data and other British, American and Australian results on wings, tailplanes and fabricated beams, has been made by Payne and others [572] for the aluminium alloy 24S–T, and from as many as 230 results representing eighteen different types of failure from eight different sources they derived the $R$–$M$ diagram shown in Fig. 144. An analysis of the scatter of the results showed that on the assumption of a log-normal distribution, the standard deviation with respect to the mean life lines was $s = 0.32$; this corresponds to a 1% probability of failure at 0.20 of the mean life. The failures most often occurred

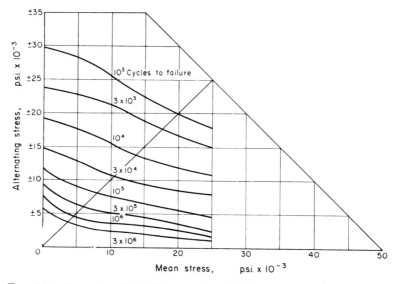

FIG. 144. Tentative $R$–$M$ Diagram for 24S–T structures. (Payne and others [572])

either at points of severe stress concentration, caused by non-uniform load distribution between redundant members, or started at a cut-out in the skin and developed along a multi-row riveted joint. The initial crack usually appeared after 30–50% of the total life, and then propagated at a practically constant rate for a further 20–30% of the life and then at a progressively increasing rate until final fracture occurred. The same authors also demonstrated the beneficial effect of applying a static pre-load on the fatigue life of Mustang aircraft wings. The optimum pre-load was found to be about 90% of the ultimate failing load and this produced an increase in fatigue life at low load ranges of more than 4 times: a similar result has been obtained from tests on Meteor tailplanes [573]. The improvement in fatigue life is attributed to the local effects of stress redistribution and cold working of the material at stress concentrations and also to load redistribution between members. A similar beneficial effect is expected to occur in aircraft structures during service from the occasional occurrence of high loads, and this is supported by the results of variable amplitude tests on the wings of C-46 aircraft reported by Whaley [574]. Six wings were subjected to a spectrum of loads derived from gust-frequency statistics and their average life was 4·8 times that predicted by the linear damage law from the results of constant amplitude tests.

Two reports of conferences on the fatigue of aircraft structures have been published recently [684, 685].

CHAPTER X

# ENGINEERING DESIGN TO PREVENT FATIGUE

DESIGNING engineering parts to avoid fatigue failure is a more complex process than designing on the basis of static strength, because of the necessity to take account of stress concentrations and the many other factors that affect resistance to fatigue such as loads of varying amplitude and combined static and dynamic loads. The methods of procedure can be conveniently summarized under the following headings:

1. Selection of material
2. Detail design
3. Estimation of fatigue strength
4. Estimation of fatigue life.

These will be considered briefly in relation to the background of fatigue information discussed in the preceding nine chapters.

## Selection of material

For components that are subjected in service to fluctuating loads, the choice of materials should be based on fatigue strength, but in practice it is more often based on static strength, either yield stress or tensile strength. To a certain extent the choice of tensile strength is a satisfactory criterion because of the fairly close relation between tensile and fatigue strength, but it can be unreliable in some circumstances, for example, for short endurances or where fretting corrosion occurs.

A comparison of fatigue strengths (determined in bending on unnotched specimens) and tensile strengths was made in Chapter III. For steels (Fig. 28), the fatigue strength increases approximately in direct proportion to the tensile strength up to a value of about 40 tons/in² at a tensile strength of 80 tons/in² and within this range the tensile strength provides a fairly reliable guide to the influence on fatigue strength of alloying additions, heat treatment and cold working. There is little further improvement in fatigue strength, however, with further increase in tensile strength. Consequently, for a part whose strength is limited by its resistance to fatigue, there may be little benefit in using a steel with a static strength above 80 tons/in². Indeed, it may be detrimental to use a material of higher strength because the adverse effects of scatter, and sensitivity to notches

320

and fatigue cracks are likely to be greater. The behaviour of aluminium alloys is somewhat similar to steel, there being only a small increase in fatigue strength beyond a tensile strength of 25–30 tons/in$^2$.

The presence of a distinct fatigue limit is a desirable property and this occurs in low and medium-strength steels, cast iron, aluminium–magnesium alloys and some titanium alloys. There is a tendency, however, to over-emphasize its value, for in those materials where it is absent, including high-strength steels and aluminium alloys, the downward slope of the $S$–$N$ curve (in the absence of corrosion) is usually small at long endurances, see for example, Fig. 37.

The results of fatigue tests on small notched specimens show that the increase in notched fatigue strength obtained by increasing the tensile strength is generally quite small (see for example, Fig. 77), but selection cannot be based simply on such results, because notch sensitivity cannot be dissociated from size effect. For large size pieces it is wise to assume that under alternating stresses, all materials will be fully notch sensitive, that is the notched fatigue strength will be equal to the plain fatigue strength divided by $K_t$. In these circumstances, the plain fatigue strength is therefore a more suitable criterion by which to select material. This should be borne in mind when comparing the relative merits of cast and wrought materials. On plain specimens the fatigue strength of a material is generally higher in the wrought than in the cast condition, but cast materials are less sensitive to notches, so that a comparison of the results of tests on small notched specimens often shows little difference between the two.

The assumption that large pieces are fully notch sensitive neglects the beneficial effect of plastic deformation. While this has only a limited effect on alternating fatigue strengths (see page 134), it can be important when static stresses are superimposed. The advantage of a relatively low yield stress under these conditions is well illustrated by the results obtained for aluminium alloys. A comparison of Figs. 87 and 88 for example, shows that the notched fatigue strength of the aluminium–copper alloy 24S–T3 under fluctuating tensile stresses is superior to the aluminium–zinc–magnesium alloy 75S–T6 despite its lower tensile strength and this behaviour is supported by fatigue tests on aircraft joints (see Fig. 129). Comparative tests of these two materials have also shown that the 24S alloy is more resistant to the propagation of fatigue cracks and its static strength is less affected by the presence of cracks (see Chapter V). On this basis, the 24S alloy is likely to be more resistant to fatigue, while the 75S alloy is more resistant to static stress and the choice of material will depend on the stress conditions for the particular application envisaged.

Material selection will be dependent to some extent on the surface treatments to be used. If no treatment at all is envisaged after processing, little may be gained by selecting a high-strength material, but the benefit derived from surface treatments such as shot-peening and surface rolling are greater for high-strength materials. The highest fatigue strengths are achieved by case-hardening and if this is required, appropriate case-hardening steels should be chosen.

Applications where the number of stress reversals during the life of a part are relatively small need special consideration. The resistance to alternating stress for short endurances is quite closely related to tensile strength, but on parts with stress concentrations, fatigue resistance may be more dependent on alternating strain (see page 88), and for endurances between 100 and 10,000 cycles, resistance to alternating strain is about the same for a wide range of materials. Consequently, for these low endurances the fatigue resistance of components may be little improved by increasing the static strength of the material.

Fatigue failures frequently result from vibrations, particularly when these are amplified by resonance, and to prevent such failures it may be advantageous to use a material with a high damping capacity. It is sometimes claimed that material damping is small compared with structural and aerodynamic damping and may therefore be neglected. This may be true in some circumstances, but if the vibration is sufficiently severe to produce stresses high enough to cause fatigue failure, then material damping can become important. This was first appreciated by Foppl [575], who quoted a number of examples where the substitution of a lower strength material with higher damping capacity had improved fatigue resistance. These included overhead cables subject to resonant vibrations from winds, where failures were prevented by substituting copper for an aluminium alloy, and crankshafts which were improved by the use of a steel of 35–40 tons/in$^2$ tensile strength in place of one of 55–60 tons/in$^2$. Material damping arises almost entirely from plastic deformation and is directly related to the area of the stress–strain hysteresis loop (see page 17). It is, in effect, a measure of the ability of a material to withstand repeated plastic deformation without failure, and this can be determined only from measurements during fatigue tests of both stress and strain or of energy dissipated. It bears no simple relation to the damping capacity measured at low stress amplitudes nor to any other mechanical property. It is markedly dependent on the range of stress and also varies with time, so that it is difficult to apply a damping criterion directly to design. The problem has been considered in some detail by Lazan, however, and he has measured the material damping during fatigue tests for a wide range of materials [576]. High values of material damping are found in mild steel and cast iron and particularly in stainless steels, while high strength steels and aluminium alloys show low values.

Although increasing the tensile strength of a material generally improves the fatigue strength, it will not always increase the fatigue resistance of a part under service conditions. A more ductile metal which is not so strong may be better, for example, for joints where the effects of stress concentration and fretting are combined, or for parts subjected to vibrations or operating under corrosive conditions. When fatigue failures do occur it should always be remembered that only a small proportion of service failures can be attributed to defective material. Attention should therefore be paid, firstly, to faults in design or assembly or misuse in service, before a change in material is considered.

## Detail design

Of the many factors that must be considered in the design of components and structures to resist fatigue failure, attention to detail is the most important. A great many of the fatigue failures that occur in service could be prevented by improving detail design, and there is more scope for improvements in fatigue strength by this means than by any other. This theme is constantly reiterated, but good detail design is not easy to maintain in practice [81]. The most important aspect of the problem is avoiding or alleviating stress concentration, although attention must also be paid to surface treatments and fabrication methods.

Determination of the stress distribution is thus an essential part of detail design to resist fatigue. Much of the stress analysis for parts of simple shape, such as a shaft with a transverse hole or a fillet, may be made by reference to previously published results and this has been discussed in Chapters V and IX. For more complex shapes there is little hope of obtaining theoretical solutions and experimental stress analysis is often tedious and costly. In these circumstances it may be more convenient to rely on component fatigue testing, for this can effectively demonstrate the most highly stressed regions and at the same time take account of additional factors such as defects in manufacture, residual stress and fretting corrosion.

The first step towards the reduction of stress concentration is to avoid all abrupt changes in cross-section. In particular, generous fillets should be provided at the intersections of all integral structural elements and sharp corners and edges should be avoided. Tapered sections should be used instead of stepped changes, if possible, for even small steps can produce high stress concentration (see Fig. 138). Holes and secondary attachments should be avoided, but when they must be used, they should be placed in regions of low stress. This also applies to the positioning of identification stamps, which can be a source of fatigue failure in highly stressed areas. Considering the whole structure, a symmetrical design should be used and offset loads avoided. Where this cannot be achieved, the local bending stress introduced must be considered and if necessary, reinforcements provided. The deflection pattern of the design and the secondary strains resulting from the deflections must also be considered. Particular attention must be paid to the joints between the individual components (see Chapter IX) and a thicker section should be provided to counteract the low fatigue resistance of joints. Bolts are more resistant than rivets to fluctuating tensile loads and rivets should be subjected only to very small ranges of tensile stress. Fatigue failures in shear joints usually occur through the plate or sheet, so that either bolts or rivets are suitable, but the two should not be mixed indiscriminately in the same joint. It should be remembered that in a multi-riveted (or bolted) joint, the load is not uniformly distributed between the rivets; the outermost rivets are usually the most severely loaded and allowance for this should be made. In welded joints, butt welds should be used, if possible, because they are more resistant to fatigue than fillet welds: the highest fatigue strength is obtained if the butt weld is machined flush with the plate.

A further factor that must be considered in connection with the reduction of stresses is that of vibration. Where vibration is unavoidable, it may be necessary to provide sufficient damping by means of vibration dampers, structural or material damping, in order to ensure that the vibration stresses will be restricted to safe values. The prevention of fatigue failures from vibration has become a serious problem in the design of jet aircraft, where damage to the airframe structure may result from the vibrations set up by the jet exhaust. This is known as acoustical or sonic fatigue, and a symposium has been held recently to discuss the problems involved [660].

Untreated surfaces show poor resistance to fatigue, in general, because of the stress concentrations introduced by the imperfections and the presence of adverse residual stresses and, in steels, from surface decarburization. Surface treatments to counteract these effects, such as shot-peening, surface rolling or case-hardening should therefore be specified in the design of parts liable to fatigue failure (see Chapter VI). High speed and rough grinding processes should be avoided, on the other hand, because they may introduce residual tensile stresses in the surface and result in a reduction of fatigue strength.

Even if great care is taken in detail design, points of weakness may be overlooked or the fatigue strength overestimated, so that it is often useful to carry out fatigue tests on critical components of a structure, in order to check the design. If, in these circumstances, a component is found not to have the required fatigue strength, modifications can be made in design, followed by further fatigue tests, the process being continued until an adequate resistance to fatigue is achieved. An illustration of this procedure, applied to the design of a "quick-disconnect" fitting has been described by Schleicher [577] and is illustrated in Fig. 145. Parts A and B were steel fittings attached to an aluminium alloy structure. Parts C and D were alloy steel (SAE 4340) studs heat-treated to 90–100 tons/in² tensile strength and the coupling nut, part E, was made of an alloy steel (SAE 4140) heat-treated to 80–90 tons/in² tensile strength. For part D, the calculated design stress in the root section of the thread was 71 tons/in²; this corresponded to a static margin of safety of 38% and a static test of the stud gave a margin of 40%. However, a pulsating fatigue test at a stress range of 47·5 tons/in² (based on the thread root section) resulted in failure at 1400 cycles, at the first thread (Fig. 145b). In the original design, the stud was permitted to bottom in the tapped hole, leaving the threads without pre-stress. The first modification consisted of shortening the stud to allow pre-stressing and a pre-stress of 53 tons/in² was applied. This resulted in no increase in fatigue life, but failure was transferred to the head, as shown in Fig. 145c. An attempt to alleviate the stress concentration under the head was then made by introducing a circular boss (Fig. 145d) and this increased the life, but only to 1800 cycles. The smallness

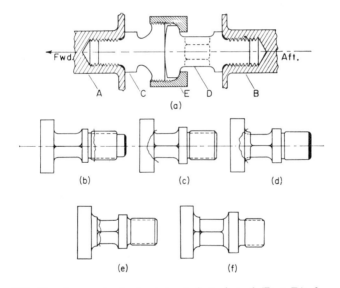

FIG. 145. Development of a heat-treated steel stud (Part D), for use in (a) "Quick-disconnect joint", (b) original design and (c, d, e, f), successive modifications of part D. (R. L. Schleicher [577])

of the gain was attributed to the presence of two fillets in close proximity and, accordingly, the boss diameter was increased by ⅛ in. (Fig. 145e) and a life of 9800 cycles was then obtained. Finally, the fillet under the head was rolled after heat treatment. This increased the fatigue life to 20,900 cycles (Fig. 145f) and the part proved satisfactory in service.

Information from behaviour in service can also be a useful aid to the development of fatigue resistance in design. As an illustration, Fig. 146a shows an axially loaded part of a fatigue testing machine that itself succumbed to fatigue failure after a life of $80 \times 10^6$ cycles, owing to an inadequate fillet radius. The replacement was provided with a more generous fillet radius (Fig. 146b) and this survived for $240 \times 10^6$ cycles. The second modification was to drill four stress deflecting holes as shown in Fig. 146c, to alleviate the stress concentration further. This was successful and the part has now been in service for more than 10 years without further failure.

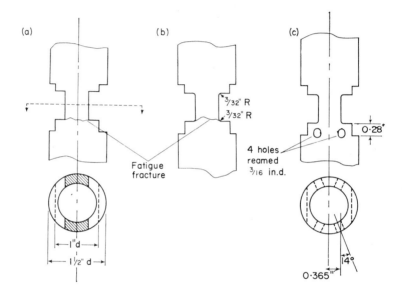

FIG. 146. Modifications to part of a fatigue machine to withstand fatigue.

### Estimation of fatigue strength

The most reliable means of estimating the fatigue strength of a component is from the results of fatigue tests on actual parts, but at the preliminary design stage, such information will not usually be available and the fatigue strength must then be estimated from fatigue data on laboratory specimens. It will then be necessary to make due allowance for the influence of stress conditions, size and stress concentration and surface condition.

Considering firstly the alternating fatigue strength of plain unnotched specimens, data are available for a wide range of materials and some typical results are quoted in Table 82, page 362. If little or no fatigue information can be found, an approximate value can be estimated from the tensile strength; this is discussed in detail in Chapter III and curves of rotating bending fatigue strength plotted against tensile strength are given in Figs. 28, 35, 38, 40 and 43.

A static tensile stress superimposed on the alternating stress reduces the fatigue strength and allowance for this may be made by reference to the $R$–$M$ diagrams given in Chapter IV (Figs. 50–56). In general, for plain specimens, the experimental results for ductile metals lie between the Goodman line and the Gerber parabola, so that the Goodman line can be recommended as a conservative design rule. Under conditions of combined bending and torsion, the fatigue strength may be estimated with sufficient accuracy for design purposes from Gough's ellipse quadrant relation for wrought metals without stress concentration and his ellipse arc relation for cast materials and for wrought materials with stress concentration (see page 110). To apply these relations, a value for the fatigue strength in torsion is required, and if this is not known, it may be estimated from the bending fatigue strength in conjunction with the data given in Figs. 58 and 59 and Table 19.

Allowance for size and stress concentration is the most important factor and the most difficult to achieve accurately. In the absence of stress concentration, the results of fatigue tests on laboratory specimens of different size have indicated a relatively small effect, but the fatigue strength of very large shafts and of large sheets is much lower than that of small specimens (see Tables 28 and 29, pp. 139 and 141), and this must be taken into account in the design of large components. A great deal of experimental work has been carried out on the effects of stress concentration, but the results are difficult to interpret and cannot be applied directly to design problems because of the decrease in fatigue strength that occurs with increase in size. It is possible to estimate the reduction in fatigue strength $K_f$, from the value of the stress concentration factor $K_t$, by means of Neuber's empirical relation (equation 33, page 145), by substituting the appropriate material constant and notch radius, and this is discussed in some detail in Chapter V. However, the value obtained in this way may be considerably in error ($\pm 20\%$ has been quoted for steels and a larger error may be expected for non-ferrous metals because of the smaller amount of experimental evidence) and unless the stress concentration is small, for example less than about $\frac{1}{8}$ in. notch radius for mild steel or aluminium alloys, it is advisable to use unnotched fatigue data and make an allowance for a reduction in fatigue strength of the full factor $K_t$.

To estimate the fatigue strength of parts containing stress concentrations in the presence of a superimposed static tensile stress, a fairly good approximation can be obtained by assuming that the alternating stress is reduced by $K_t$, but that the mean stress is unaffected. The Goodman line drawn on the $R$–$M$ diagram from a value of the alternating fatigue strength divided by $K_t$ to the static tensile strength therefore usually gives a conservative estimate of the fatigue strength. This method is not reliable, however, for materials with a high ratio of yield strength to tensile strength, such as the high-strength aluminium alloys, and Gunn's construction should then be used (see page 163).

The methods described above may be used with a fair degree of confidence to estimate the fatigue strength of integral components containing stress concentrations, but cannot, in general, be applied to joints. This is partly because of the difficulty of determining $K_t$ accurately and, more important, because the fatigue failures of joints are so often associated with fretting corrosion, the influence of which is extremely difficult to predict. The fatigue strength of joints must therefore be estimated from the results of previous fatigue tests on joints and the information available has been reviewed in Chapter IX. Even using this method, the accuracy of prediction will not be high, because the fatigue strength is markedly dependent on the design of the joint; this is illustrated by the range of results that have been obtained for typical aircraft joints (see Fig. 131). It is therefore particularly important to check the design of joints by subsequent component fatigue testing.

The next stage in estimating the fatigue strength of an engineering part is the consideration of the surface condition, in particular the effect of the surface finish and of any special surface treatments such as shot-peening, case-hardening or plating. This can only be achieved by reference to the available information and this has been reviewed in Chapter VI. Finally, it may be necessary to make allowance for the effects of corrosion (discussed in Chapter VII) and temperature (discussed in Chapter VIII).

### Estimation of fatigue life

For applications where it is possible to restrict the fluctuating stresses to values below the fatigue limit or long-life fatigue strength of the part, design on the basis of fatigue strength, as described above, is adequate. In some circumstances, however, repetitions of stress above the fatigue limit cannot be avoided. It must then be accepted that fatigue failure will eventually occur if the part is not removed from service and the design problem is to estimate the safe life. This is a more difficult problem than estimating fatigue strength because it involves estimating the magnitude and frequency of the fluctuating loads that will occur in service and their combined effect on the fatigue life. Furthermore, the slope of the $S$–$N$ curves for commercial alloys are such that a 10% increase in stress will halve the life, so that it is much more difficult to predict fatigue life accurately than fatigue strength—for instance, the scatter in life for a given stress range will be about ten times as great as the scatter in fatigue strength for a given life. The problem of estimating fatigue life has received most attention in connection with design of aircraft and the method of procedure developed for this purpose will be described briefly to illustrate the problem; much more detailed accounts are available elsewhere [578–580].

Fatigue failure in aircraft has become a serious problem only comparatively recently. Its increasing importance can be attributed primarily to
the much longer lives now expected of transport aircraft and to the improvements achieved in static structural efficiency which have resulted in
the use of high stresses. Modern aluminium alloys have been developed
with very high static strengths that have not been matched by corresponding increases in fatigue strength. The aircraft loads likely to lead to fatigue
failures arise primarily from gusts, manoeuvres (including take-off,
landing and taxiing) and cabin pressurization. The effects of gusts and
manoeuvres are most severe on the wings, but they can also lead to fatigue
in the tailplane, while the effects of pressurization are confined almost
entirely to the fuselage. Before any attempt can be made to estimate the
fatigue life of a wing or tail component, the magnitude and frequency of
the gust and manoeuvre loads must be estimated. This information is
obtained from counting accelerometers that have been developed to record
automatically the frequency and magnitude of the accelerations occurring
during flight. As these vary in an almost random manner, a large amount
of data must be collected and analysed on a statistical basis. Extensive
records have now been obtained of the gusts occurring on all the regular
air routes and from these the magnitude and frequency of the load distribution, known as load spectra, can be calculated [581, 582].

To determine the fatigue life accurately it would then be necessary to
subject each component in the laboratory to the loading sequence occurring
in service. Clearly, this is impracticable and a number of simplifications
have to be made. The closest approach to service conditions is obtained
by programme testing the components, that is subjecting them to stress
cycles at a number of different stress amplitudes in proportion to the
service frequency distribution (see page 120 and Fig. 62). Whilst this
method is probably the most accurate, there are relatively few suitable
testing machines available, so that it is often necessary to predict the fatigue
life from the results of tests at constant stress amplitude. For this purpose
the most suitable method is to use the linear damage law, although this can
result in fairly large discrepancies (see Chapter IV). For conditions where
the applied stresses are predominantly in one direction, in other words
where there is a high mean stress, a condition applicable to most aircraft
parts, the linear damage law is usually conservative because the occurrence
of a few high loads can introduce beneficial residual stresses. To take account of this effect, the Royal Aircraft Establishment make it a standard
practice to precede their constant amplitude fatigue tests on aircraft
parts by one application of a high static load [583]. For predominantly
alternating stresses, on the other hand, the linear damage law has sometimes
yielded very unconservative results (see Table 25).

The application of the linear damage law to the design of a spar joint to

withstand gust loading is illustrated in Fig. 147 [578]. The fluctuating
stresses, expressed as a percentage of the static ultimate stress have been
derived from measurements of gust velocity. To simplify the procedure
these stresses have been grouped into intervals covering a range of 4%
of the ultimate stress, and the number of stress fluctuations within each
interval is plotted—thus, $10^4$ stress fluctuations occurred with a magnitude
between 10% and 14% of the ultimate stress. The damage caused by each
group of stress fluctuations, according to the linear damage law, is equal to
the ratio of the number of cycles to the number required to cause fatigue

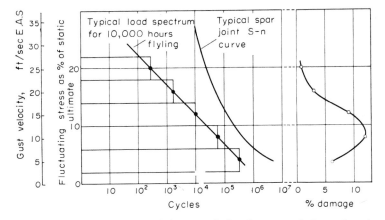

FIG. 147. Example of the use of the cumulative damage rule for estimating
spar life. (Tye [578])

failure in the joint at that stress range, and this is plotted as percentage
damage in the right-hand curve. The cumulative damage is then equal to
the sum of the damage caused by each group. In this example this amounts
to about 30%, giving an estimate of the life of the joint subjected to the
gust loading shown, of a little over 30,000 hr. It can be seen from Fig. 147
that most of the damage, according to the linear damage law, is caused by
gusts within the relatively narrow band of 4 to 14% of the ultimate stress,
the maximum damaging effect occurring at about 8%, corresponding to a
gust of about 10 ft/sec. This stress range is often chosen, therefore, for
constant amplitude laboratory tests on aircraft components.

A further problem involved in the estimation of fatigue life is the scatter
in endurance of nominally identical parts. Difficulty arises because it is
not the mean life that is required but the minimum or safe life below which
no failures will occur. It is, of course, never possible to quote a safe life with
absolute certainty, but it is possible by statistical analysis of fatigue results
to establish a safe life with a certain known degree of confidence. It has
been argued that the design of aircraft to resist fatigue should be based

on a given life with a given probability of failure [584], and this is discussed in more detail in Chapter II. It has been found from experience that if a large number of aluminium alloy components are fatigue tested at the same stress range, there will be a scatter in endurance of about 9 to 1 with the weakest showing an endurance of about one third of the average. Consequently, it is now customary to test about six identical components under the same conditions, determine the logarithmic mean and divide by a factor of about 3 to obtain a safe life. (An alternative procedure is to use a stress equal to 70% of that corresponding to the required life on the mean $S$–$N$ curve.) The confidence with which one can ensure that a given life is safe increases with the number of tests that are made, or to put it another way, the safe life for a given degree of confidence increases with the number of tests. This is an added reason for using component fatigue tests to estimate fatigue life, because these may be easily duplicated while it is not usually feasible to test more than one full-scale structure.

It will be apparent from this short summary that estimating the safe fatigue life of an engineering part is fraught with difficulties. This situation has produced a school of thought that insists that aircraft should be designed not only for a safe life, but to "fail safe", that is, they should be designed so that cracked parts can be detected and replaced before complete collapse of the structure results. The application of the fail safe philosophy to design has been discussed by Spaulding [507, 585]. The properties required in a structure are a slow rate of fatigue crack propagation and a lack of sensitivity of static strength to the presence of fatigue crack. Vital areas of the structure should be accessible for inspection, and where this cannot be arranged, parts should be designed conservatively. As an example, design in which all the tension load is carried by one or two heavy spars should be avoided because cracks are difficult to detect and, when present, they reduce the static strength by a factor much greater than the reduction in cross-section. Instead, Spaulding recommends a conventional box beam with small spars, many moderately heavy stringers and thin skins.

The application of the fail safe method to the design of aircraft has aroused a certain amount of controversy. On the one hand it is argued that design on the basis of a safe life is dangerous and must be conservative, whilst on the other hand it is argued against the fail safe approach that rigorous inspection is required, that replacing cracked parts is uneconomic, and that it has yet to be established that the method is safer. The argument has not yet been resolved, but it seems certain that in practice a compromise between the two methods will be adopted.

## CHAPTER XI

# THE MECHANISM OF FATIGUE

THIS chapter includes a brief historical survey of fatigue of metals and a short account of the more recent developments towards an understanding of the mechanism of fatigue. A more detailed history of fatigue has been written recently by Mann [586] and a review of recent developments by Thompson and Wadsworth [587].

## Historical survey

That metals might break under the repeated application of a stress insufficient to cause failure on the first application was first realized towards the middle of the nineteenth century, mainly as a result of experience in railway engineering. For example, Rankine [588] in 1843, discussed the unexpected fractures which sometimes occurred in originally good railway axles after running for several years, and he attributed this behaviour to a gradual deterioration of the metal during the course of working. It is interesting that he appreciated the detrimental effect of sharp corners and he demonstrated that the introduction of a larger radius of curvature improved the resistance to repeated impact. At about the same time a Commission was appointed to inquire into the suitability of iron as a material of construction for railway bridges and a number of experiments were carried out on cast iron beams [589]. It was shown that the beams could withstand a static load almost as great as the breaking load for as long as four years without failure, but if beams were repeatedly strained to the deflection produced by only half the breaking load, they broke in less than 1000 reversals. In 1864 Fairbairn [590] described a fatigue test he had carried out on a built-up girder, which had fractured under a repeated load equal to 40% of the breaking load.

The first comprehensive investigation of the fatigue of metals was carried out by Wöhler between 1858 and 1870 [46]. He designed testing machines for carrying out fatigue tests under various stress conditions, and his rotating bending machine forms the basis of design for the most widely used type of fatigue machines now in operation. From his experiments on wrought iron and steel he showed that fatigue failures could occur below the elastic limit, and that there was a limiting range of stress below which fatigue failure would not occur. In addition, he investigated the effects on fatigue strength of a superimposed static load and of stress concentrations. The first attempt to relate fatigue failure with the occurrence of plastic deformation was made by Bauschinger [22]. He observed that the limits of proportionality measured in static tension and compression tests could be changed by the application of a fluctuating stress, but reached stable values after a few reversals of stress. He regarded the stable values as the "natural" elastic limits and suggested that these corresponded with the limiting fatigue range.

Until almost the end of the nineteenth century, however, there was little knowledge of the structure of metals and the most generally accepted explanation of fatigue was that the fibrous texture of metals gradually changed to a crystalline structure. The first microscopic observations of deformation caused by fluctuating stresses were made by Ewing and Humfrey [591] and this represented a big step forward towards an understanding of fatigue behaviour. They carried out rotating bending fatigue tests on annealed Swedish iron, examining the specimens at intervals during the course of the tests. They found that if the limit of proportionality was exceeded, the metal deformed by slipping on certain planes within the crystals. After a few reversals of stress the appearance of the surface was similar to that observed after static stressing, slip lines occurring on only a few of the crystals at a comparatively low stress range and appearing in more crystals as the stress range was increased. Viewed under vertical illumination the slip lines appeared as fine dark lines. After more reversals of stress additional slip lines appeared, but the most conspicuous feature was that the original slip lines became more distinct and showed a tendency to broaden. After many reversals they changed into comparatively wide bands with rather hazily defined edges, and as the number of reversals increased this process of broadening continued and some parts of the surface became almost covered with dark markings made up of groups of broadened lines. At this stage it was found that some of the crystals had cracked along the broadened slip bands. In some instances the cracks were first seen on a single crystal, but soon they joined up from crystal to crystal forming a long continuous crack and when this happened a few more reversals resulted in fracture.

Following this demonstration that fatigue cracking was associated with slip, a number of theories of fatigue were put forward. Ewing and Humfrey considered that repeated slipping occurred on a slip band and, in a process similar to solid friction, resulted in the wearing away of the slipped surface by attrition, leading to a broadening of the slip band and, eventually, the formation of a crack. In support of this theory, they were able to detect a piling-up of debris on the surface. Other theories suggested were based on the "amorphous" theory of Beilby. It was argued that the surfaces of the slip planes underwent a phase change, the crystalline material changing to a less ductile but stronger amorphous phase. Further stressing, therefore, resulted in further slip in the crystalline material with a consequent increase of amorphous material, until cracking occurred as a result of the stresses induced by the phase change.

The main criticism of these theories was that they did not explain the observation that plastic deformation could occur repeatedly without leading to failure and, in addition, there was no experimental evidence of the existence of an amorphous phase. An alternative explanation of the mechanism of fatigue failure was put forward by Gough and Hanson [592] in 1923. They considered that the repeated plastic deformation occurring during cyclic stressing gradually decreased owing to work- or strain-hardening. If the stress range was below the fatigue limit the deformation would finally stop, but if not, a limit to the strain hardening would be reached and a crack would be formed. To elucidate the mechanism further a comprehensive series of experiments was undertaken on single crystals of pure metals, and the results of ten years' work on this programme were summarized by Gough [593] in 1933. The ductile crystals tested were aluminium, copper and silver (all with a face-centred cubic atomic lattice) and iron (body-centred cubic). In these metals, plastic deformation under repeated stresses occurred by slip along the same crystallographic planes and directions as under static stresses and fatigue cracks were observed to propagate from regions of heavy slip. Both elastic failure under static stress and fatigue failure were found to depend almost entirely on the criterion of maximum resolved shear stress. From the results of tests on specimens of aluminium containing a few large crystals, it was apparent that the essential characteristics of deformation and failure were substantially the same in single crystals as in polycrystals, although the presence of a grain boundary tended to inhibit slip and reduce the rate of crack propagation.

On the basis of these results, Gough argued that fatigue failure of ductile metals must be considered as a consequence of slip. From microscopic measurements of hardness it was clear that the initiation of a fatigue crack did not mean that the whole crystal had reached a maximum value of strain hardening. He therefore concluded that fatigue failure did not result from the consequences of slip and strain hardening on the crystal in general, but in certain local regions, where the limiting lattice strains were exceeded, resulting in rupture of atomic bonds and discontinuities in the lattice.

Tests were also made on single crystals of two "brittle" metals, antimony and bismuth, each having a rhombohedral lattice. These metals deformed not by slipping, but by twinning. (Twinning occurs by a co-ordinated pattern of movement of very large numbers of atoms by which the original crystal structure is abandoned and converted within the twin to a new crystal, oriented so that the atoms form a mirror image of the parent crystal about the twinning plane.) The crystals did not fatigue, but fractured only as the stress was increased. The most common method of failure was by direct cleavage on clearly defined crystallographic planes, but cracks were sometimes observed along the edges of twins. In zinc single crystals (hexagonal lattice) deformation occurred both by slip and by twinning and the fatigue cracks followed the traces of the slip plane and the twinning plane.

Orowan [594] restated Gough's strain-hardening theory on a semi-quantitative basis. He considered a metal to consist of a number of structural inhomogeneities embedded in an elastic matrix. The stress at the inhomogeneities would be higher than in the elastic matrix, so that yield would occur first at these points. This would result in a transfer of the load from the inhomogeneities to the elastic matrix. However, with continued stress cycling the inhomogeneities would work- or strain-harden, that is, their ability to yield would gradually decrease; the stress on them would, therefore, gradually increase. If complete strain-hardening could occur without the stress reaching the fracture stress at any of these points, then the applied stress would be in the safe range; if not, then failure would occur. The theory is able to account qualitatively for the shape of the S–N curve, but to make a quantitative comparison, an assumption of the rate of strain-hardening during the fatigue process is necessary.

The main criticism of the theory was that the rate of strain-hardening required to satisfy the observed fatigue behaviour of metals was very much less than that found in static tests; in other words, the theory did not explain adequately the large number of stress cycles required to produce a fatigue crack. Furthermore, the occurrence of strain-hardening was not supported, in general, by experimental evidence obtained, for example, from damping measurements during fatigue tests.

## Metallographic observations

Many metallographic observations have been made in recent years of the surface of fatigued metals and while these have confirmed that both static and fatigue deformation in ductile metals occur by slip on the same crystallographic planes, they have also shown a number of distinguishing features between the two processes. Slip bands produced by static stress generally appear as sharp lines fairly evenly distributed over each grain, and under high magnification each band can be seen to consist of parallel lines of various heights. The slip lines formed during cyclic stressing, on the other hand, usually appear close to, or within existing slip bands so that the bands gradually broaden, but there may be extensive regions between them which appear free from slip. Unlike slip bands produced by static stress, those produced by fatigue are often confined to the middle of grains and do not extend to the grain boundaries. Wood [595, 596] suggested that an essential difference between the two slip processes is that static deformation occurs by coarse slip, that is, by an avalanche of slip movements on closely spaced planes producing a coarse step of about $10^{-4}$ or $10^{-5}$ cm, whereas fatigue deformation occurs by fine slip on individual slip planes producing a step of about $10^{-7}$ cm. This is supported by observations of fine slip in fatigued copper [597] and by evidence that appreciable hardening occurs in the early stages of fatigue tests on soft materials before slip bands can be detected [598].

Another most important difference between static and fatigue deformation is that slip bands produced by static stress consist of a series of steps on the surface while in fatigue, owing to the reversal of stress, the slip bands consist of grooves and ridges as illustrated in Fig. 148 [599]. If

Fig. 148. Pure aluminium, surface grooves and ridges, ×1500. (Forsyth [599])

slip occurs on many planes the grooves and ridges may be shallow and undulating, but if slip is restricted to a few closely spaced planes, sharply defined crevices and walls may be formed. In some materials this process results in the extrusion of thin ribbons of metal from the surface. This was observed by Forsyth in an aluminium–4% copper alloy, and is illustrated in Fig. 149; the thickness of the ribbons was less than 0·1 $\mu$ (0·0001 mm), but they projected as much as 20 $\mu$ (0·02 mm) from the surface of the slip band. The effect has subsequently been observed in other materials although the size of the ribbons varies with different materials and fatigue

FIG. 149. Extrusion in aluminium + 4% copper alloy, × 1500. (Forsyth [599])

conditions. Forsyth has also shown that reversed slip and extrusion occurs in silver chloride as a result of cyclic stress [600]. This material is transparent and by using transmitted light to examine below the surface he was able to demonstrate the presence of crevices or intrusions which were about the same size as the extrusions. Cottrell and Hull [601, 602] have also observed both extrusions and intrusions by examining replicas of the surface of copper specimens previously subjected to alternating stress. There is some evidence that intrusions formed in the slip bands by reversed slip can be the source of fatigue cracks.

It was shown by Ewing and Humfrey that fatigue cracks propagated from regions of dense slip and further information of the origin and growth of fatigue cracks has been obtained by Thompson and others [587, 603, 604] in a series of experiments on copper. Unnotched specimens were tested in direct stress and cracks were detected by electropolishing the surface at intervals during the tests. It was found that a light electropolish, removing a layer about 2 $\mu$ (0·002 mm) thick from the surface, resulted in the disappearance of most of the slip bands, but a few became more distinct. These were called persistent slip bands and it was found that the fatigue cracks eventually grew from them. A similar behaviour was subsequently observed in other metals. Forsyth [599] found persistent slip bands in an age-hardened aluminium–zinc–magnesium alloy and observed a series of holes along them in regions where extrusions had occurred (see Fig. 150). Subsequent solution treatment eliminated the persistent slip bands but

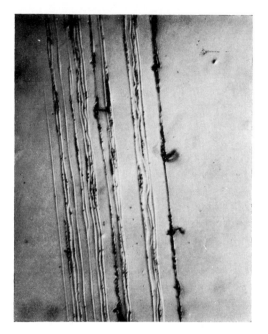

Fig. 150. Aluminium + 7·5% zinc + 2·5% magnesium alloy showing persistent bands and holes, × 1500. (Forsyth [599])

not the holes. In experiments on aluminium, Smith [605] observed that persistent slip bands were preceded by the appearance of a series of dots which appeared to be small hemispherical or conical shaped pits penetrating into the metal along planes parallel to the slip plane. These were particularly marked at low stress ranges and if the stress was increased they joined together to form continuous markings. Similar effects have been observed in copper and brass.

In his experiments on copper, Thompson investigated the development of persistent slip bands into cracks and the growth of the fatigue cracks. The behaviour is illustrated by a series of photomicrographs in Fig. 151. The first persistent slip bands appeared after about 5% of the specimen life of a few million cycles, and at half the life some had usually spread through two or three grains. To determine at what stage the persistent bands became cracks, a static tensile strain of 5% was applied to a partially fatigued specimen. Those bands which were more than one grain long opened into cavities, showing clearly that they had been cracks, but there was not generally much change in the appearance of bands confined to one grain, although some of them showed a slight broadening. These may, therefore, have been cracks, but the evidence was not conclusive. Thus, at least 50% of the fatigue life was spent in crack propagation and possibly a much higher proportion.

This behaviour was somewhat unexpected and it was thought at first that the behaviour of copper might be exceptional, but subsequent observations on other metals have shown that it is typical, at least for pure metals. In tests on nickel, Thompson [604] observed persistent slip bands which looked like cracks on electropolishing a specimen after 4% of the life and these subsequently grew longer in the same way as the cracks in copper. Similar results were obtained by Smith and Harries [605] on high purity aluminium and an aluminium–1% magnesium alloy, the chief difference being that persistent slip bands and cracks sometimes developed in grain boundaries. This was attributed to the low melting point of aluminium and the effect was much reduced when tests were made at −73°C. Hunter and Fricke [606] tested a number of aluminium–magnesium alloys and found that over 90% of the fatigue life was spent in crack propagation. The behaviour of mild steel has been examined by Hempel [607]; the repolishing technique was not used, but with the electron microscope fine dark lines were observed on the slip bands, which were claimed to be sub-microscopic fissures and these occurred even at stress ranges below the fatigue limit. Earlier observations with the electron microscope were made by Craig [608] who claimed that fatigue cracks could be detected as early as 0·1% of the fatigue life.

The stage in a fatigue test at which a persistent slip band can be regarded as a crack and not merely as a region of highly distorted metal cannot be definitely established from metallographic observation, but there is other evidence that cracks are formed at an early stage in the fatigue life. This has been obtained from fatigue tests in which the specimen has been re-annealed at intervals during the test. If the fatigue crack formed at a late stage, then an intermediate anneal ought to restore the specimen to its initial condition and so extend its total life. Sinclair and Dolan [609] investigated this on α-brass by means of three groups of tests, each on 10 to 15 specimens. Fatigue tests were carried out on one group without intermediate annealing and on the second and third groups with annealing treatment at every 50% and 20% respectively of the mean life of the first group. The endurances of the specimens in each group were compared statistically and no significant difference was found. Similar results, though less well established, have been obtained on nickel, copper, aluminium [587] and mild steel [610].

It may be noted that although persistent slip bands may extend right

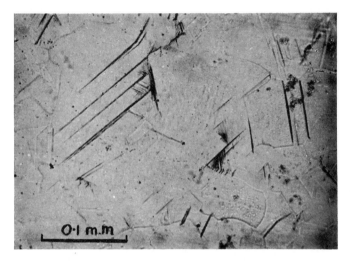

(a)

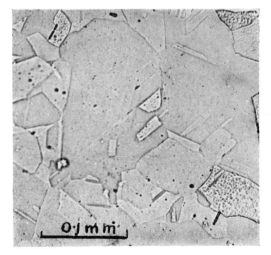

(b)

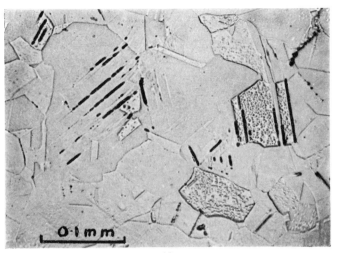

(c)

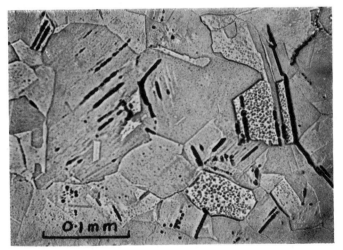

(d)

FIG. 151. Development of a fatigue crack in copper. (a) after $7\frac{1}{2}\%$ of life, (b) as (a) electropolished, (c) after $42\%$ of life, electropolished, (d) after $77\%$ of life, electropolished. (Thompson, Wadsworth and Louat [603])

across a crystal in the metal at an early stage in the fatigue test, they are essentially surface markings and do not extend far downwards into the metal. This was shown by Thompson [587] who progressively electropolished layers from the surface of a copper specimen. He found that after $25\%$ of the fatigue life most of the persistent slip bands were less than $10\ \mu$ ($0 \cdot 01$ mm) deep and none was deeper than $30\ \mu$ ($0 \cdot 03$ mm), and that during the polishing no fresh bands were exposed. He also showed that if the persistent bands were polished away at regular intervals, the life of the specimen could apparently be extended indefinitely, thus demonstrating that the fatigue damage only occurred at the surface and was probably associated with the persistent bands. This behaviour has also been observed subsequently in other metals [587, 610]. There are a number of reasons why the surface is more susceptible to fatigue cracking than the interior, and these have been discussed in Chapter VI.

Wood [596] has recently used the technique of taper sectioning for obtaining magnifications up to 30,000 times. This is achieved by sectioning the specimen at a specially small angle to the surface, after protecting the surface by an electrodeposited layer. The method has proved valuable for demonstrating persistent slip bands, extrusions and intrusions.

## Changes in mechanical and physical properties accompanying fatigue

Many attempts have been made to trace the progressive development of fatigue in metals by means of changes in mechanical or physical properties. One of the earliest methods used was to measure the change in internal friction or damping capacity in a specimen during a fatigue test. The damping capacity is a measure of the energy required to apply a cycle of stress to a material and can be determined either by measuring the stress–strain hysteresis loop during a stress cycle (see page 17), or, because almost all the work done on the material is dissipated as heat, by measuring the change in temperature of the specimen during the fatigue test. The latter method was adopted by Haigh [611] and he showed that, in general, the damping behaviour during a fatigue test could be divided into three stages. In annealed metals the damping was high at the beginning of the fatigue test and decreased rapidly during the primary stage. Haigh showed that this stage was accompanied by an increase in hardness and attributed the behaviour to normal work-hardening; it did not occur in initially hardened metals. The secondary stage occupied the greater part of the fatigue test and during this stage there was little variation in the damping and no change in the hardness. In the tertiary stage, which was usually brief, the damping rose gradually at first and then with increasing rapidity until the specimen broke. This last stage was attributed to the plastic flow associated with the gradual opening of a crack, which was often visible during the last part of the tertiary stage, but never in the secondary stage. Subsequent experiments have, in general, confirmed Haigh's results, although during the second stage the damping is often found to increase gradually and in initially hardened metals this may be accompanied by softening.

In his experiments on copper, Thompson showed that the damping was unaffected by electropolishing the specimen to a sufficient depth to remove the persistent slip bands, though this increased the fatigue life; on the other hand, annealing a partially fatigued specimen restored the damping capacity almost to its initial value, but did not affect the fatigue life [587]. It is therefore clear that the damping is not directly related to crack formation but is a measure of the state of deformation of the specimen as a whole. This also applies to other "bulk" physical properties such as electrical resistance and thermal and magnetic properties, and probably accounts for the lack of success in the attempts to correlate changes in these properties with the fatigue limit (see page 22).

Experiments have also been made to show the effect of fatigue on the static mechanical properties by interrupting a fatigue test and determining the static stress–strain curve or hardness. Unless the prior fatigue has produced macroscopic cracks there is usually no reduction in tensile strength, but there is often a change in the stress–strain curve. The results of such experiments have been used recently in an attempt to explain the differences between work-hardening produced by static stress and the hardening produced by cyclic stress [597].

Structural changes in the surface of metals resulting from the application of stress can be detected by means of X-ray diffraction, and this technique has been used to supplement the metallographic observations of deformation occurring during fatigue. The method usually adopted is to direct a monochromatic beam of X-rays at a small area of the specimen surface and to detect the diffracted beam on a photographic film or plate [612]. The diffraction of an X-ray beam by an atomic plane obeys the optical laws of reflection and refraction, so that an annealed specimen consisting of undistorted crystals produces a series of sharp spots on the photographic plate. If the specimen is deformed statically the sharp spots become diffuse arcs, indicating that the crystals have been distorted. Fatigue deformation also produces some blurring of the sharp X-ray spots, but the X-ray diffraction patterns show clearly that the disorientation produced during fatigue by an alternating stress is negligible compared with that produced by static deformation [595, 596]. Wood's suggestion that static deformation occurs by coarse slip while fatigue deformation occurs by fine slip is based primarily on this evidence, for he argues that fine slip can more easily be accommodated without distorting the crystal.

A number of attempts have been made to detect progressive fatigue damage by examining the same area of the specimen by X-ray diffraction at intervals during a fatigue test. Gough and Wood [613] tested a mild steel and observed that if the applied stress was above the fatigue limit, there was a progressive change during the fatigue test, which they interpreted as a gradual breakdown of the original grains into slightly misoriented subgrains or crystallites between $10^{-5}$ and $10^{-4}$ cm in size. At a stress range below the fatigue limit no change in the X-ray pattern was observed after the first cycle and it was therefore claimed that the technique could be used to distinguish between a safe and an unsafe range of stress, but this has not been found to be generally true [614].

An alternative method recently adopted to investigate the structural changes accompanying fatigue is the measurement of the change in a physical property of a fatigued specimen while its temperature is increased. Clarebrough and others [615], for example, have compared the release of the energy of deformation of statically stressed and fatigued specimens of both copper and nickel. They found appreciable differences in behaviour between the two and observed that for the statically stressed specimen the process occurred primarily by recrystallization, while for the fatigue specimen, recovery occurred with little or no recrystallization.

There is considerable evidence that cyclic stressing produces metallurgical changes similar to those produced by an increase in temperature. For example, by means of damping measurements on precipitation-hardened aluminium alloys, Hanstock [139] showed that cyclic stressing resulted in overageing, that is a coarsening of the precipitate, and it is likely that this accounts for the disappointing fatigue properties of these alloys. The behaviour is attributed to an increase in the rate of atomic diffusion induced by cyclic stress. It is generally believed that the effect does not result simply from a local increase in temperature produced by the deformation, but by the movement of vacant lattice sites produced by the cyclic stress [587].

## The fatigue behaviour of iron and steel

The fatigue behaviour of iron and steel differs in a number of ways from most other metals. The most important distinguishing feature is that they show a distinct fatigue limit; in addition, their fatigue strength can be appreciably increased by understressing or by coaxing (see page 117), and thirdly, the fatigue strength increases with increase in the temperature above about 100°C, reaching a maximum value between 200° and 400°C (see Fig. 119, page 254). These three features are probably interrelated and there is considerable evidence that they may all be attributed to strain ageing.

Strain ageing is a process usually associated with static loading. If, in a static tensile test on mild steel, the load is removed after the specimen has yielded and is then immediately reapplied, a smooth curve without a yield point is obtained. If, on the other hand, the specimen is rested, or aged, after the initial loading, either for several days at room temperature or for a shorter time at a higher temperature, the yield point reappears at a higher stress than the initial yield point; the tensile strength is also increased by the ageing. An explanation of this behaviour based on the theory of dislocations has been put forward by Cottrell [616] and this is now generally accepted in principle. The behaviour is attributed to the presence of carbon and nitrogen atoms in the iron lattice. Slip is considered to occur by the movement of dislocations and it is argued that the carbon and nitrogen atoms congregate at the dislocations, thus restricting their movement, and increasing the stress required to start slip. However, once the dislocations have been pulled away from the carbon and nitrogen atoms, a smaller force is sufficient to keep them moving and this accounts for the yield behaviour. If the metal is subsequently rested the carbon and nitrogen atoms gradually diffuse back to the dislocations and the yield point is restored. The yield phenomenon and strain ageing occur in some other metals, but the effects are not so marked as in steel.

The diffusion rates of carbon and nitrogen atoms in iron are markedly dependent on temperature, so that the strengthening process occurs more rapidly as the temperature is raised. This can account for the increase in fatigue strength as the temperature is increased and the maximum strength probably occurs at the temperature where the carbon and nitrogen atoms are just able to diffuse to the dislocations in one stress cycle. It has been shown that the fatigue strength reaches a maximum value at a lower temperature if the cyclic frequency is reduced [442], and the effect is very much reduced if the steel is decarburized. It has been shown by Sinclair [236] that an increase in fatigue strength by coaxing occurs only in materials susceptible to strain ageing; he observed the effect in ingot iron and two steels, but not in 70/30 brass, an aluminium–zinc–magnesium alloy, nor in ingot iron previously strained and aged. A distinct fatigue limit does not occur in many non-ferrous metals, nor does it occur in steel if the carbon and nitrogen contents are reduced to very low values [617] nor in high strength alloy steels which are not susceptible to strain ageing (see, for example, Fig. 27, page 57).

### The fatigue process

For ductile metals there is now considerable evidence of the metallographic and physical changes accompanying fatigue. Recent work has, in general, confirmed the results of the early investigations, and Haigh's division of the fatigue process into three parts, work-hardening, crack formation and crack propagation is generally accepted. Work-hardening occurs quickly and is virtually complete at an early stage in the fatigue life, probably after a few thousand stress cycles. The process is, in principle, similar to work-hardening under static stress, though differing in detail.

One of the principal difficulties encountered in attempting to provide a satisfactory explanation of the fatigue process has been to explain the long second stage between the completion of work-hardening and the appearance of a fatigue crack. In the early investigations little or no metallographic or physical change could be detected during this stage and it was difficult to reconcile this behaviour with the theories of Gough and Orowan that fatigue cracks were formed as a consequence of work-hardening in certain local regions. An alternative theory was put forward that the fatigue process was not essentially one of progressive damage associated with plastic deformation, but a statistical process of sub-microscopic cracking [618]. This explanation was not generally accepted, however, partly because of the considerable experimental evidence demonstrating the association of fatigue cracks with slip and partly because the scatter in fatigue life, at least for ductile metals, is much less than one would expect from a random process. It now seems that the difficulty may be resolved by the recent observations using more sensitive metallographic techniques, that fatigue cracks are formed at an early stage in the fatigue life. If fatigue cracks are formed towards the end of the work-hardening stage the mechanism becomes easier to explain; it is, for instance, then consistent with the theories of Gough and Orowan.

A number of mechanisms, based on the theory of dislocations [616], have been proposed to explain the way in which fatigue cracks are formed. The movement of dislocations in a metal can produce vacant lattice sites, that is, positions in the lattice where atoms are missing, and it has been suggested that as a result of repeated slip, a sufficiently large number might be produced to form a void. The evidence that diffusion rates are considerably increased by cyclic stress lends support to this suggestion. An alternative proposal is that repeated slip occurs on the same plane and that a film of oxide or absorbed gas is drawn into the crystal along the slip plane [587]. This suggestion is supported by the evidence that fatigue cracks usually start at a free surface and that fatigue strengths are often influenced by the nature of the environment. However, the results of recent tests, showing that metals fatigue when tested in liquid helium [127] indicates that while these processes may influence the behaviour they are not essential to it, for at the temperature of liquid helium ($4°K$) the rates of diffusion are too low for the formation of voids and no gases are present. A process for which there is direct experimental evidence is the formation of intrusions from the surface and these have been observed at $4°K$ [602]. At present this seems the most likely explanation of the way fatigue cracks are formed in ductile metals, because an intrusion is, in effect, a micro-crack. It would seem that these are formed as a result of reversed slip and a number of dislocation mechanisms have been proposed to explain their formation [124, 601]. A technique has recently been developed which enables dislocations to be observed directly by the observation of thin metal foils with the electron microscope. This is now being applied to fatigued specimens [619, 620] and it is hoped that this will show more clearly how fatigue cracks are formed.

With the demonstration that fatigue cracks can be formed at an early stage in the fatigue life, the stage of crack propagation assumes a much greater importance. If crack propagation occupies most of the life, then fatigue strength is determined primarily by the stress required to propagate a crack rather than the stress required to form it. Unfortunately, the subject has not received a great deal of attention. There is a certain amount of data on the rate of propagation of fatigue cracks (see page 167) although this has been confined to macroscopic cracks that can be easily detected. This work has shown that at a constant stress range the growth of fatigue cracks generally proceeds in a regular manner, although at low stresses there may be periods during which no growth can be detected. The regular growth of fatigue cracks is also demonstrated by the appearance of the beach markings on surfaces fractured by fatigue, see, for example, Fig. 91, page 171. By examination with a high-power microscope, a similar regularity can be observed. This is illustrated in Fig. 152, which shows photomicrographs by Forsyth and Ryder [304] of the fracture surface of an aluminium alloy wing spar, which had been subjected to a programmed fatigue test consisting of the application of a stress of 12,000 lb/in$^2$ and then superimposing 18 cycles of $\pm 3000$ lb/in$^2$ on the mean stress, followed by removal of the stress. Fig. 152a shows fairly widely spaced striations on a portion of the fracture surface, while Fig. 152b at a higher magnification shows that there are 18 finer evenly spaced striations between each. This demonstrates clearly that one striation was produced by each cycle of stress.

More recently Forsyth [686] has demonstrated that the growth of fatigue cracks occurs in two distinct stages, which he calls stage 1 and stage 2 fatigue crack growth. In stage 1, slip band cracks are formed by the growth of crevices or intrusions on planes closely aligned to the maximum shear stress directions, and may propagate, apparently by the same mechanism, for an appreciable proportion of the life. The change to stage 2 growth usually occurs when a crack meets a slip obstacle such as a grain boundary. The criterion for growth in the second stage is the maximum principal tensile stress and it is during this stage that striations or beach markings may occur.

The problem of crack propagation is a difficult one to tackle theoretically, but a simplified treatment has been attempted by Head [621, 622]. The high stress at the end of a crack will cause plastic deformation, so that elastic theory cannot be applied. Head based his analysis on Orowan's theory (see page 335) arguing that with repeated stressing the plastic zone at the end of the crack would gradually work-harden causing a gradual increase in stress range in that region. If the fracture stress were reached before complete work-hardening occurred the crack would advance through the plastic zone. With some simplifying assumptions Head deduced that the rate of crack propagation would be given by the following expression:

$$\frac{\mathrm{d}l}{\mathrm{d}N} = \frac{l^{3/2}}{a^{\frac{1}{2}}} \, f(\sigma) \tag{43}$$

where $l$ is the length of the crack after $N$ cycles at a stress $\sigma$ and $a$ is the length of the plastic zone ahead of the crack. He showed that the dependence of the rate of crack propagation on $l^{3/2}$ was in quite good agreement with the experimental evidence and was consistent with the premise that crack propagation proceeded slowly in the early stages and could therefore occupy a large proportion of the fatigue life. (It may be noted that the above expression may be rewritten: $[(1/l)(\mathrm{d}l/\mathrm{d}n)] = (l/a)^{\frac{1}{2}}f(\sigma)$, which is consistent with the observations of crack propagation rates made by Frost and Dugdale [305] if $l/a$ is a constant. In fact, Frost and Dugdale argued that $l/a$ must be a constant by geometric similitude and checked it by direct observation.)

The extent to which the fatigue process described can be applied to metals with little or no ductility is much less certain. Precipitation-hardened metals, such as the fully heat-treated commercial aluminium alloys, may be weakened by overageing resulting from cyclic stress, and it is possible in these circumstances that fatigue cracks are not formed until a much later stage of the life. The possibility that the fatigue process in high-strength alloys may be primarily a statistical process cannot be entirely discounted. For example, Cox [623] has pointed out that even on the extreme view that the average endurance $N$ need be no more than the

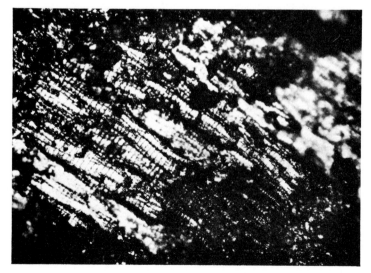

(a)

(b)

FIG. 152. Fracture surface of an aluminium alloy wing spar. (a) coarse striations on fracture surface, ×250, (b) showing batches of fine striations between regularly spaced coarse ones, ×1500. (Forsyth and Ryder [304])

expression of an equal chance $1/N$ of failure in each and every cycle, the scatter about $N$ would not be much greater than that actually observed on hard alloys.

It is now almost universally accepted that plastic deformation plays an essential part in the fatigue of ductile metals, but the claim that it is essential for all fatigue failures cannot so easily be accepted. There is some evidence that fatigue will not occur in very brittle metals. In other words, during a fatigue test the specimen either breaks while the stress is being increased, or it does not break at all. This behaviour has been observed in single crystals of zinc tested in liquid oxygen and in $\gamma$-brass [587], and it also occurred in single crystals of antimony and bismuth tested by Gough and Cox [593]. On the other hand, there is abundant evidence that fatigue failure can occur in a wide range of non-metals in which the deformation processes are quite different from those in metals.

## CHAPTER XII

# FATIGUE OF NON-METALLIC MATERIALS

THE great majority of engineering parts that are subjected to fluctuating loads are metallic, so that the problem of fatigue failure is usually associated with metals. It is by no means confined only to metals, however, for almost all non-metallic materials will also fatigue and the failures show many of the characteristics of fatigue in metals.

## Wood

Wood will fail by fatigue from the repeated application of a stress considerably below its static breaking strength, but unlike metals, failures resulting from the fatigue of wood often have the same appearance as static failures; as a result, fatigue failures in service may not always be recognized as such.

The behaviour of wood in fatigue has been investigated most fully at the U.S. Forest Products Laboratory, and some of their results from completely reversed and repeated bending tests are shown in Figs. 153 and 154. There is little difference between the different woods tested but each shows a considerable scatter. To reduce the scatter as much as possible, the fluctuating stress is plotted as a ratio of the static strength, determined on specimens cut from the same piece of wood. This procedure is commonly adopted and fatigue strengths are usually quoted as a proportion of the static strength. It may be noted that there is no indication of a distinct fatigue limit, at least up to $50 \times 10^6$ cycles, and Fuller and Oberg [625] have reported a failure on a specimen of yellow birch after $435 \times 10^6$ cycles.

Wood is usually weaker in compression than in tension. In a completely reversed bending test the first failure, therefore, usually occurs in compression, although the specimen may finally fail in tension In a repeated bending fatigue test the failure consists of a compression wrinkle. Reversed bending tests are usually conducted at a constant range of strain; this may not lead to complete fracture and the tests are stopped when the outside fibres have failed.

The effects of repeated bending stress on the subsequent static strength has been investigated by Kommers [626]. He found that 5000 repetitions of a stress up to 85% of the static strength did not affect the strength

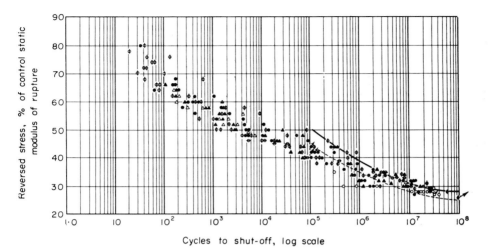

FIG. 153. Results of tests to determine endurance of wood and plywood when subjected to completely reversed bending stress. (W. C. Lewis [624])

● Sitka spruce—solid plank No. 1          △ Yellow poplar—5 ply.
ϕ Sitka spruce—solid plank No. 2.          ▲ Douglas fir—solid plank No. 1.
⊖ Yellow birch—5 ply panel No. 1.          O➤ Arrow indicates unfailed specimen.
O Yellow birch—5 ply panel No. 2.          —— Solid yellow birch—rotating beam
          — — —Solid maple—rotating beam

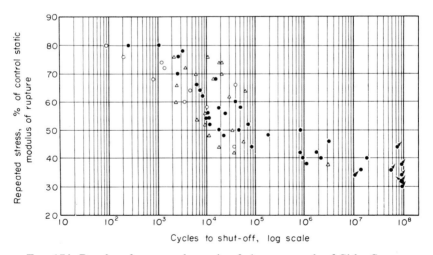

FIG. 154. Results of tests to determine fatigue strength of Sitka Spruce and Douglas Fir when subjected to repeated bending stress. (W. C. Lewis [624])

O Sitka spruce—solid plank No. 1.          △ Douglas fir—solid plank No. 1.
● Sitka spruce—solid plank No. 2.          ●➤ Arrow indicates unfailed specimen

adversely for loading in the same direction as the repeated loadings, but if the static test was made in the opposite direction, a reduced strength was obtained after repetitions of stress exceeding 30 or 40% of the static strength. This was attributed to a reduction in tensile strength resulting from the prior deformation in compression.

Other results of fatigue tests on wood from various sources are summarized in Table 80. All the data show considerable scatter, and the fatigue strengths quoted represent average values. The tests were made on smooth-grained specimens not containing knots or other obvious defects. The results obtained by Fuller and Oberg [625], in rotating bending, indicate a considerable influence of size on fatigue strength. Most of the tests were made on specimens $\frac{1}{3}$ in. diameter, and increasing this size to 1 in. diameter reduced the fatigue strength by about 20%. There was a corresponding decrease in the static strength, however, so that the endurance ratio was unaffected. The same authors also carried out tests at two different frequencies, 3450 and 10,600 cycles/min. At high ranges of stress the fatigue strength was lower at the higher frequency, but there was no significant difference at long endurances. The effect may perhaps be explained by the rise in temperature which occurs in wood undergoing fatigue, for this would be greater at the higher frequency. The fatigue strength of wood is reduced by stress concentrations, such as abrupt changes in section, bolt holes, slope of the grain and knots [630], but tests on small notched specimens have shown that it is less notch sensitive than most metals [625].

A number of results quoted by Lewis [627] for glued joints are included in Table 80. For specimens containing a single scarf joint with a 1:8 slope, both the static strength and the fatigue strength were about 80% of the values for solid specimens. The specimens were glued with a room-temperature-setting resorcinol-resin adhesive with mechanical pressure applied while the glue was setting; no failures occurred by breakdown of the glue. In the laminated glue shear specimens which were designed so that tension loading produced shear along the glue line, the failures occurred almost entirely by shear of the wood in an area immediately adjacent to one of the glue lines.

Little attempt has been made to test large specimens of wood, but Leggett [631] has reported the results of tests on full-size timber stringers for bridges. The tests were made on beams 8 in. wide and 16 in. deep with a span of 13 ft. With this ratio of span-to-depth of about 10:1, all the beams failed in horizontal shear and this was attributed to the presence of checks (cracks) formed during seasoning. The tests were made in repeated bending, and the fatigue range for an endurance of 2 million cycles, based on very few tests on Douglas fir and Southern pine, was about 25–30% of the static strength determined on 2 × 2 × 32 in. specimens free from defects. Lewis [628] has carried out a series of fatigue tests on quarter-

| Stressing conditions | Frequency cycles/min | Fatigue strength / Static rupture strength | | | | Source | Ref. |
|---|---|---|---|---|---|---|---|
| | | $10^5$ | $10^6$ | $10^7$ | $10^8$ | | |
| Reversed bending | 1750 | 0·34 0·33 0·37 0·35 | 0·27 0·27 0·30 0·27 | | | Dietz and Grinsfelder | 629 |
| Rotating bending on polished specimens | 3450 and 10,600 | 0·40 0·34 0·51 0·48 | 0·36 0·34 0·32 0·39 0·45 | 0·28 0·28 0·28 0·28 0·32 0·41 | 0·20 0·21 0·25 0·24 0·30 0·37 | Fuller and Oberg | 625 |
| Fluct. tension | 900 | 0·43 ± 0·35 0·41 ± 0·33 0·35 ± 0·29 0·39 ± 0·32 0·39 ± 0·32 0·37 ± 0·31 | 0·37 ± 0·30 0·35 ± 0·28 0·29 ± 0·24 0·33 ± 0·27 0·33 ± 0·27 0·31 ± 0·25 | 0·31 ± 0·25 0·30 ± 0·24 0·26 ± 0·21 0·29 ± 0·23 0·29 ± 0·24 0·25 ± 0·20 | | Lewis | 627 |
| Fluct. bending | 500 | | | 0·27 ± 0·23 0·31 ± 0·25 0·31 ± 0·25 0·27 ± 0·23 | | Lewis | 628 |

TABLE 80. FATIGUE STRENGTH OF

| Material | Specific gravity | Static strength, tons/in² | | | | Fatigue specimen details |
|---|---|---|---|---|---|---|
| | | Tensile | Compressive | Bending | Shear | |
| Laminated birch bonded with thermo-setting phenol–formaldehyde fibres | | | | 11·4 | | 2 ply |
| | | | | 10·4 | | 3 ply |
| Birch plywood bonded with phenol–formaldehyde | | | | 9·2 | | 3 ply |
| Birch plywood bonded with cold-setting urea–formaldehyde resin | | | | 7·8 | | 3 ply |
| Hard maple | 0·70 | | 4·3 | 8·7 | | Solid 0·33 in dia. |
| Hard maple | 0·68 | | 6·3 | 8·5 | | ⅛ in. laminations, 0·33 in. dia. bonded with phenolic resin |
| Hard maple compressed wood | 1·23–1·38 | 13–15 | 10·5–12 | 18 | | do. impregnated and non-impregnated 0·33 in. dia. |
| Hard maple compressed wood | | 11 | 11·4 | 14·5 | | do. 1 in. dia. |
| Yellow birch | 0·69 | | 5·0 | 9·7 | | Solid 0·33 in. dia. |
| Yellow birch compressed wood | 1·25 | 14 | | 14 | | 1/16 in. laminations with phenolic resin — impregnated. 0·33 in. dia. |
| Douglas fir | | 4·0–9·4 Av. 6·4 | | | | Solid plank ¼ in × ½ in. |
| Douglas fir | | 3·9–7·2 Av. 5·2 | | | | Single scarf joint with 1 : 8 slope |
| Douglas fir | | | | | 0·27–0·40 Av. 0·33 | Laminated glue shear |
| White oak | | 4·0–10·9 Av. 7·4 | | | | Solid plank ¼ in. × ½ in |
| White oak | | 2·9–9·6 Av. 5·9 | | | | Single scarf joint with 1 : 8 slope |
| White oak | | | | | 0·48–0·65 Av. 0·58 | Laminated glue shear |
| Green southern pine: Straight grained | | | | 2·7–3·9 Av. 3·3 | | 2 × 4 × 43 ins loaded at third points of a 39 in span |
| 1 : 12 slope of grain | | | | 2·6–3·9 Av. 3·1 | | |
| Dry southern pine: Straight grained | | | | 4·5–7·3 Av. 6·0 | | |
| 1 : 12 slope of grain | | | | 3·3–5·7 Av. 4·5 | | |

scale bridge stringers and his results obtained on specimens free from defects are included in Table 80. Some of the specimens were notched, reducing the width by one-half at mid-height, to simulate checks and these failed in fatigue by shear along the notch. The maximum stresses based on the gross sections, which these could withstand for 10 million cycles with a stress ratio of 0·1, were about 300 lb/in² for straight grained material and 250 lb/in² for that with 1:12 slope of grain; these values corresponded to about 35% of the static strength.

### Plastics

Considerable interest has developed recently in the mechanical properties of reinforced plastics, for if weight is taken into consideration, their specific strength is comparable with that of high-strength metals. A review of their fatigue properties has been written by Heywood [632], and some data are quoted in Table 81. In determining the fatigue strength of these materials it is desirable to control both the temperature and humidity. They exhibit considerable internal damping during fatigue tests and it is, therefore, necessary to limit the frequency of the stress cycle to prevent the specimens overheating; Heywood recommends a limit of 900 cycles/min.

The results given in Table 81 show that glass reinforced plastics exhibit a stress-endurance relation similar to that of high-strength metals with a comparable ratio of fatigue-to-tensile strength. The fatigue strength is little influenced by the type of fabric or by the finish, but there are considerable differences between the various resins. These materials are resistant to moderately high temperatures and a further, most important attribute is a low fatigue notch sensitivity. As with cast iron this may be attributed to the presence of internal stress raisers in the material itself, and this is confirmed by the shape of the R–M diagram (see Fig. 155) which is similar to that of cast iron and of high-strength wrought metals containing stress concentrations (see page 166). Some results for other types of plastic are also included in Table 81. It can be seen that the fatigue strength of perspex is markedly dependent on the frequency.

### Rubber

Rubber is liable to fail by fatigue, and its fatigue resistance is important for such applications as rubber springs and engine mountings. Fatigue failure may occur by the development of cracks, as in other materials, but alternatively, failure may result from overheating, caused by the considerable hysteresis developed by repeated stressing. A number of testing machines have been designed for carrying out fatigue tests on rubber specimens [638, 639]; these usually operate at a constant range of strain and the frequency is restricted to avoid the overheating type of failure.

TABLE 81. FATIGUE STRENGTH OF PLASTICS

| Material | Static strength tons/in² | Type of fatigue stress | Alternating fatigue strength, tons/in², in longitudinal direction | | | | | Source | Ref. |
|---|---|---|---|---|---|---|---|---|---|
| | | | $10^3$ | $10^4$ | $10^5$ | $10^6$ | $10^7$ | | |
| Glass reinforced polyester laminates. Various finishes {fast cure, slow cure | (Bending) 21·7–23·3 26·0–27·5 | B | | | | 5·3–6·5 6·7–7·8 | 4·5–5·0 | Hooper | 633 |
| Polyester resins reinforced with various glass fabrics | (Tensile) | Ax | 12–14 | 9–10 | 6·5–8·0 | 5·5–6·0 | 4·5–5·0 | Boller | 634 |
| Various resins reinforced with 181 glass fabric: | | | | | | | | | |
| Polyester, tested at room temperature | 20·7 | | 12·7 | 10·0 | 7·6 | 5·8 | 4·6 | | |
| Polyester, tested at 500°F (260°C) | | | 6·1 | 5·6 | 4·6 | 3·2 | 1·9 | | |
| Epoxy, tested at room temperature | 19·2 | | 15·6 | 11·7 | 8·8 | 6·8 | 4·9 | | |
| Epoxy, tested at 500°F | | | 5·9 | 5·3 | 4·6 | 4·0 | 3·3 | | |
| Phenolic, tested at room temperature | 20·0 | | 17·8 | 13·7 | 9·7 | 7·3 | 5·6 | | |
| Phenolic, tested at 500°F | | | 8·6 | 7·1 | 6·0 | 4·5 | 1·4 | | |
| Silicone, tested at room temperature | 15·8 | | 7·7 | 6·6 | 5·6 | 4·5 | 3·5 | | |
| Silicone, tested at 500°F: | | | 3·1 | 2·9 | 2·8 | 2·7 | 2·5 | | |
| Cellulose acetate (transparent thermoplastic) | | B | 2·8 | 2·1 | 1·4 | 1·0 | 1·0 | Findley and Hintz | 635 |
| Acrylic (non-crystalline thermoplastic) as received | | R.B. 1789 c/min | | | | | 0·40 | Lazar | 636 |
| Polystyrene (non-crystalline thermoplastic) as received | | 1900 c/min | | | | | 0·20 | | |
| Polystyrene (non-crystalline thermoplastic) annealed | | 1900 c/min | | | | | 0·20 | | |
| Polystyrene (non-crystalline thermoplastic) annealed | | 360 c/min | | | | | 0·23 | | |
| Nylon. As received | | Ax 1800 | | | | | 1·5 | | |
| Unplasticized polymethyl methacrylate (Perspex) | | R.B. 95 c/min | | 2·4 | 2·0 | 1·9 | 1·9 | Zarek | 637 |
| | | 190 c/min | | 2·0 | 1·6 | 1·5 | 1·5 | | |
| | | 950 c/min | | 1·6 | 1·2 | 1·2 | 1·2 | | |
| | | 1700 c/min | | 1·5 | 1·2 | 1·1 | 1·0 | | |
| | | 2250 c/min | | 1·5 | 1·1 | 0·9 | 0·9 | | |

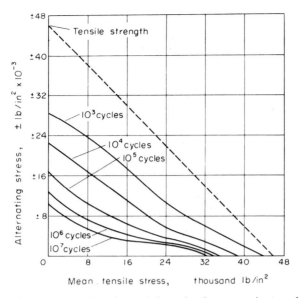

FIG. 155. *R–M* diagram for glass reinforced polyester resin tested at 23°C.
(Boller [634])

Some results obtained by Cadwell and others in direct stress tests are shown in Fig. 156. These tests were made on specimens bonded to metal ends and were tested at 180 or 3600 cycles/min, depending on the strain range. The influence of mean strain is most unusual; the fatigue resistance has a minimum value under an alternating strain and is increased by a superimposed static strain either tensile or compressive. The results shown are for a rubber with a hardness of 50 on a type A Shore durometer, but similar results were obtained on other rubbers with hardness values ranging from 30 to 80. The same authors carried out a few fatigue tests in shear and found that the resistance to fluctuating shear strain was about the same as for axial strain. Results quoted by Moulton and Turner [639] from torsion tests, however, indicated a considerably higher fatigue resistance, as shown in Fig. 157. These results are applicable to spring type rubbers with shear moduli between 70 and 110 lb/in² (corresponding to a Shore hardness range of about 42 to 55). They showed a good correlation with the behaviour of road vehicle springs tested on the Motor Industry Research Association pavé track [640].

Fatigue cracks in rubber progress slowly, so that in service it should usually be possible to detect a failure before complete fracture occurs. In fatigue tests at a constant range of strain complete fracture may never occur and it is then necessary to define failure in some arbitrary manner, such as a reduction in stiffness of 10%, the criterion adopted by Moulton

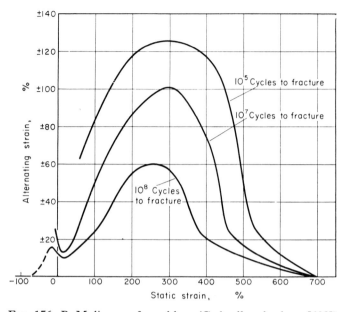

FIG. 156. *R–M* diagram for rubber. (Cadwell and others [638])

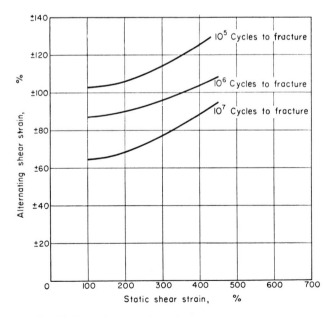

FIG. 157. *R–M* shear diagram for rubber. (Moulton and Turner [639])
Static breaking strain 1400%

and Taylor. The fatigue resistance of rubber is dependent on the temperature; results quoted by Cadwell and others [638] show that the resistance is a maximum at about 60°F, and decreases appreciably above 120°F and below 0°F. As for other materials, the fatigue resistance is adversely affected by geometrical discontinuities and by non-uniform loading, and this must not be neglected in the design of rubber components subjected to fluctuating loads.

## Glass

Glass is apparently one of the few materials that is not liable to failure by fatigue as a result of repeated loading. Its static strength is appreciably reduced by increasing the time under load, and this behaviour is usually known as "fatigue" although it is not affected by cyclic loading. This was demonstrated by Gurney and Pearson [641] by means of bending tests on $\frac{1}{4}$ in. diameter specimens of annealed soda-glass. Three stress–endurance (time to failure) curves were obtained, one for specimens which were not rotated, the second for specimens rotated at 14 rev/min, and the third for specimens rotated at 10,000 rev/min. There was no significant difference between the results of the three series of tests, showing that the behaviour was a time-dependent deterioration of the material, quite distinct from the process of fatigue failure in metals. The behaviour is thought to be associated with the effect of the atmosphere, for much higher static strengths are obtained in a vacuum.

## Concrete

For many applications concrete is subjected to static loads with little or no fluctuation, but when appreciable variations in load do occur, fatigue is a likely source of failure. It is generally agreed, for example, that the cracking of concrete road surfaces results from the repeated applications of load. Consequently, the fatigue behaviour of concrete has been widely investigated, both on plain and on reinforced and prestressed concrete; two recent reviews on the subject are available [642, 643].

The results of fatigue tests on plain concrete have demonstrated a striking resemblance between the fatigue behaviour of concrete and metals. An S–N curve obtained from fluctuating bending tests on plain concrete beams is shown in Fig. 158. There is no evidence of a fatigue limit up to $10^7$ cycles and few tests have been continued beyond this endurance because of the long testing times involved. Because of the inhomogeneous nature and large particle size of concrete, large specimens are necessary, and this requires large testing machines which operate relatively slowly. The test results shown in Fig. 158 were obtained on beams 6 × 6 in. in cross section, and 64 in. long, tested in machines operating at about 400 cycles/min. Despite this large size there is still an appreciable scatter in the results.

It is common practice to quote fatigue strengths for concrete as a proportion of the static strength because of the difficulty of reproducing similar materials. On a basis of $10^7$ cycles to fracture, the fatigue range in pulsating or repeated compression (from zero stress to a maximum stress in compression) is usually between 50 and 55% of the ultimate crushing strength, while values quoted for the repeated bending fatigue strength range from 33 to 64% of the static ultimate flexural stress, with an average value of about 55% [642]. Typical values of the static strength of concrete are 300–450 lb/in² tensile strength and 1600–3500 crushing strength [645].

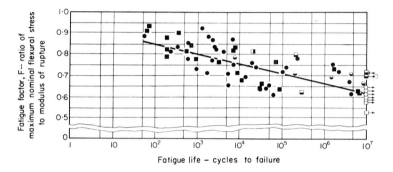

FIG. 158. Behaviour of plain concrete under fatigue loading, $R = 0.13$ to 0.18. (J. W. Murdock and C. E. Kesler [644])

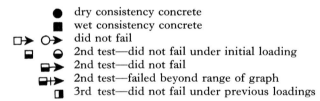

If a specimen of concrete is subjected to a constant range of repeated stress, both the range of strain and the permanent deformation gradually increase, tending towards steady values at low stress ranges, but increasing continuously until fracture at high stress ranges. The fatigue strength can be increased by understressing and by rest periods even when the concrete has been well aged before testing. The frequency of the stress cycle has little effect on the fatigue strength. In fluctuating compression the effect of mean stress can be represented approximately by the Goodman relation.

In reinforced concrete beams, cracking of the concrete may be produced by the repeated application of about half the static breaking load, but complete failure does not occur unless the repeated load is between 60 and 80%

of the static strength. Under static loading, a beam with a normal proportion of reinforcement fails as a result of yield of the steel leading to crushing of the concrete. Under repeated loading, a beam with mild steel reinforcement is likely also to fail in this way (with some reduction in strength), but a beam with medium-tensile steel or cold-worked mild steel reinforcements may fail by fatigue of the steel [643].

Higher fatigue strengths can be obtained with prestressed concrete beams than with reinforced beams. Fatigue failures in prestressed beams occur almost always by fatigue fracture of the wire and only rarely by crushing of the concrete or by slip at the bond between the wire and the concrete. Consequently, the prime consideration for adequate fatigue resistance is the fatigue strength of the wire. The fatigue behaviour of hard drawn steel wire is discussed in Chapter III, and more direct information is available from the results of fatigue tests on actual prestressed concrete beams [642, 643].

A number of such tests have been carried out at the Building Research Station on T section beams 16 in. wide and 12 in. deep, tested on a span of 10 ft [646]. The beams were designed so that the stress in the wire could be estimated, and it was found that they could withstand a million cycles of a stress range not less than 0·2 of the static strength, when the minimum value of the range was equal to 0·55 of the static strength. The fatigue strength was appreciably greater for beams with plain rust-free wires from coils of large diameter than for most of those tested with deformed wires. However, rusting of the plain wire sufficiently to improve the bond, without producing noticeable pitting of the surface, had little adverse effect. Fatigue failure of the wires was always preceded by severe cracking and deformation so that there was a clear warning before collapse was imminent. Furthermore, even when one wire had fractured, the beam was usually able to sustain an appreciable number of further load reversals. The static strength of the beams was not reduced by prior repeated loading even when the applied load range approached that causing fatigue failure.

In general, fatigue cracking of the concrete can be avoided by limiting the maximum stress of the range to half the static stress required to produce cracking, which is usually about 1000 lb/in². It has also been shown that the fatigue strength is not improved by a reduction in the pre-stress.

# FATIGUE DATA

THE following tables contain some data on the fatigue strength and other mechanical properties of metals, mainly from British sources. The results shown in Table 82 were all obtained at air temperature; low-temperature results are quoted in Table 83 and high-temperature results in Table 84. The following abbreviations are used:

N = normalized
A = annealed
A.R. = as received
O.Q. = oil quenched
W.Q. = water quenched
T = tempered
B = Brinell hardness number
D.P.N. = diamond pyramid number
R.B. = rotating bending
B = plane bending
Ax = axial or direct stress

The chemical compositions are quoted in weight per cent.

The fatigue results quoted in these tables are all alternating fatigue strengths for unnotched polished specimens stressed either in bending or direct stress. Data showing the effect of a superimposed static tensile stress on direct stress fatigue strengths are quoted in Tables 14, 15 and 16 pages 96, 98, 100. A comparison of fatigue strengths in bending and torsion is made in Figs. 58 and 59 and the results are summarized in Table 19, page 110. The influence of stress concentrations is discussed in Chapter V and results showing the effects of surface treatments on fatigue strength are included in Chapter VI. Some data of fatigue strengths in corrosive environments are quoted in Chapter VII, see Tables 46–51.

TABLE 82. FATIGUE STRENGTHS

INGOT IRON, WROUGHT

| No. | Material | Condition | Yield stress | Tensile strength |
|-----|----------|-----------|--------------|------------------|
|     |          |           | tons/in² | |
| 1 | Armco iron, 0·012 C, 0·07 Mn | A 1000°C | 6·8 | 18·7 |
| 2 | Ingot iron, 0·015 C, 0·03 Mn | A | 10·3 | 19·6 |
| 3 | Ingot iron, 0·014 C, 0·015 Mn | N 940°C | 10·7 | 19·6 |
| 4 | Wrought iron, 0·017 C, ·122 Si, 0·004 Mn, 2·24 slag | Longitudinal A.R. | 13·4 | 21·0 |
| 5 | Wrought iron, 0·017 C, ·122 Si, 0·004 Mn, 2·24 slag | Transverse A.R. | 13·0 | 21·0 |
| 6 | 0·12 C steel, 0·61 Mn | N 900°C | 16·6 | 27·9 |
| 7 | 0·13 C steel | N | 20·0 | 30·6 |
| 8 | 0·15 C steel, 0·66 Mn | Longitudinal | 21·2 | 25·5 |
| 9 | | Transverse | — | — |
| 10 | 0·25 C steel, 0·65 Mn | A.R. | 15·5 | 29·2 |
| 11 | 0·30 C steel | A.R. | 21·7 | 37·5 |
| 12 | 0·31 C steel | A.R. | 31·0 | 42·3 |
| 13 | 0·33 C steel, 0·59 Mn | N 850°C | 22·4 | 37·3 |
| 14 | 0·36 C steel, 0·66 Mn | N 850°C | 24·9 | 37·9 |
| 15 | 0·36 C steel, 0·66 Mn | O.Q. 850°C, T 600°C | 31·5 | 46·8 |
| 16 | 0·39 C steel, 0·65 Mn, 0·12 Ni | N 850°C | 23·4 | 42·0 |
| 17 | 0·39 C steel, 0·65 Mn, 0·12 Ni | Spheroidized, N 900°C 6 days at 650°C | 18·6 | 30·9 |
| 18 | 0·42 C steel, 0·62 Mn | A.R. | 25·0 | 40·8 |
| 19 | 0·45 C steel, 0·54 Mn | N | 22·9 | 42·0 |
| 20 | 0·60 C steel, 0·77 Mn, 0·21 Si, 0·08 Ni, 0·09 Cr | O.Q. 950°C, T 400°C | — | 109 |
| 21 | | O.Q. 950°C, T 450°C | 83 | 92 |
| 22 | | O.Q. 950°C, T 500°C | 73 | 78 |
| 23 | | O.Q. 950°C, T 550°C | 68 | 74 |
| 24 | 0·65 C steel, 0·11 Mn, 0·14 Si, 0·20 S | N 800°C | 22·8 | 50·0 |
| 25 | 0·82 C steel, 0·41 Mn, 0·25 Si | O.Q. 900°C, T 500°C | 65 | 82 |
| 26 | | O.Q. 900°C, T 550°C | 58 | 77 |
| 27 | 0·86 C steel, 0·13 Mn | N 820°C | — | 54·9 |

OF METALS AT AIR TEMPERATURE

IRON AND CARBON STEEL

| Reduction in area % | Brinell hardness number | Izod impact strength ft-lb | Diameter of fatigue specimen in. | Fatigue limit tons/in² | | Source | Ref. |
|---|---|---|---|---|---|---|---|
| | | | | R.B. | Ax. | | |
| 80 | — | — | — | 12·6 | 9·9 | N.P.L. | 24 |
| 75 | 83 | — | 0·33 | 12·0 | — | Kommers | 231 |
| 47 | — | — | 0·33 | 13·0 | — | Russell and Welcker | 291 |
| 16 | — | — | | 13·4 | — | | |
| 16 | — | — | | 12·5 | — | | |
| 70 | 127 | 89 | 0·3 | 17·0 | — | Gough, Pollard and Clenshaw | 56 |
| 72 | 126 | — | — | 16·3 | 13·8 | N.P.L. | 24 |
| — | — | — | — | 14·6 | — | Morrison, Crossland and Parry | 118 |
| — | — | — | — | 12·3 | — | | |
| — | 128 | — | — | 12·4 | 12·3 | N.P.L. | 24 |
| — | — | — | — | 16·7 | — | | |
| — | — | — | — | 21·5 | — | | |
| 59 | 149 | — | — | 17·5 | 14·0 | | |
| 58 | — | — | — | 17·0 | 15·0 | | |
| 62 | — | — | — | 19·0 | 18·0 | | |
| 58 | 195 | 30 | 0·3 | 20·8 | — | Gough, Pollard and Clenshaw | 56 |
| 67 | 144 | 32 | | 15·9–17·4 | — | | |
| — | — | — | — | 17·3 | — | N.P.L. | 24 |
| 46 | 182 | — | — | 18·3 | — | | |
| — | 455 | 4 | 0·2 | 47·0 | — | Hankins, Hanson and Ford | 647 |
| 10 | 422 | 12 | | 41·0 | — | | |
| 17 | 370 | 18 | | 38·0 | — | | |
| 21 | 353 | 18 | | 37·5 | — | | |
| 27 | 222 | — | — | 20·5 | 19·2 | N.P.L. | 24 |
| 19 | 377 | 12 | 0·2 | 40·0 | — | Hankins, Hanson and Ford | 647 |
| 26 | 344 | 12 | | 38·5 | — | | |
| 18 | 248 | 3½ | 0·3 | 22·2 | — | Gough, Pollard and Clenshaw | 56 |

TABLE 8

ALLO

| No. | Material | Condition | Yield stress | Tensile strength | Elongation per cent |
|---|---|---|---|---|---|
| | | | tons/in$^2$ | | on 8 in. |
| 1 | Silico-manganese steel | O.Q. 950°C, T 450°C | 103 | 108 | 4 |
| 2 | 0·54 C, 1·95 Si, 0·94 Mn | O.Q. 950°C, T 500°C | 83 | 91 | 8 |
| 3 | | O.Q. 950°C, T 550°C | 72 | 80 | 10 |
| 4 | | O.Q. 950°C, T 600°C | 63 | 72 | 13 |
| 5 | | W.Q. 870°C, T 450°C | 109 | 112 | 4 |
| 6 | | W.Q. 870°C, T 500°C | 85 | 91 | 8 |
| 7 | | W.Q. 870°C, T 550°C | 77 | 85 | 9 |
| 8 | | W.Q. 870°C, T 600°C | 69 | 78 | 10 |
| 9 | Chrome–vanadium steel | O.Q. 850°C, T 400°C | 106 | 112 | 6 |
| 10 | 0·55 C, 0·29 Si, 0·68 Mn, | O.Q. 850°C, T 475°C | 103 | 105 | 5 |
| 11 | 0·10 Ni 1·16 Cr, 0·27 V | O.Q. 850°C, T 550°C | 82 | 84 | 7 |
| 12 | | O.Q. 850°C, T 600°C | 76 | 79 | 7 |
| | BS 970 En 100 acid open-hearth | | | | On 4√A |
| 13 | Ingot 1, top, 0·37 C, 1·48 Mn, 0·58 Ni, 0·42 Cr, 0·17 Mo | O.Q. 850°C, T 625°C | 57·4 | 63·9 | 22 |
| 14 | Ingot 1, middle, 0·35 C, 1·48 Mn, 0·58 Ni, 0·42 Cr, 0·18 Mo | | 56·5 | 62·3 | 22 |
| 15 | Ingot 1, bottom, 0·36 C, 1·47 Mn, 0·58 Ni, 0·43 Cr, 0·17 Mo | | 55·7 | 62·1 | 23 |
| 16 | Ingot 15, middle, 0·37 C, 1·50 Mn, 0·58 Ni, 0·42 Cr, 0·18 Mo | | 56·6 | 62·7 | 23 |
| 17 | Ingot 31, middle, 0·38 C, 1·48 Mn, 0·57 Ni, 0·42 Cr, 0·18 Mo | | 56·3 | 62·7 | 22 |
| 18 | BS 970 En 24, 0·37 C, 0·64 Mn, 1·53 Ni, 1·06 Cr, 0·21 Mo | O.Q. 840°C, T 700°C | 50·0 | 56·0 | 24 |
| 19 | BS 970 En 24, 0·37 C, 0·64 Mn, 1·53 Ni, 1·06 Cr, 0·21 Mo, 0·19 lead | | 49·7 | 55·5 | 24 |
| 20 | BS 970 En 24, 0·37 C, 0·64 Mn, 1·53 Ni, 1·06 Cr, 0·21 Mo | O.Q. 840°C, T 600°C | 42·0 | 68·3 | 21 |
| 21 | BS 970 En 24, 0·37 C, 0·64 Mn, 1·53 Ni, 1·06 Cr, 0·21 Mo, 0·19 lead | | 38·0 | 67·5 | 19 |
| 22 | BS 970 En 24, 0·37 C, 0·64 Mn, 1·53 Ni, 1·06 Cr, 0·21 Mo | O.Q. 840°C, T 300°C | 103·7 | 109·3 | 15 |
| 23 | BS 970 En 24, 0·37 C, 0·64 Mn, 1·53 Ni, 1·06 Cr, 0·21 Mo, 0·19 lead | | 104·0 | 108·5 | 13 |
| 24 | BS 970 En 36, 0·11 C, 0·45 Mn, 3·08 Ni, 0·76 Cr | O.Q. 780°C, T 400°C | 49·7 | 54·9 | 24 |
| 25 | BS 970 En 36, 0·11 C, 0·45 Mn, 3·08 Ni, 0·76 Cr, 0·18 lead | | 49·7 | 53·8 | 22 |

*—continued*

STEELS

| Reduction in area % | Brinell hardness number | Izod impact strength ft-lb | Diameter of fatigue specimen in. | Endurance basis N | Rotating bending fatigue strength tons/in² | Source | Ref. |
|---|---|---|---|---|---|---|---|
| 20 | 470 | 9 | 0·20 | $10^7$ | 47·8 | Hankins, | 647 |
| 21 | 415 | 12 | | | 46·0 | Hanson | |
| 25 | 390 | 14 | | | 44·0 | and | |
| 30 | 337 | 17 | | | 35·4 | Ford | |
| 28 | 470 | 11 | | | 50·0 | | |
| 22 | 420 | 13 | | | 47·0 | | |
| 25 | 370 | 15 | | | 41·4 | | |
| 26 | 342 | 19 | | | 39·0 | | |
| 12 | 516 | 9 | | | 47·0 | | |
| 19 | 460 | 13 | | | 43·5 | | |
| 32 | 415 | 20 | | | 43·5 | | |
| 31 | 390 | 30 | | | 42·5 | | |
| 54 | — | — | 0·30 | $3 \times 10^7$ | 35·5 (50% confidence) 34·3 (95% confidence) | Ineson, Clayton-Cave and Taylor | 86 |
| 54 | — | — | | | 34·1 (50% confidence) 32·9 (95% confidence) | | |
| 55 | — | — | | | 33·9 (50% confidence) 32·5 (95% confidence) | | |
| 57 | — | — | | | 33·9 (50% confidence) 32·5 (95% confidence) | | |
| 56 | — | — | | | 34·1 (50% confidence) 33·0 (95% confidence) | | |
| 63 | — | 59 | 0·30 | $10^7$ | 31·7 | Bardgett | 103 |
| 62 | — | 63 | | | 31·0 | | |
| 58 | — | 52 | | | 39·5 | | |
| 56 | — | 42 | | | 37·0 | | |
| 49 | — | 3 | | | 51·2 | | |
| 42 | — | 7 | | | 41·5 | | |
| 64 | — | 56 | | | 28·0 | | |
| 60 | — | 51 | | | 26·0 | | |

TABLE 82
ALLOY STEELS

| No. | Material | Condition | Yield stress | Tensile strength | Elongation per cent |
|---|---|---|---|---|---|
| | | | tons/in² | | on $4\sqrt{A}$ |
| 26 | BS 970 En 36, 0·14 C, 0·48 Mn, 3·16 Ni, 0·88, Cr | O.Q. 780°C, T 400°C | 71·1 | 74·3 | 16 |
| 27 | BS 970 En 36, 0·14 C, 0·48 Mn, 3·16 Ni, 0·88 Cr, 0·19 lead | | 67·3 | 70·7 | 19 |
| 28 | 3% nickel steel, 0·11 C, 0·42 Mn, 3·18 Ni | O.Q. 850°C, T 700°C | — | 34·1 | 40 |
| 29 | 3–3½% nickel steel, 0·34 C, 0·57 Mn, 3·25 Ni | O.Q. 850°C, T 610°C | 38·0 | 46·8 | 26 |
| 30 | Cr–V steel, 0·41 C, 0·71 Mn, 1·27 Cr, 0·28 V | O.Q. 850°C, T 700°C | 44·1 | 48·7 | 26 |
| 31 | 3½% nickel chromium, 0·3 C, 0·58 Mn, 3·62 Ni, 0·85 Cr (normal impact) | O.Q. 830°C, T 620°C | 49·2 | 58·0 | 25 |
| 32 | 3½% nickel chromium, 0·3 C, 0·58 Mn 3·62 Ni, 0·85 Cr (low impact) | O.Q. 830°C, T 1¾ hr at 620°C and cooled to 100°C in 42 hr | 48·9 | 58·1 | 24 |
| 33 | Ni, Cr, Mo steel, 0·24 C, 0·57 Mn, 3·06 Ni, 1·29 Cr, 0·54 Mo, 0·25 V | O.Q. 850°C, T 640°C | 61·3 | 64·8 | 23 |
| 34 | Ni, Cr, Mo steel, 0·24 C, 0·57 Mn, 3·10 Ni, 1·33 Cr, 0·41 Mo, 0·25 V | O.Q. 850°C, T 600°C | — | 80·5 | 20 |
| 35 | Ni, Cr, steel, 0·28 C, 0·48 Mn, 4·42 Ni, 1·36 Cr | A.C. 820°C, T 200°C | — | 108 | 16 |
| | | | 0·1% proof stress tons/in² | | On 1 in. |
| 36 | Basic electric arc, 0·31 C, 0·62 Mn, 3·76 Ni, 0·91 Cr, 0·24 Mo | O.Q. 830°C, T 650°C longitudinal | 42·9 | 62·6 | 26 |
| 37 | | O.Q. 830°C, T 650°C transverse | 46·6 | 62·6 | 21 |
| 38 | | A.C. 830°C, T 200°C longitudinal | 75·8 | 113·9 | 16 |
| 39 | | A.C. 830°C, T 200°C transverse | 73·9 | 119·0 | 11 |
| 40 | | A.C. 830°C, T 200°C and 250°C longitudinal | 81·1 | 108·1 | 15 |
| 41 | Basic electric arc, 1·00 C, 0·40 Mn, 1·50 Cr, 0·09 Mo | O.Q. 850°C, T 185°C | | | |
| 42 | | O.Q. 850°C, T 185°C | | | |
| 43 | Acid high frequency, 0·94 C, 0·46 Mn, 1·40 Cr | O.Q. 850°C, T 250°C | | | |
| 44 | Acid high frequency, 0·87 C, 0·44 Mn, 1·39 Cr, 2·11 Co | O.Q. 850°C, T 250°C | | | |
| 45 | Acid open hearth, 0·32 C, 0·65 Mn, 3·06 Ni, 0·84 Cr, 0·04 Mo | O.Q. 830°C, T 620°C longitudinal | 50·0 | 61·3 | (12) |

—*continued*
—*continued*

| Reduction in area % | Brinell hardness number | Izod impact strength ft-lb | Diameter of fatigue specimen in. | Endurance basis N | Rotating bending fatigue strength tons/in$^2$ | Source | Ref. |
|---|---|---|---|---|---|---|---|
| 60 | — | 17 | | | 35·5 | Bardgett | 103 |
| 56 | — | 16 | | | 30·0 | | |
| 72 | 163 | 100 | 0·30 | 10$^7$ | 20·3 | Gough, Pollard and Clenshaw | 56 |
| 67 | 237 | 86 | | | 26·5 | | |
| 66 | 229 | 96 | | | 26·5 | | |
| 65 | 282 | 76 | | | 33·7 | | |
| 60 | 278 | 5½ | | | 31·9 | | |
| 67 | 325 | 90 | | | 37·5 | | |
| 60 | 394 | 55 | | 3 × 10$^7$ | 39 | | |
| 52 | 479 | 24 | | 2 × 10$^7$ | 45 | | |
| | Brinell or diamond pyramid number | | | | | | |
| 64 | 293 (B) | | 0·275 | 3 × 10$^7$ | 32·5 | Frith | 92 |
| 60 | | | | 3 × 10$^7$ | 29·0 | | |
| 59 | 572 (D.P.N.) | | | 10$^8$ | 38·0 | | |
| 32 | | | | 10$^8$ | 30·0 | | |
| 47 | 523 (D.P.N.) | | | 10$^8$ | 40·0 | | |
| | 819 (D.P.N.) | | | 10$^8$ | 37·5 | | |
| | 748 (D.P.N.) | | | 10$^8$ | 38 | | |
| | 760 (D.P.N.) | | | 10$^8$ | 45·0 | | |
| | 751 (D.P.N.) | | | 10$^8$ | 39·5 | | |
| 47 | 293 (B) | | | 2 × 10$^7$ | 33·0 | | |

TABLE 82

ALLOY STEELS

| No. | Material | Condition | 0·1% proof stress | Tensile strength | Elongation per cent on 1 in. |
|-----|----------|-----------|-------------------|------------------|------------------------------|
| | | | tons/in² | | |
| 46 | | O.Q. 830°C, T 620°C transverse | 46·3 | 57·1 | 21 |
| 47 | Acid open hearth, 0·32 C, 0·54 Mn, 3·56 Ni, 0·94 Cr, 0·25 Mo | O.Q. 830°C, T 655°C longitudinal | 54·2 | 61·0 | 17 |
| 48 | | O.Q. 830°C, T 655°C transverse | 51·7 | 61·1 | 13 |
| 49 | Acid open hearth, 0·32 C, 0·56 Mn, 3·82 Ni, 1·31 Cr, 0·32 Mo | O.Q. 820°C, T 200°C longitudinal | 73·0 | 113·0 | 14 |
| 50 | | O.Q. 820°C, T 200°C transverse | 83·1 | 111·8 | 4 |
| 51 | Acid open hearth, 0·90 C, 1·02 Mn, 0·91 Cr | O.Q. 850°C, T 185°C longitudinal | | | |
| 52 | Acid open hearth, 0·95 C, 0·36 Mn, 1·55 Cr | O.Q. 850°C, T 185°C | | | |
| 53 | Neutral open hearth, 0·3 C, 0·63 Mn, 2·37 Ni, 0·84 Cr, 0·45 Mo | O.Q. 830°C, T 575°C longitudinal | 72·7 | 79·0 | 15 |
| 54 | | O.Q. 830°C, T 575°C transverse | 74·9 | 82·0 | 11 |
| 55 | Neutral open hearth, 1·00 C, 0·41 Mn, 0·30 Ni, 1·29 Cr | O.Q. 850°C, T 185°C | | | |
| 56 | Basic open hearth, 0·4 C, 0·65 Mn, 2·62 Ni 0·81 Cr, 0·55 Mo | O.Q. 830°C, T 590°C longitudinal | 69·8 | 79·1 | 21 |
| 57 | | O.Q. 830°C, T 590°C transverse | 68·7 | 74·5 | 7 |
| 58 | | A.C. 830°C, T 200°C and 250°C longitudinal | 92·6 | 120·7 | 9 |
| 59 | | A.C. 830°C, T 200°C and 250°C transverse | 88·1 | 120·0 | 3 |
| 60 | BS 970 En 40 (basic electric arc) 0·24 C, 0·55 Mn, 3·18 Cr, 0·53 Mo | O.Q. 900°C, T 595°C | 50·1 | 61·3 | — |
| 61 | | O.Q. 900°C, T 595°C nitrided 72 hr at 485–490°C | | | |
| 62 | Cr–Mo–W (acid high frequency), 0·5 C, 0·61 Mn, 8·28 Cr, 3·68 Mo, 4·04 W, 0·22 Cu | O.Q. 1100°C, T 550°C | | | |
| 63 | Cr–Mo (acid high frequency), 1·72 C, 0·21 Mn, 13·86 Cr, 0·49 Mo | O.Q. 1050°C, T 500°C | | | |
| 64 | Cr–Co–Mo (basic high frequency), 1·41 C, 0·39 Mn, 13·93 Cr, 0·41 Mo, 3·27 Co | O.Q. 1050°C, T 500°C | | | |
| 65 | W–Cr–V (acid high frequency), 0·67 C, 0·26 Mn, 3·57 Cr, 0·25 Mo, 13·61 W, 0·32 V | A.C. 1280°C, T 550°C | | | |

—*continued*

—*continued*

| Reduction in area % | Brinell or diamond pyramid number | Izod impact strength ft-lb | Diameter of fatigue specimen in. | Endurance basis N | Rotating bending fatigue strength ton/in² | Source | Ref. |
|---|---|---|---|---|---|---|---|
| 47 | | | | $4 \times 10^7$ | 24·7 | Frith | 92 |
| 72 | 293 (B) | | | $5 \times 10^7$ | 33·5 | | |
| 42 | | | | $5 \times 10^7$ | 25·5 | | |
| 38 | 560 (D.P.N.) | | | $10^8$ | 45·5 | | |
| nil | | | | $10^8$ | 29 | | |
| | 808 (D.P.N.) | | | $10^8$ | 47·0 | | |
| | 866 (D.P.N.) | | | $10^8$ | 43·5 | | |
| 68 | 375 (B) | | | $4 \times 10^7$ | 41·2 | | |
| 26 | | | | $4 \times 10^7$ | 29·2 | | |
| | 831 (D.P.N.) | | | $10^8$ | 51·0 | | |
| 67 | 387 (B) | | | $4 \times 10^7$ | 42·0 | | |
| 23 | | | | $4 \times 10^7$ | 29·0 | | |
| 45 | 590 (D.P.N.) | | | $10^8$ | 47·0 | | |
| 9 | | | | $10^8$ | 27·5 | | |
| 74 | | | 0·3 | $2 \times 10^7$ | 33·7 44·0 | Frith | 93 |
| | 766 (D.P.N.) | | | $10^8$ | 40 | | |
| | 821 (D.P.N.) | | | $10^8$ | 40 | | |
| | 841 (D.P.N.) | | | $10^8$ | 39 | | |
| | 854 (D.P.N.) | | | $10^8$ | 41 | | |

TABLE 82

ALLOY STEELS

| No. | Material | Condition | Yield stress | Tensile strength | |
|---|---|---|---|---|---|
| | | | tons/in² | | |
| 66 | W–Cr–V (acid high frequency), 0·68 C, 0·19 Mn, 4·90 Cr, 0·19 Mo, 18·46 W, 0·88 V | A.C. 1280–1300°C, T 560°C | | | |
| 67 | W–Cr–V (basic high frequency), 0·68 C, 0·18 Mn, 4·77 Cr, 0·15 Mo, 18·32 W, 0·88 V | A.C. 1280–1300°C, T 560°C | | | |
| 68 | Cr–V–W, 0·75 C, 0·26 Mn, 4·34 Cr, 0·46 Mo, 18·5 W, 0·33 Co, 1·29 V | A.C. 725–730°C | | | |
| 69 | | A.C. 650–660°C, A.C. 670°C | | | |
| 70 | | A.C. 610°C (twice) A.C. 630°C | | | |
| 71 | En 56A 0·10 C, 0·50 Mn, stainless iron type F.I. 13·0 Cr | O.Q. 1000°C, T 750°C | 24·5 | 37·2 | |
| 72 | En 56C 0·22 C, 0·30 Mn, stainless steel type F.G. 13·0 Cr | O.Q. 960°C, T 700°C | 41·3 | 49·1 | |
| 73 | En 56CM free cutting 0·20 C, 1·3 Mn, 0·23 S, stainless steel 13·0 Cr, 0·28 Mo | O.Q. 1000°C, T 700°C | 28·9 | 44·5 | |
| 74 | En 57, S 80, 0·16 C, 0·50 Mn, 16·5 Cr, 2·5 Ni | O.Q. 975°C, T 650°C | 45 | 57 | |
| 75 | F.V. 520 (B) 0·06 C, 0·80 Mn, 15·0 Cr, 5·5 Ni, 1·5 Mo, 1·5 Cu, 0·3 Nb | Hardened and tempered | 54 | 63 | |
| 76 | | Precipitation hardened | 65 | 76 | |
| 77 | En 58A Staybright–FST. 0·08 C, 0·80 Mn, 18·0 Cr, 8·75 Ni | Softened | 18 | 40 | |
| 78 | En 58B Staybright–FDP 0·08 C, 0·80 Mn, 18·0 Cr, 9·0 Ni, 0·50 Ti | Softened | 18 | 42 | |
| 79 | En 58F Staybright–FCB 0·08 C, 0·80 Mn, 18·0 Cr, 9·0 Ni, 0·85 Nb | Softened | 17·2 | 40·8 | |
| 80 | En 58J Staybright–FMB 0·07 C, 1·5 Mn, 17·75 Cr, 10·0 Ni, 2·75 Mo | Softened | 18 | 40 | |

—continued

—continued

| Reduction in area % | Brinell hardness number | Izod impact strength ft-lb | Diameter of fatigue specimen in. | Endurance basis N | Rotating bending fatigue strength tons/in$^2$ | Source | Ref. |
|---|---|---|---|---|---|---|---|
| | 760 (D.P.N.) | | | $10^8$ | 44·5 | Frith | 93 |
| | 740 (D.P.N.) | | | $10^8$ | 44·0 | | |
| | 400–415 (D.P.N.) | | 0·3 | $2 \times 10^7$ | 42·6 | Russell and Walker | 99 |
| | 595–615 (D.P.N.) | | | | 47·0 | | |
| | 790–815 (D.P.N.) | | | | 50·8 | | |
| 75 | 172 | 98 | | $10^7$ | 15·5 | Firth-Vickers Stainless Steel Ltd, Sheffield | |
| 65 | 223 | 69 | | | 22 | | |
| 54 | 220 | 36 | | | 24·7 | | |
| 55 | 270 | 25 | | | 24 | | |
| 60 | 310 | 75 | | | 36 | | |
| 50 | 380 | 25 | | | 38 | | |
| 50 | 170 | 110 | | | 17 | | |
| 50 | 180 | 80 | | | 17·5 | | |
| 65 | 175 | 80 | | | 19·5 | | |
| 50 | 180 | 80 | | | 17·5 | | |

TABLE 82

CAST

| No. | Material* | Cast diameter in. | Tensile strength tons/in² |
|---|---|---|---|
| 1 | M 305 flake–pearlitic, 2·78 C, 1·75 Si, 0·80 Mn | 0·875 | 18·3 |
| 2 | A flake–pearlitic, 3·13 C, 2·31 Si, 0·69 Mn, 0·67 P, 0·12 Ni, 0·12 Cr | 1·2 | 18·3 |
| 3 | V 216 flake–pearlitic, 2·99 C, 2·09 Si, 0·60 Mn | 0·875 | 18·8 |
| 4 | B flake–pearlitic, 3·02 C, 1·57 Si, 0·87 Mn, 0·17 P, 0·16 Ni, 0·11 Cu, 0·10 Cr, 0·57 Mo | 1·2 | 21·7 |
| 5 | M 309 flake–pearlitic, 2·56 C, 1·63 Si, 0·76 Mn | 0·875 | 23·6 |
| 6 | M 540 flake–acicular, 3·08 C, 2·00 Si, 0·68 Mn, 2·21 Ni, 0·71 Mo | 0·875 | 28·6 |
| 7 | M 528 flake–acicular, 3·09 C, 2·19 Si, 0·64 Mn, 1·58 Ni, 0·59 Mo | 0·875 | 29·1 |
| 8 | V 531 flake–acicular, 2·93 C, 2·11 Si, 0·60 Mn, 1·25 Ni, 0·65 Mo | 0·875 | 29·4 |
| 9 | V 636 flake–acicular, A. 320°C, 2·91 C, 2·16 Si, 0·64 Mn, 1·92 Ni, 1·18 Mo | 0·875 | 33·9 |
| 10 | NOD 67 nodular (cerium treated) 3·85 C, 2·69 Si, 0·49 Mn, 0·029 Ce | 0·875 | 24·1 |
| 11 | V 980 nodular (cerium treated) 3·86 C, 2·49 Si, 0·85 Mn, 0·020 Ce | 0·875 | 25·4 |
| 12 | W 16 nodular (cerium treated) 3·59 C, 2·79 Si, 0·85 Mn, 0·038 Ce | 0·875 | 31·0 |
| 13 | V 895 nodular (cerium treated) 3·67 C, 3·01 Si, 0·88 Mn, 0·050 Ce | 0·875 | 35·2 |
| 14 | W 3 nodular (cerium treated) 3·60 C, 2·33 Si, 0·84 Mn, 2·20 Cu, 0·047 Ce | 0·875 | 38·2 |
| 15 | W 105 nodular (cerium treated) 3·68 C, 2·13 Si, 0·74 Mn, 2·38 Cu, 0·052 Ce | 0·875 | 40·9 |
| 16 | NOD 517 as cast, nodular (magnesium treated) ⎤ 3·01 C, 1·98 Si, 0·47 Mn, 1·93 Ni, 0·089 Mg | 3·0 | 42·7 |
| 17 | NOD 517 annealed | 3·0 | 28·0 |
| 18 | NOD 518 as cast, nodular (magnesium treated) ⎤ 3·00 C, 2·01 Si, 0·42 Mn, 1·83 Ni, 0·096 Mg | 3·0 | 46·0 |
| 19 | NOD 518 annealed | 3·0 | 30·2 |

* Total carbon values are quoted for all materials.

*—continued*

RON

| Elongation on 2 in. % | Brinell hardness number | Izod impact strength ft-lb | Diameter of fatigue specimen in. | Rotating bending fatigue limit tons/in² | Source | Ref. |
|---|---|---|---|---|---|---|
| | | Modified Izod BS 1349 Unnotched 0·798 in. dia. | | | | |
| | 244 | — | 0·331 | 11·5 | Grant | 648 |
| | 244 | 10 | | 8·5 | | |
| | 211 | — | | 8·5 | | |
| | 259 | 17–19 | | 9·5 | | |
| | 245 | — | | 10·5 | | |
| | 343 | 19–24 | | 11·0 | | |
| | 312 | 18–28 | | 11·0 | | |
| | 283 | — | | 11·5 | | |
| | 331 | 28–38 | | 11·5 | | |
| | 198 | 22–23 | | 12·0 | | |
| | 204 | 75–110 | | 15·0 | | |
| | 224 | — | | 17·5 | | |
| | 249 | 109–>120 | | 16·0 | | |
| | 290 | 106–>120 | 0·301 | 18·5 | | |
| | 305 | — | | 20·0 | | |
| | | BS 131 Notched 0·45 in. dia. | | | | |
| 3 | 260 | 1 | | 16·0 | | |
| 10 | 155 | 9 | | 13·0 | | |
| 3 | 269 | 1 | | 18·0 | | |
| 18 | 158 | 11 | | 13·0 | | |

TABLE 8

WROUGH

| No. | Material | Specification BS 1470–1477 | Form | Condition |
|---|---|---|---|---|
| 1 | 2 S, 99¼ Al | 1 C | 1 in. extrusion | M |
| 2 | 26 S, 4¼ Cu, ¾ Si, ¾ Mn, ½ Mg | H 15 | 1 in. extrusion | W |
| 3 | | | | WP |
| 4 | | | Rolled bar 1⅛ in. square | W |
| 5 | | | | WP |
| 6 | | | Forging—airscrew blade | W |
| 7 | | | | WP |
| 8 | 50 S, ⅝ Mg, ½ Si | H 9 | 1 in. extrusion | W |
| 9 | | | | WP |
| 10 | 51 S, 1 Si, ⅝ Mg | H 10 | 1 in. extrusion | W |
| 11 | | | | WP |
| 12 | 54 S, 3½ Mg, ⅓ Mn | N 5 | 1 in. extrusion | M |
| 13 | B 54 S, 4¼ Mg, ¾ Mn | NP 5/6 | ⅝ in. plate | M |
| 14 | A 56 S, 5 Mg, ⅓ Mn | N 6 | 1 in. extrusion | M |
| 15 | M 57 S, 2 Mg, ¼ Mn | N 4 | 1 in. extrusion | M |
| 16 | 58 S, 7 Mg, ⅓ Mn | N 7 | 1 in. extrusion | M |
| 17 | 62 S, 1½ Cu, ¾ Mn, 1 Si, 1 Mg | H 11 | 1 in. extrusion | W |
| 18 | | | | WP |
| 19 | | | Forging 2in. slab | W |
| 20 | | | | WP |
| 21 | 65 S, 1 Mg, ½ Si, ¼ Cu, ¼ Cr | | 1 in. extrusion | W |
| 22 | | | | WP |
| 23 | M 75 S, 6 Zn, 2½ Mg, 1⅓ Cu, ¼ Mn, ⅛ Cr | (DTD 683) (DTD 687) | 5 in. extrusion | WP |
| 24 | Hiduminium 55, 2·4 Cu, 1·0 Mg, 1·0 Si, 1·0 Fe, 0·7 Ni, 0·3 Mn | | Extrusion | W |
| 25 | | | | WP |
| 26 | RR 56, 2·1 Cu, 0·9 Mg, 0·9 Si, 0·9 Fe, 1·1 Ni 0·1 Ti | HF 12 | Forged bar | WP |
| 27 | RR 57, 6·0 Cu, 0·25 Mn, 0·1 Ti | | Forged bar | WP |
| 28 | RR 58, 2·5 Cu, 1·5 Mg, 1·0 Fe, 1·2 Ni, 0·1 Ti | | Forged bar | WP (special) |
| 29 | RR 59, 2·2 Cu, 1·5 Mg, 0·85 Si, 1·0 Fe, 1·2 Ni, 0·1 Ti | HF 18 | Forged bar | WP |
| 30 | | | Forged bar | O |
| 31 | RR 77, 0·4 Cu, 2·8 Mg, 0·5 Mn, 5·5 Zn | | Forged bar | WP |
| 32 | | | Extrusion | WP |

*O = annealed, M = as manufactured, W = solution treated, WP = solution treated and

*—continued*

ALUMINIUM ALLOYS

(See Table 7, page 76 for data on aluminium alloy sheet.)

| Typical tensile properties | | | Rotating bending fatigue strength tons/in² for endurance of: | | | | Source | Ref. |
|---|---|---|---|---|---|---|---|---|
| 0.1% proof stress tons/in² | Tensile strength | Elongation per cent on 2 in | $10^5$ | $10^6$ | $10^7$ | $10^8$ | | |
| 2 | 5½ | 38 | 4.0 | 3.2 | 3.0 | | Aluminium Laboratories Ltd, Banbury. (Fatigue results for $\frac{5}{16}$ in. diameter specimens, tested at 3000 c/min.) | 136 |
| 20 | 30 | 18 | 17.7 | 14.3 | 12.2 | 10.5 | | |
| 30 | 33 | 10 | 17.8 | 15.0 | 13.0 | 11.0 | | |
| | | | 18.0 | 15.3 | 12.8 | 10.7 | | |
| | | | 18.5 | 15.2 | 12.8 | 11.0 | | |
| 14½ | 25½ | 23 | 16.2 | 13.0 | 11.0 | 9.3 | | |
| 28 | 31 | 11½ | 19.0 | 15.0 | 11.7 | 9.3 | | |
| 7 | 11 | 20 | 9.0 | 7.3 | 6.2 | 5.4 | | |
| 12 | 16 | 18 | 10.0 | 7.9 | 6.5 | 5.7 | | |
| 9 | 15 | 20 | 10.7 | 8.7 | 7.0 | 5.8 | | |
| 18 | 20 | 13 | 12.2 | 9.5 | 7.7 | 6.2 | | |
| 6½ | 14½ | 25 | 11.7 | 9.7 | 9.1 | 8.9 | | |
| 13 | 19½ | 20 | 12.0 | 9.7 | 9.0 | 8.5 | | |
| 9 | 18½ | 27 | 12.5 | 9.5 | 9.5 | — | | |
| 6 | 13 | 20 | — | 9.0 | 7.8 | 7.6 | | |
| 12½ | 22 | 35 | 14.5 | 11.5 | 10.8 | 10.7 | | |
| 15 | 24 | 17 | 13.8 | 11.2 | 9.5 | 8.5 | | |
| 26 | 28 | 12 | 16.0 | 12.0 | 10.0 | 8.5 | | |
| 11½ | 21 | 24 | 13.0 | 10.0 | 8.5 | 6.8 | | |
| 21½ | 27 | 11½ | 15.0 | 11.2 | 8.7 | | | |
| 9 | 15 | 20 | 12.0 | 10.2 | 8.9 | 8.0 | | |
| 17 | 20 | 13 | 13.2 | 11.2 | 9.5 | 8.3 | | |
| 36 | 39 | 11 | 16.5 | 13.0 | 10.7 | 9.7 | | |
| | | on 4√A | | | | | | |
| 10 | 20 | 15 | | 11.5 | 9.0 | 8.0 | High Duty Alloys Ltd, Slough, Bucks. | |
| 20 | 26 | 8 | | 10.8 | 8.4 | 7.7 | | |
| 22 | 28 | 12 | | 13.5 | 10.5 | 8.8 | | |
| 15 | 25 | 8 | | 9.6 | 7.8 | 7.0 | | |
| 17 | 27 | 12 | | 12.5 | 10.0 | 9.3 | | |
| 21 | 28 | 13 | | 13.7 | 10.8 | 9.2 | | |
| 4 | 11 | 20 | | 6.4 | 5.6 | 5.3 | | |
| 28 | 33 | 12 | | 12.5 | 10.9 | 10.0 | | |
| 34 | 38 | 8 | | 13.4 | 11.5 | 11.0 | | |

precipitation hardened, P = precipitation hardened.

z

TABLE 82

CAST ALUMINIUM

| No. | Material | Specification BS 1490 | Form |
|---|---|---|---|
| 1 | Hiduminium 40, 0·5 Mg, 5·5 Si | LM 8 | Sand cast |
| 2 | | | |
| 3 | | | |
| 4 | | | Chill cast |
| 5 | | | |
| 6 | | | |
| 7 | RR 50, 1·0 Cu, 0·1 Mg, 2·5 Si, 1·0 Fe, 0·9 Ni, 0·2 Ti | LM 23 | Sand cast |
| 8 | | | Chill cast |
| 9 | RR 53 B, 1·5 Cu, 0·8 Mg, 0·75 Si, 1·0 Fe, 1·0 Ni, 0·2 Ti | LM 15 | Sand cast |
| 10 | Hiduminium 90, 10·5 Mg | LM 10 | Sand cast |
| 11 | RR 250, 5·0 Cu, 0·25 Mn, 1·0 Ni, 0·2 Ti, 0·25 Co, 0·25 Sb | | Sand cast |
| 12 | Y alloy, 4·2 Cu, 1·5 Mg, 2·0 Ni | LM 14 | Sand cast |
| 13 | | | Chill cast |

* For abbreviations see pages 374–375.
† Specified values.

*—continued*

ALLOYS*

| Condition | Typical tensile properties | | | Rotating bending fatigue strength tons/in², for endurance of: | | | Source |
|---|---|---|---|---|---|---|---|
| | 0·1% proof stress tons/in² | Tensile strength | Elongation per cent on 4√A | $10^6$ | $10^7$ | $10^8$ | |
| M | | 8·0† | 2† | 5·0 | 3·9 | 3·7 | High Duty |
| W | | 10·5† | 2·5† | 5·5 | 3·9 | 3·5 | Alloys Ltd, |
| WP | | 15·0† | | 5·6 | 4·1 | 3·6 | Slough, |
| M | | 10·5† | 3† | 6·0 | 5·5 | 5·3 | Bucks. |
| W | | 15·0† | 5† | 6·6 | 5·7 | 5·4 | |
| WP | | 18·0† | 2† | 6·7 | 5·7 | 5·4 | |
| P | 7·0 | 11·0 | 2 | 5·6 | 4·7 | 4·6 | |
| P | 8·0 | 13·0 | 3 | 6·8 | 5·6 | 5·5 | |
| WP | 17·0 | 18·5 | 1 | 5·8 | 5·0 | 4·9 | |
| W | 10·0 | 20·0 | 15 | 4·6 | 4·1 | 4·0 | |
| WP | 10·0 | 16·0 | 2 | 5·1 | 4·1 | 4·0 | |
| WP | 14·0 | 15·0 | 1 | | 5·5 | 4 | |
| WP | 15·0 | 19·0 | 2 | | 7 | 6 | |

TABLE 82

COPPER

| No. | Material | Condition | Grain Size mm |
|---|---|---|---|
| 1 | Electrolytic copper, 99·93 Cu | Drawn 30% | 0·040 |
| 2 | Cartridge brass, 69·37 Cu, 30·61 Zn | Drawn 21% | 0·120 |
| 3 | Free cutting brass, 61·78 Cu, 34·81 Zn, 3·31 Pb | Drawn 20% | 0·040 |
| 4 | Naval brass, 59·88 Cu, 39·31 Zn, 0·68 Sn | Drawn 24% | Fine |
| 5 | Naval brass, 59·74 Cu, 39·39 Zn, 0·71 Sn | Drawn 24% | Coarse |
| 6 | 1½% Silicon bronze, 97·18 Cu, 1·35 Zn, 1·43 Si | A | 0·025 |
| 7 | 1½% Silicon bronze, 97·12 Cu, 1·39 Zn, 1·46 Si | Drawn 21% | 0·020 |
| 8 | 3% Silicon bronze, 95·88 Cu, 1·05 Zn, 3·01 Si | Drawn 10% | 0·020 |
| 9 | 3% Silicon bronze, 95·88 Cu, 1·05 Zn, 3·01 Si | Drawn 44% | 0·040 |
| 10 | Aluminium bronze, 87·84 Cu, 9·65 Al, 1·95 Fe, 0·52 Te | Drawn 10% | — |
| 11 | Cupro nickel, 68·04 Cu, 30·67 Ni, 0·49 Fe, 0·53 Mn | Drawn 33% | 0·025 |
| 12 | Phosphor bronze 316, 88·35 Cu, 9·31 Sn, 1·36 Fe, 0·78 Mn, 0·20 P | Drawn 36% | 0·020 |
| 13 | Phosphor bronze Grade A, 95·27 Cu, 4·32 Sn, 0·38 P | A. 550°C | 0·025 |
| 14 | Phosphor bronze Grade A, 95·27 Cu, 4·32 Sn, 0·38 P | Drawn 15% | 0·070 |
| 15 | Phosphor bronze Grade A, 95·27 Cu, 4·32 Sn, 0·38 P | Drawn 30% | 0·090 |
| 16 | Phosphor bronze Grade A, 95·27 Cu, 4·32 Sn, 0·38 P | Drawn 50% | 0·065 |

NICKEL

| No. | Material | Condition | |
|---|---|---|---|
| 1 | Monel, 63 min Ni, 28–34 Cu, 2·5 Max Fe, 2·0 Max Mn | Hot-rolled A | |
| 2 | | Hot-rolled, as rolled | |
| 3 | | Cold drawn | |
| 4 | Inconel, 72 min Ni, 14–17 Cr, 6·10 Fe, 1·0 Max Mn | A | |
| 5 | | Hot-rolled | |
| 6 | | Cold drawn | |
| 7 | | Cold drawn, stress equalized, A. 275°C | |

TIN

| No. | Material | Condition | Grain size mm | 0·1% proof stress | Tensile strength |
|---|---|---|---|---|---|
| | | | | tons/in² | |
| 1 | Chill cast whitemetal bearing alloys: Adastral "A", 4·85–5·33 Sb, 2·88–3·12 Cu | Chill cast | | 2·4 | 4·8–5·0 |
| 2 | Adastral "F", 6·89 Sb, 3·86 Cu | Chill cast | | 2·9 | 5·8 |

*—continued*

ALLOYS

(See Tables 9 and 10, pages 81 and 82 for data on copper alloy sheet and wire.)

| 0·2% proof stress | Tensile strength | Elongation on 2 in. | Rotating bending fatigue strength tons/in², for endurance of: | | | | | Source | Ref. |
|---|---|---|---|---|---|---|---|---|---|
| tons/in² | | | $10^5$ | $10^6$ | $10^7$ | $10^8$ | $10^9$ | | |
| 17·9 | 19·6 | 19 | | 11·2 | 8·7 | 7·3 | | Burghoff and | 150 |
| 20·3 | 25·4 | 42 | | 14·0 | 9·4 | 6·7 | | Blank (on | |
| 19·0 | 24·5 | 28 | | 13·6 | 10·5 | 8·9 | | 0·3 in. dia- | |
| 32·3 | 38·8 | 14 | | 21·4 | 16·2 | 14·8 | | meter spec- | |
| 30·7 | 38·9 | 9 | | 13·0 | 9·6 | 9·4 | | mens at | |
| 4·8 | 18·1 | 57 | | 9·1 | 7·6 | 6·7 | | 8000c/min.) | |
| 21·4 | 24·1 | 29 | | 14·7 | 12·5 | 12·5 | | | |
| 18·9 | 28·0 | 49 | | 13·2 | 11·1 | 10·7 | | | |
| 35·7 | 45·7 | 14 | | 20·2 | 16·1 | 15·4 | | | |
| 23·6 | 41·4 | 19 | | 20·6 | 14·7 | 12·7 | | | |
| | | | | | | | | | |
| 34·3 | 36·4 | 12 | | 19·1 | 16·3 | 15·4 | | | |
| 49·5 | 51·5 | 7 | 31·5 | 25·4 | 20·1 | 14·8 | | Anderson, | 149 |
| | | | | | | | | Swan and | |
| 9·0 | 22·6 | | 17·4 | 14·5 | 13·4 | 13·0 | 13·0 | Palmer (on | |
| 22·2 | 25·3 | | 19·3 | 15·2 | 13·2 | 12·5 | 12·3 | 0·3 in. dia- | |
| 27·5 | 31·2 | | 22·8 | 16·3 | 13·8 | 13·4 | 12·7 | meter speci- | |
| 37·5 | 43·1 | | 25·0 | 19·2 | 15·6 | 14·7 | 14·3 | mens at | |
| | | | | | | | | 3500c/min.) | |

ALLOYS (See Tables 11 and 12, pages 84 and 87 for data on nickel alloy sheet and wire.)

| 0·2% proof stress | Tensile strength | Elongation on 2 in. | Rotating bending fatigue strength tons/in², for endurance of: | | | | | Source | Ref. |
|---|---|---|---|---|---|---|---|---|---|
| tons/in² | | | $10^5$ | $10^6$ | $10^7$ | $10^8$ | $10^9$ | | |
| | 34 | | | | | 13 | | Henry Wiggin | |
| | | | | | | | | & Co. Ltd, | |
| | 39–45 | | | | | 18–23 | | Birming- | |
| | 44–52 | | | | | 18–21 | | ham | |
| | 39–43 | | | | | 13–16 | | | |
| | 41–44 | | | | | 17–21 | | | |
| | 56–68 | | | | | 18–25 | | | |
| | 58–73 | | | | | 20–27 | | | |

ALLOYS

| Elongation per cent on 2 in. | Rotating bending fatigue strength tons/in², for endurance of: | | | | | Source | Ref. |
|---|---|---|---|---|---|---|---|
| | $10^5$ | $10^6$ | $10^7$ | $10^8$ | $10^9$ | | |
| 13·5–14 | | | | 1·6 | | J. Stone & Co, | |
| 10 | | | | 2·0 | | Charlton, London | |

For titanium alloys see Table 84.

TABLE 82

WROUGHT MAGNESIUM

| No. | Material | Specification |
|---|---|---|
| 1 | ZW 3, 3·0 Zn, 0·6 Zr | |
| 2 | | DTD 622 A |
| 3 | ZW 1, 1·3 Zn, 0·6 Zr | DTD 5011 |
| 4 | ZW 6, 5·5 Zn, 0·6 Zr | DTD 5031 |
| 5 | ZTY, 0·5 Zn, 0·6 Zr, 0·75 Th | |
| 6 | AM 503, 1·5 Mn | DTD 142 A, BS 1355 |
| 7 | AZM, 6·0 Al, 1·0 Zn, 0·3 Mn | DTD 259 A, BS 1354 |
| 8 | | DTD 88 C, BS 1351 |
| 9 | AZ 855, 8·0 Al, 0·4 Zn, 0·3 Mn | DTD 88 C, BS 1351 |
| | | CAST MAGNESIUM |
| 1 | ZRE 1, 2·2 Zn, 0·6 Zr, 2·7 rare earth metals | DTD 708 MAG 6–MorP |
| 2 | MTZ, 0·7 Zr, 3·0 Th | |
| 3 | A 8, 8·0 Al, 0·5 Zn, 0·3 Mn | BS 2970 MAG 1–M |
| 4 | AZ 91, 9·5 Al, 0·5 Zn, 0·3 Mn | BS 2970 MAG 3–M |
| 5 | | BS 2970 MAG 3–W |
| 6 | | BS 2970 MAG 3–WP |
| 7 | C, 7·5–9·5 Al, 0·3–1·5 Zn, 0·15 min Mn | BS 2970 MAG 7–M |
| 8 | | BS 2970 MAG 7–W |
| 9 | | BS 2970 MAG 7–WP |
| 10 | MCZ, 0·71 Zr, 2·84 rare earth metals | DTD 728 |
| 11 | RZ5, 4·64 Zn, 0·7 Zr, 1·30 rare earth metals | BS 2970 MAG 5–P |
| 12 | MSR–A, 0·6 Zr, 2·50 Ag, 1·69 rare earth metals | DTD 5025 |
| 13 | MSR–B, 0·6 Zr, 2·55–2·61 Ag, 2·63–2·68 rare earth metals | DTD 5035 |

\* Minimum values quoted for the specified or proposed specified minima

| Tensile strength tons/in² | | Type of fatigue stress | Diameter of fatigue specimens in. | Endurance basis | temp |
|---|---|---|---|---|---|
| −60°C | −186°C | | | | |
| 32 | 51 | Ax | 0·35 | $10^7$ | |
| 64 | 84 | | | | |
| −78°C | −188°C | | | | |
| 32·8 | 51·1 | Ax | 0·24–0·31 | $10^6$ | |
| 47·1 | 60·4 | | | | |
| 57·3 | 64·7 | | | | |
| 57·6 | 77·0 | | 0·20–0·24 | | |
| 68·9 | 86·4 | | | | |
| 76·7 | 91·6 | | | | |
| −78°C | −196°C | | | | |
| 59 | 75 | B | 0·3 | $10^6$ | |
| 55 | 73 | | | | |
| 70 | 88 | | | | |
| 47 | 67 | | | | |
| 65 | 86 | | | | |
| 108 | 134 | | | | |
| 89 | 108 | | | | |
| | 126 | B | 0·3 | $10^6$ | |
| | 92·8 | | | | |
| | 129 | | | | |
| −40°C | | | | | |
| 40·3 | | RB | 0·4 | $10^7$ | |
| 32·4 | | | | | |
| −78°C | −196°C | | | | |
| 10 | 14 | B | 0·5 | $10^6$ | |
| 34 | 39 | | | | |
| 22 | 27 | | | | |
| 39 | 44·4 | | | | |
| 21 | 28 | | | | |
| 37 | 43 | | | | |
| | 83·2 | B | 0·25 | $10^6$ | |
| 78 | 110 | B | 0·25 | $10^6$ | |
| 76 | 114 | | | | |
| 33°C | −253°C | −269°C | | | |
| | 31 | 32·5 | Ax | 0·02 | $10^5$ |
| ·5 | 22 | 23 | | | |
| ·5 | 23·5 | 24·5 | | | |
| | 19·5 | 20·5 | | | |
| | 20 | 22·5 | | | |
| | 29·5 | 33 | | | |

TABLE 83. FATIGUE STRENGTHS OF ME

| Condition | Yield stress tons/in² | | | Air temperature | |
|---|---|---|---|---|---|
| | Air temperature | | | | |
| N 950°C | | | | 29 | |
| T 670°C | | | | 59 | |
| | | −78°C | −188°C | | |
| | 16·3 | 24·6 | — | 27·0 | |
| | 22·4 | 31·8 | — | 39·6 | |
| | 0·2% proof stress | | | | |
| | 26·0 | 29·5 | 63·4 | 50·6 | |
| | 42·4 | 48·2 | 73·2 | | |
| | | | | 51·0 | |
| | 53·9 | 62·5 | 82·5 | 60·6 | |
| | 56·7 | 63·5 | 82·1 | 66·7 | |
| | | −78°C | −196°C | | |
| .C., 1 hr, 788°C, A.C., , A.C. | — | 39 | — | 52 | |
| | 40 | 45 | — | 49 | |
| T 496°C | 62 | 66 | — | 64 | |
| | 35 | 40 | — | 40 | |
| T 454°C | 53 | 60 | — | 63 | |
| | 66 | 88 | — | 94 | |
| aged 40 mins 538°C | 78 | 88 | — | 81 | |
| | 87·6 | | 104 | 103 | |
| C | 60·7 | | 89·1 | 65·1 | |
| C | 95·5 | | 119 | 103 | |
| | 0·1% proof stress | | | | |
| | 34·8 | | | 38·5 | |
| | 28·9 | | | 32·3 | |
| | 0·2% proof stress | | | | |
| | | −78°C | −196°C | | |
| | 8 | 8 | | 9 | |
| | 21·6 | 22 | 28·1 | 31·4 | |
| | 17 | 18 | | 20 | |
| | 32·2 | 33 | 40 | 37·4 | |
| | 14 | 17 | 21·6 | 17·9 | |
| | 22 | 24 | | 35 | |
| | 32·2 | | 79·2 | 40·0 | |
| | 64 | 76 | 110 | 68 | |
| | 63 | 75 | 113 | 66 | |
| | | | | | −1 |
| | | | | 18 | 2 |
| | | | | 12 | 1 |
| | | | | 12 | 1 |
| | | | | 5 | 1 |
| | | | | 12·5 | 1 |
| | | | | 8 | 1 |

| air temperature | Fatigue strength tons/in² | | | Source | Ref. |
|---|---|---|---|---|---|
| | −60°C | −186°C | | Kenneford and Nichols | 427 |
| 12·5 | 15·5 | 29 | | | |
| 28 | 28 | 43 | | | |
| | −78°C | −188°C | | Hempel and Luce | 426 |
| 13 | 18 | 37 | | | |
| 15 | 21 | 42 | | | |
| 18 | 24 | 44 | | | |
| 26 | 30 | 44 | | | |
| 51 | 36 | 48 | | | |
| 36 | 40 | 51 | | | |
| | −78°C | −196°C | | Zambrow and Fontana | 649 |
| 34 | 39 | 44 | | | |
| 26 | 30 | 50 | | | |
| 33 | 42 | 54 | | | |
| 21 | 30 | 40 | | | |
| 30 | 40 | 57 | | | |
| 50 | 56 | 68 | | | |
| 42 | 55 | 72 | | | |
| 46 | | 58 | | Spretnak, Fontana and Brooks | 650 |
| 34 | | 58 | | | |
| 18 | | 61 | | | |
| | −40°C | | | Gunn | 651 |
| 11·6 | 12·9 | | | | |
| 7·8 | 7·4 | | | | |
| | −78°C | −196°C | | Zambrow and Fontana | 649 |
| 6 | 7 | | | | |
| 15 | 17 | 24 | | | |
| 11 | 13 | | | | |
| 15 | 17 | 26 | | | |
| 10 | 11·5 | | | | |
| 18 | 22 | 27 | | | |
| 33 | | 46 | | Spretnak et al. | 650 |
| 49 | 54 | 63 | | Bishop, Spretnak and Fontana | 652 |
| 38 | 43 | 58 | | | |
| | −183°C | −253°C | −269°C | McCammon and Rosenberg | 127 |
| 9·5 | 13 | 17·5 | 19 | | |
| 5·5 | 8 | 10·5 | 12 | | |
| 8 | 12 | 14·5 | 15·5 | | |
| 2·1 | 5·1 | 6·8 | 8·5 | | |
| 3·2 | 5·7 | 8·9 | 9·4 | | |
| 3·5 | 9·9 | 16 | 17·5 | | |

| No. | Material | |
|---|---|---|
| 1 | Free cutting mild steel, En 1B, 0·13 C, 1·2 Mn, 0·18 Pb | Cold drawn, |
| 2 | Alloy steel, En 25, 0·29 C, 2·44 Ni, 0·74 Cr, 0·52 Mo | O.Q. 950°C, |
| 3 | Mild steel, 0·08 C, 0·59 Mn | N |
| 4 | 0·4% C steel, 0·40 C, 0·78 Mn, 0·43 S | A |
| 5 | 0·64% C steel, 0·64 C, 0·75 Mn | N |
| 6 | Cr, Mo, steel, 0·22 C, 0·60 Mn, 0·83 Cr, 0·22 Mo | W.Q. & T. |
| 7 | Cr, Mo, steel, 0·22 C, 0·60 Mn, 0·83 Cr, 0·22 Mo | W.Q. & T. |
| 8 | Cr, Ni, Mo, steel, 0·34 C, 0·45 Mn, 2·27 Ni, 1·88 Cr, 0·40 Mo | O.Q. & T. |
| 9 | 8½% Ni, steel, 0·10 C, 0·77 Mn, 8·6 Ni | 1 hr 899°C, A 2 hr 566°C |
| 10 | 3½% Ni, steel, SAE 2330, 0·28–0·33 C, 0·6–0·8 Mn, 3·25–3·75 Ni | N |
| 11 | 3½% Ni, steel, SAE 2330, 0·28–0·33 C, 0·6–0·8 Mn, 3·25–3·75 Ni | O.Q. 815°C, |
| 12 | Ni, Cr, Mo, steel, NE 8630  0·27–0·33 C  0·7–0·9 Mn | N |
| 13 | 0·48–0·67 Ni, 0·49–0·56 Cr, 0·18 Mo | O.Q. 815°C, |
| 14 | Stainless steel type 304, 18·50 Cr, 8·82 Ni | Cold rolled |
| 15 | Stainless steel type 322, 17·0 Cr, 6·5 Ni, 0·37 Ti, 0·12 Al | A.C. 1038°C |
| 16 | Hy–Tuf, 0·26 C, 1·26 Mn, 1·37 Si, 1·91 Ni, 0·43 Mo | N |
| 17 | SAE 4340, 0·46 C, 0·70 Mn, 1·78 Ni, 0·95 Cr, 0·23 Mo | O.Q. T 649° |
| 18 | SAE 4340, 0·46 C, 0·70 Mn, 1·78 Ni, 0·95 Cr, 0·23 Mo | O.Q. T 427° |
| 19 | Aluminium alloy DTD 363 A, 5 in. extrusion (Al–Zn–Mg) | Longitudinal |
| 20 | | Transverse |
| 21 | 2 S aluminium, 99 Al | ¾ hard |
| 22 | 24 S–T aluminium alloy, 3·8–4·4 Cu | — |
| 23 | 61 S–T aluminium alloy, 0·5–0·7 Si, 0·8–1·0 Mg | |
| 24 | 75 S–T aluminium alloy, 5·7 Zn, 2·8 Mg, 1·5 Cu | |
| 25 | FS 1 magnesium alloy, 3·1 Al, 1·05 Zn | |
| 26 | Aluminium bronze, 9·0 Al | |
| 27 | Titanium | Hot swaged |
| 28 | Titanium alloy 150 A, 1·3 Fe, 2·7 Cr | |
| 29 | Titanium alloy RC-130-B, 3·8 Al, 3·8 Mn | |
| 30 | Copper (0·03 oxygen) | A 600°C |
| 31 | Silver (99·995) | A 620°C |
| 32 | Gold (99·997) | A 660°C |
| 33 | Cadmium (>99·95) | A 60°C |
| 34 | Magnesium (99·98) | A 380°C |
| 35 | Aluminium (>99·99) | A 400°C |

*—continued*

ALLOYS

(See Table 8, page 78 for data on magnesium alloy sheet.)

| Form and condition | Typical tensile properties | | | Rotating bending fatigue strength for endurance of 5 × 10⁷ cycles tons/in². | Source |
|---|---|---|---|---|---|
| | 0·1% proof stress tons/in² | Tensile strength | Elongation per cent on 2 in. | | |
| Plate ¼–1 in. | 9 | 16 | 8 | 5·25–6·5 | Magnesium |
| Extrusions ⅜–4 in. | 14–17* | 20–23* | 10–25* | 7·75–8·75 | Elektron |
| Extrusions ⅜–2 in. | 11–14* | 17–20* | 10–20* | 7·25–8·0 | Ltd, |
| Extrusions | 13* | 19* | 10* | 6·0 | Manchester |
| Extrusions up to 1 in. | 9 | 14 | 30 | 5·0 | |
| Extrusions | 8–13* | 15–20* | 4–10* | 4·5 –5·25 | |
| Extrusions up to 3 in. | 11–14* | 17–22* | 10–18* | 8·0 –8·75 | |
| Forgings | 10–13* | 18–20* | 8–14* | 7·5 –8·25 | |
| Press forgings | 10–14 | 18–22* | 8–14* | 8·0 –8·75 | |
| ALLOYS | | | | | |
| As cast and annealed | 5–6 | 9–11* | 3–6* | 4·25–4·75 | Magnesium Elektron |
| Fully heat-treated | 5 | 13 | 5 | 4·0 –4·5 | |
| As cast | 4·5–5·5 | 9–11* | 2–5* | 5·0 –5·5 | |
| As cast | 4·5–6 | 8–10·5* | 1–3 | 5·0 –5·5 | |
| Solution treated | 4·5–6 | 13–16* | 4–8* | 5·0 –6·0 | |
| Fully heat-treated | 6·5–8·5 | 13–16·5* | 1–4 | 4·5 –5·0 | |
| As cast | 4–5·5 | 8–11 | 2–5 | 4·75–5·25 | |
| Solution treated | 4–5·5 | 12–16 | 4–10 | 5·0 –5·5 | |
| Fully heat-treated | 5–7·5 | 12–16 | 1–3 | 4·0 –4·75 | |
| | | | | 10⁸ cycles | |
| As cast | 6·0 | 10·6 | 8·5 | 4·2 | J. Stone & Co, |
| 2 hr at 330°C | 9·1 | 15·1 | 6 | 7·6 | Charlton, London |
| 4 hr at 535°C quenched, 16 hr at 200°C | 12·0 | 18·6 | 9 | 6·4 | (Fatigue results for ¾ in. diameter speci- |
| 4 hr at 535°C quenched, 8 hr at 200°C | 12·2–12·7 | 16·4–17·6 | 2·5–4 | 7 | mens at 3000 c/min) |

# REFERENCES

1. G. A. COTTELL, "Lessons to be Learnt from Failures in Service". *Int. Conf. on Fatigue of Metals, Inst. Mech. Engrs.* (1956) 563.
   See also Brit. Engine Boiler and Electrical Insurance Co., Ltd., Manchester, Tech. Rpt. New Series **2** (1954) 221; **3** (1957) 91.
2. *Handbook of Expt. Stress Analysis.* John Wiley and Sons, New York. Chapman and Hall, London. (1950).
3. C. W. ORR, "The Detection of Fatigue Cracks". Symposium *The Failure of Metals by Fatigue.* Melbourne Univ. Press (1946) 95.
4. L. J. DEMER, "Fatigue Crack Detection Methods", *Wright Air Development Center. Tech. Rpt.* 55–86 (1955).
5. J. M. McLEOD, "Non-Destructive Testing", *Iron and Steel* **28** (June 1955) 301, (July 1955) 339, (Aug. 1955) 383.
   Reprinted in *Metallurgical Progress* **3**. Iliffe & Sons. (1957).
6. D. M. LEWIS, *Magnetic and Electrical Methods of Non-Destructive Testing.* George Allen & Unwin, London (1951).
7. ANON. "Rail-Defect Detecting Car". *Engineering* **150** (1940) 223.
8. B. CARLIN, *Ultrasonics.* McGraw Hill, New York (1949).
9. J. SCHIJVE, "Ultrasonic Testing of Compressor and Turbine Blades for Fatigue Cracks". *Aircraft Engng.* **31** (1959) 51.
10. M. J. McGUIGAN, D. F. BRYAN and R. E. WHALEY, "Fatigue Investigation of Full-Scale Transport Airplane Wings". *National Advisory Co. for Aeronautics Tech. Note* 3190 (1954).
11. ANON. "Failure of Rotating Shafts due to Repairs by Welding". British Engine Boiler and Electrical Insurance Co., Manchester. *Tech. Rpt. New Series* **1** (1952) 114.
12. S. WISE, "Strength of Components Repaired by Welding". *Brit. Welding J.* **6** (1959) 345.
13. O. J. HORGER and W. I. CANTLEY, "Design of Crankpins for Locomotives". *Trans. Amer. Soc. Mech. Engrs.* **68** (1946) A17.
14. P. G. FORREST, "The Influence of Plastic Deformation on Notch Sensitivity in Fatigue". *Int. Conf. on Fatigue. Inst. Mech. Engrs.* (1956) 171.
15. P. G. FORREST and H. J. TAPSELL, "Experiments on the Fatigue of a Mild Steel and an Aluminium Alloy at Elevated Temperatures". *Proc. Instn. Mech. Engrs.* **168** (1954) 763.
16. A. A. BLATHERWICK and B. J. LAZAN, "Effect of Changing Cyclic Modulus on Bending Fatigue Strength". *Proc. Amer. Soc. Test. Mat.* **56** (1956) 1012.
17. ANON. "The Effect of Type of Testing Machine on Fatigue Test Results". *Proc. Amer. Soc. Test. Mat.* **41** (1941) 133.
18. T. T. OBERG and R. J. ROONEY, "Fatigue Characteristics in Reversed Bending as affected by Type of Machine and Specimen". *Proc. Amer. Soc. Test. Mat.* **49** (1949) 804.
19 T. J. DOLAN, J. H. McCLOW and W. J. CRAIG, "The Influence of Shape of Cross Section on the Flexural Fatigue Strength of Steel". *Trans. Amer. Soc. Mech. Engrs.* **72** (1950) 469.

20. H. T. CORTEN and T. J. DOLAN, "Shape as a Factor in Flexural Fatigue Strength". *Univ. Illinois. Dept. of Theoretical and Applied Mechanics. Tech. Rept.* **42** (1955).

21. F. H. VITOVEC and B. J. LAZAN, "Review of Previous Work on Short-time Tests for Predicting Fatigue Properties of Materials". *Wright Air Development Center. Tech. Rpt.* 53-122 (1953).

22. J. BAUSCHINGER, "On the Change of the Position of the Elastic Limit of Iron and Steel under Cyclic Variations of Stress". *Mitthlg. des. Mechanisch-Technischen Laboratoriums in Munchen*, **13** (1886). *English abstract: J. Inst. Civil Engrs.* **2** (1886–7) 463.

23. L. BAIRSTOW, "The Elastic Limits of Iron and Steel under Cyclical Variations of Stress". *Phil. Trans. Roy. Soc.* **A210** (1910) 35.

24. H. J. GOUGH, *The Fatigue of Metals*. Scott, Greenwood & Son, London (1924).

25. S. IKEDA, "Rapid Method of Determining Endurance Limit by Means of Measuring Electrical Resistance". *Tech. Reports Tohoku Univ.* **8** (1929) 167.

26. E. RAVILLY, "Fracture of Metal Wires under Alternating Torsion". *Publ. Scientifiques et Techniques du Ministere de l'Air.* No. **120** (1938) 52.

27. A. LANGEVIN, E. PAUL and M. REIMBERT, "Electromagnetic Method for Determining the Fatigue Limit". *Comptes Rendus de l'Academie des Sciences.* **230** (1950) 1138.

28. P. E. CAVANAGH, "Progress of Failure in Metals as Traced by Changes in Magnetic and Electrical Properties". *Proc. Amer. Soc. Test. Mat.* **47** (1947) 639.
    See also: *Wright Air Dev. Center. Tech. Rpt.* 53–184 (1953).

29. J. L. ROSENHOLTZ and D. T. SMITH, "Dilastrain Method for Determining Endurance Limit of Materials". *Metal Progress* **61** (1952) 85.

30. M. PROT, "Fatigue Testing under Progressive Load". *Rev. Metal.* **34** (1937) 440, **48** (1951) 822.
    See also: *Wright Air Develop. Center. Tech. Rept.* 52-148 (1952).

31. P. W. RAMSEY and D. P. KEDZIC, "Prot Fatigue Study of an Ultra-High-Strength Steel". *Trans. Amer. Inst. Min. Met. Engrs.* **209** (1957) 401.

32. E. J. WARD, R. T. SCHWARTZ and D. C. SCHWARTZ, "An Investigation of the Prot Accelerated Fatigue Test". *Proc. Amer. Soc. Test. Mat.* **53** (1953) 885.

33. A. P. BORESI and T. J. DOLAN, "An Appraisal of the Prot Method of Fatigue Testing". *Univ. Illinois Dept. Theoretical and Applied Mech.* "Behaviour of Materials under Repeated Stress". *Tech. Rpt.* 34 (1953).

34. A. FERRO and U. ROSSETTI, "Fatigue of Metals under Progressive Load". *Colloquium on Fatigue. Stockholm* 1955. Springer-Verlag Berlin (1956) 24.

35. F. BASTENAIRE, R. CAZAUD and M. WEISZ, "Fatigue of Materials under Progressive Loading". *Colloquium on Fatigue, Stockholm* 1955. Springer-Verlag Berlin (1956) 14.

36. W. A. HIJAB, "Appraisal of the Prot Method". *J. Appl. Mech.* **24** (1957) 214.

37. H. T. CORTEN, T. DIMOFF and T. J. DOLAN, "An Appraisal of the Prot Method of Fatigue Testing". *Proc. Amer. Soc. Test. Mat.* **54** (1954) 875.

38. J. McKEOWN, "A Rapid Method of Estimating the Fatigue Limit". *Metallurgia* **54** (1956) 151.

39. ANON. "Manual on Fatigue Testing". *Amer. Soc. Test. Mat. Spec. Tech. Publ.* No. 91 1949.

40. Symp. on "Large Fatigue Testing Machines and their Results". *Amer. Soc. Test Mat. Spec. Tech. Publ.* No. 216 (1957).

41. N. B. OWEN and H. L. COX, "Slipping Clutch Fatigue Testing Machine". *Engineering* **186** (1958) 84.

42. T. HAAS, "Simulated Service Life Testing". *Engineer* **206** (1958) 754.

43. G. VIDAL, F. GIRARD and P. LANUSSE, "A Small Tension–Compression Fatigue Machine Operating at 5000 Cycles per sec". *Rev. Metal.* **55** (1958) 613.

44. F. GIRARD and G. VIDAL, "Micro Fatigue Machine in Tension–Compression at 92,000 Cycles per sec". *Rev. Metal* **56** (1959) 25.

45. E. A. NEPPIRAS, "Metal Fatigue at High Frequency". *Proc. Phys. Soc.* **70**B (1957) 393.

46. A. WÖHLER, "Tests to Determine the Forces Acting on Railway Carriage Axles and the Capacity of Resistance of the Axles". English Abstract *Engineering* **11** (1871) 199.

47. H. E. GRESHAM and B. HALL, "Hot Fatigue Testing". Symp. "High Temperature Steels and Alloys for Gas Turbines". *Iron and Steel Inst. Special Rpt. No.* 43 (1952) 181.

48. J. McKEOWN and L. H. BACK, "A Rotating-Load, Elevated Temperature Fatigue-Testing Machine". *Metallurgia* **38** (1948) 247.

49. W. N. FINDLEY, P. G. JONES, W. I. MITCHELL and R. L. SUTHERLAND, "Fatigue Machines for Low Temperatures and Miniature Specimens". *Amer. Soc. Test. Mat. Bull.* No. 184 (1952) 53.

50. J. P. ROMUALDI, C. L. CHANG and C. F. PECK, "A Fatigue Testing Machine for Range of Stress". *Amer. Soc. Test Mat. Bull.* No. 200 (1954) 39.

51. F. H. HOOKE, "The Effects of Mean Stress and of Preloading on the Fatigue Life of a High Tensile Structural Steel". *Part* 1, *M.O.S. S. & T. Memo* 20/58 (1958).

52. W. W. JOHNSTONE, "Methods of Investigating the Fatigue Properties of Materials". Symp. *The Failure of Metals by Fatigue.* Melbourne (1946) 135.

53. G. R. GOHN and E. R. MORTON, "A New High Speed Sheet Metal Fatigue Testing Machine for Unsymmetrical Bending Studies". *Proc. Amer. Soc. Test Mat.* **49** (1949) 702.

54. K. W. MITCHELL and H. KING, "Fatigue Testing Machine for Hot Sheet. *Engineering* **185** (1958) 402.

55. ANON. "Fatigue Bending Test Machine for Electric Cables". *Engineering* **180** (1955) 184.

56. H. J. GOUGH, H. V. POLLARD and W. J. CLENSHAW, "The Resistance of Metals to Fatigue under Combined Stress". *Aero. Res. Council R. & M. 2522* (1951).

57. H. J. GOUGH and H. V. POLLARD, "The Strength of Metals under Combined Alternating Stresses". *Proc. Inst. Mech. Engrs.* **131** (1935) 3.

58. W. P. WELCH and W. A. WILSON, "A New High Temperature Fatigue Machine". *Proc. Amer. Soc. Test Mat.* **41** (1941) 733.

59. T. J. DOLAN, "Electrically Excited Resonant-Type Fatigue Testing Equipment". *Amer. Soc. Test Mat. Bull* No. 175 (1951).

60. A. R. WADE and P. GROOTENHUIS, "Very High-Speed Fatigue Testing". *Inst. Mech. Engrs. Int. Conference on Fatigue* (1956) 361.

61. C. F. JENKIN and G. D. LEHMAN, "High Frequency Fatigue". *Proc. Roy. Soc.* A**125** (1929) 83.

62. F. B. QUINLAN, "Pneumatic Fatigue Machines". *Proc. Amer. Soc. Test Mat.* **46** (1946) 846.

63. T. W. LOMAS, J. O. WARD, J. R. RAIT and E. W. COLBECK, "The Influence of Frequency of Vibration on the Endurance Limit of Ferrous Alloys at Speeds up to 150,000 Cycles per Minute Using a Pneumatic Resonance System". *Inst. Mech. Engrs. Int. Conference on Fatigue* (1956) 375.

64. H. W. Foster and V. Seliger, "Fatigue Testing Methods and Equipment". *Mech. Engng.* **66** (1944) 719.

65. B. J. Lazan, J. Brown, A. Gannett, P. Kirmser and J. Klumpp, "Dynamic Testing of Materials and Structures with a New Resonance Vibration Exciter and Controller". *Proc. Amer. Soc. Test Mat.* **52** (1952) 858.

66. R. P. Newman, "The Fatigue Testing of Welded Structures". Chapter in *Metal Fatigue*. Chapman & Hall (1959) 348.

67. S. F. Dorey, "Large Scale Torsional Fatigue Testing of Marine Shafting". *Proc. Inst. Mech. Engrs.* **159** (1948) 399.

68. R. J. Atkinson, "The Fatigue Testing of Aircraft Structures". Chapter in *Metal Fatigue*. Chapman & Hall (1959) 366.

69. H. L. Cox and E. P. Coleman, "A Note on Repeated Loading Tests on Components and Complete Structures". *J. Royal Aero. Soc.* **54** (1950) 1.

70. L. Baes and Y. Verwilst, "A Large Mechanical Installation for Endurance Tests". *Proc. Soc. Exp. Stress Analysis* **16.1** (1959) 39.

71. B. Thurlimann and W. J. Ewey, "Modern Installation for Testing of Large Assemblies Under Static and Fatigue Loading". *Proc. Soc. Exp. Stress Analysis* **16.2** (1959) 81.

72. H. Neuber, *Theory of Notch Stresses*. J. W. Edwards, Ann Arbor, Michigan 1946.

73. T. S. Braithwaite, "Production of Specimens for Static and Fatigue Testing". *Machinery* **86** (1955) 34.

74. B. F. Billing, "Measurement of Fluctuating and Mean Loads in Haigh Fatigue Testing Machines". *J. Royal Aero. Soc.* **58** (1954) 508.

75. M. H. Roberts, "Precise Measurement of Fatigue Test Load". *Metallurgia* **46** (1952) 107.

76. T. M. Dowell, "Dynamic Calibration of Fatigue Testing Machines". *Engineering* **185** (1958) 693.

77. R. C. A. Thurston, "Dynamic Calibration Method using Modified Proving Ring". *Amer. Soc. Test. Mat. Bull.* **154** (1948) 50.

78. P. G. Forrest, "Optical Dynamic Weighbar for a Fatigue Testing Machine". *Engineering* **174** (1952) 801.

79. G. M. Sinclair and T. J. Dolan, "Effect of Stress Amplitude on Statistical Variability in Fatigue Life of 75 S–T6 Aluminium Alloy". *Trans. Amer. Soc. Mech. Engrs.* **75** (1953) 867.

80. "A Tentative Guide for Fatigue Testing and the Statistical Analysis of Fatigue Data". *Amer. Soc. Testing Mat. Spec. Tech. Publ.* No. **91-A** (1958).

81. "Data Sheets on Fatigue". *Royal Aero. Soc.* (1959).

82. J. T. Ransom and R. F. Mehl, "The Statistical Nature of the Fatigue Properties of SAE 4340 Steel Forgings". Symp. on Fatigue with emphasis on Statistical Approach II. *Amer. Soc. Test Mat. Spec. Tech. Publ.* **137** (1952) 3.

83. J. Clayton-Cave, R. J. Taylor and E. Ineson, "Reproducibility of Wohler Fatigue Tests". *J. Iron and Steel Inst.* **180** (1955) 161.

84. F. A. McClintock, "A Criterion for Minimum Scatter in Fatigue Testing". *J. Appl. Mech.* **22** (1955) 427.

85. F. A. McClintock, "Variability in Fatigue Testing". *Colloquium on Fatigue: Stockholm* 1955. Springer-Verlag Berlin (1956) 171.

86. E. Ineson, J. Clayton-Cave and R. J. Taylor, "Variation in Fatigue Properties over Individual casts of Steel—Investigation of a Cast of Steel to B.S. 970, Specification En. 100". *J. Iron and Steel Inst.* **184** (1956) 179.

87. G. Forrest, "The Fatigue Properties of Aluminium Alloys". Chapter in *Metal Fatigue*. Chapman & Hall (1959) 189.

88. N. T. BLOOMER, "Time Saving in Statistical Fatigue Experiments". *Engineering* **184** (1957) 603.
89. H. L. COX, "Reproducibility of Results in Fatigue Testing". Chapter in *Metal Fatigue*. Chapman & Hall, London (1959).
90. W. WEIBULL, "Statistical Design of Fatigue Experiments". *J. Appl. Mech.* **19** (1952) 109.
91. A. M. FREUDENTHAL and E. J. GUMBEL, "Physical and Statistical Aspects of Fatigue". *Advances in Appl. Mech.* **4** (1956) 117.
92. P. H. FRITH, "Fatigue Tests on Rolled Alloy Steels". *Iron and Steel Inst. Special Report* No. 50 (1954).
93. P. H. FRITH, "Fatigue of Wrought High-Tensile Alloy Steels". *Int. Conf. on Fatigue Instn. Mech. Engrs.* (1956) 462.
94. H. F. MOORE and J. B. KOMMERS, *Fatigue of Metals*. McGraw Hill, New York (1927).
95. D. K. BULLENS, *Steel and its Heat-Treatment* **1** (1938) 37.
96. R. CAZAUD, "Mechanical Properties of Steel of Varying Nickel Content". *Rev. Metal* **52** (1955) 579.
97. M. F. GARWOOD, H. H. ZURBURG and M. A. ERICKSON, "Interpretations of Tests and Correlation with Service". Symp. "Correlation of Laboratory Tests and Service Performance". *Amer. Soc. Met.* (1951).
98. J. H. MOORE, "Vacuum Melting Lengthens Fatigue Life, Improves Impact Properties". *Iron Age* **171** (1953) 154.
99. J. E. RUSSELL and D. V. WALKER, "Fatigue Results on a Steel of up to 800 V.P.N. Hardness, using Notched and Unnotched Specimens". *Int. Conf. on Fatigue, Instn. Mech. Engrs.* (1956) 459.
100. M. L. BECKER, *Int. Conf. on Fatigue, Instn. Mech. Engrs.* (1956) 770.
101. D. O. MORRIS, "Composition and Physical Properties of Steel in Relation to Fatigue". *Symposium on Fatigue, Univ. of Melbourne* (1946) 336.
102. ANON. "Effect of Sulphur on the Endurance Properties of Rivet Steels". *Proc. Amer. Soc. Test. Mat.* **24** I (1924) 96.
103. W. E. BARDGETT, "Effect of Lead Additions on the Fatigue Properties of En 24 and En 36 Steels". *Iron and Steel* **29** (August 1956) 392.
104. J. WOOLMAN and A. JACQUES, "Influence of Lead Additions on the Mechanical Properties and Machinability of some Alloy Steels". *J. Iron and Steel Inst.* **165** (1950) 257.
105. G. M. SINCLAIR and T. J. DOLAN, "Effects of Austenitic Grain Size and Metallurgical Structure on the Mechanical Properties of Steel". *Proc. Amer. Soc. Test Mat.* **50** (1950) 587.
106. T. J. DOLAN and C. S. YEN, "Effect of Metallurgical Structure on Fatigue Strength and Notch Sensitivity of Steel". *Proc. Amer. Soc. Test. Mat.* **48** (1948) 664.
107. F. BORIK, R. D. CHAPMAN and W. E. JOMINY, "The Effect of Percent Tempered Martensite on the Endurance Limit". *Trans. Amer. Soc. Metals* **50** (1958) 242.
108. H. E. FRANKEL, J. A. BENNETT and W. A. PENNINGTON, "Fatigue Properties of High Strength Steels". *Trans. Amer. Soc. Metals* **52** (1960) 257.
109. P. L. TEED, "The Influences of Metallographic Structure on Fatigue". *Symp. Fatigue and Fracture of Metals M.I.T.* John Wiley, New York (1950) 252.
110. J. T. RANSOM and R. F. MEHL, "Anisotropy of the Fatigue Properties of SAE 4340 Steel Forgings". *Proc. Amer. Soc. Test. Mat.* **52** (1952) 779.
111. J. T. RANSOM, "Effect of Inclusions on the Fatigue Strength of SAE 4340 Steels". *Trans. Amer. Soc. Met.* **46** (1954) 1254.

112. W. C. STEWART and W. L. WILLIAMS, "Effect of Inclusions on the Endurance Properties of Steels". *J. Amer. Soc. Naval Engrs.* **60** (1948) 475.

113. H. N. CUMMINGS, F. B. STULEN and W. C. SCHULTE, "Tentative Fatigue Strength Reduction Factors for Silicate-Type Inclusions in High-Strength Steels. *Proc. Amer. Soc. Test. Mat.* **58** (1958) 505.

114. E. EPREMIAN and R. F. MEHL, "Statistical Behaviour of Fatigue Properties and the Influence of Metallurgical Factors". *Amer. Soc. Test. Mat. Spec. Tech. Publ.* 137 (1953).

115. H. STYRI, "Fatigue Strength of Ball-Bearing Races and Heat-Treated 52100 Steel Specimens". *Proc. Amer. Soc. Test. Mat.* **51** (1951) 682.

116. R. CAZAUD, *Fatigue of Metals*, 4th ed. Dunod, Paris (1959). 3rd ed. Translated by A. J. Fenner, Chapman and Hall, London (1953).

117. B. B. MUVDI, G. SACHS and E. P. KLIER, "Axial Load Fatigue Properties of High-Strength Steels". *Proc. Amer. Soc. Test. Mat.* **57** (1957) 655.

118. J. L. M. MORRISON, B. CROSSLAND and J. S. C. PARRY, "Strength of Thick Cylinders Subjected to Repeated Internal Pressure". *Proc. Inst. Mech. Engrs.* **174** (1960) 95.

119. E. T. GILL and R. GOODACRE, "The Fatigue Properties of Patented Steel Wire". *J. Iron and Steel Inst.* **130** (1934) 293. *J. Iron and Steel Inst.* **132** (1935) 143.

120. R. J. LOVE, "The Influence of Surface Condition on the Fatigue Strength of Steel". Symp. *Properties of Metallic Surfaces.* Inst. of Metals (1952) 161. Also "The Fatigue Strength of Steels". *Motor Industry Res. Ass. Rpt.* (1950) 9.

121. B. CINA, "Effect of Cold Work on the Fatigue of an Austenitic Alloy Steel". *J. Iron and Steel Inst.* **190** (1958) 144.

122. S. M. SHELTON and W. H. SWANGER, "Fatigue Properties of Steel Wire". *J. Res. Nat. Bureau Standards* **14** (1935) 17.

123. H. J. GODFREY, "The Fatigue and Bending Properties of Cold Drawn Steel Wire". *Trans. Amer. Soc. Met.* **29** (1941) 133.

124. *Fracture.* Int. Conf. Swampscott, Massachusetts (1959). Tech Press M.I.T. and John Wiley, New York. Chapman & Hall, London (1959).

125. N. P. ALLEN and C. C. EARLEY, "Effect of Phosphorus Content on Impact Values of Steels". *J. Iron and Steel Inst.* **182** (1956) 375.

126. R. D. CHAPMAN and W. E. JOMINY, "The Endurance Limit of Temper-Brittle Steel". *Trans. Amer. Soc. Met.* **45** (1953) 710.

127. R. D. MCCAMMON and H. M. ROSENBERG, "The Fatigue and Ultimate Tensile Strengths of Metals Between 4·2 and 293°K". *Proc. Roy. Soc.* **A242** (1957) 203.

128. C. W. MACGREGOR, "Significance of Transition Temperature in Fatigue". *Fatigue and Fracture of Metals. Symposium M.I.T.* (1950). John Wiley, New York. Chapman and Hall, London (1952), p. 229.

129. R. H. RARING and J. A. RINEBOLT, "Static Fatigue of High Strength Steel". *Trans. Amer. Soc. Met.* **48** (1956) 198.

130. E. B. EVANS, L. J. EBERT and C. W. BRIGGS, "Fatigue Properties of Comparable Cast and Wrought Steels". *Proc. Amer. Soc. Test. Mat.* **56** (1956) 979.

131. H. MORROGH, "Fatigue of Cast Iron". Chapter in *Fatigue of Metals*. Chapman and Hall, London (1959) 220; also *Foundry Trade J.* **102** (1957) 197 and 239.

132. G. N. J. GILBERT and K. B. PALMER, "Tensile and Fatigue Tests on Normalised Pearlitic Nodular Irons". *Brit. Cast Iron Res. Assoc. J. Research and Development* **6** (1957) 498.

133. G. N. J. GILBERT and K. B. PALMER, "Tensile and Fatigue Tests on Hardened and Tempered Nodular Irons". *Brit. Cast Iron Res. Assoc. J. Research and Development* **5** (1955) 604.

134. R. L. TEMPLIN, "Fatigue of Aluminium". *Proc. Amer. Soc. Test. Mat.* **54** (1954) 641.

135. H. J. GROVER, S. A. GORDON and L. R. JACKSON, *Fatigue of Metals and Structures.* U.S. Bureau of Aeronautics (1954). Thames & Hudson, London (1956).

136. ANON. "Fatigue Properties of Some Noral Wrought Aluminium Alloys". *Aluminium Labs. Ltd. Research Bulletin No.* 1 (1952).

137. T. T. OBERG, "When Will It Fail?" *Metal Progress* **60** (July 1951) 74.

138. J. Y. MANN, "Survey of Fatigue Data of DTD 363 and 364 Aluminium Alloys". *Aero. Res. Lab. Melbourne. S & M Note* 248 (1958).

139. R. F. HANSTOCK, "The Reactions of High Strength Aluminium Alloys to Alternating Stresses". *Int. Conf. on Fatigue, Instn. Mech. Engrs.* (1956) 425.

140. T. BROOM, J. H. MOLINEUX and V. N. WHITTAKER, "Structural Changes During the Fatigue of Some Aluminium Alloys". *J. Inst. Met.* **84** (1956) 357.

141. T. BROOM, J. A. MAZZA and V. N. WHITTAKER, "Structural Changes Caused by Plastic Strain and by Fatigue in Al–Zn–Mg–Cu Alloys". *J. Inst. Met.* **86** (1957) 17.

142. J. L. WAISMAN, L. SOFFA, P. W. KLOERIS and C. S. YEN, "Effect of Internal Flaws on the Fatigue Strength of Aluminium Alloys". *Nondestructive Testing* **16** (1958) 477.

143. R. L. TEMPLIN, F. M. HOWELL and E. C. HARTMANN, "Effect of Grain Direction on Fatigue Properties of Aluminium Alloys". *Prod. Engng.* **21** (July 1950) 126. See also A.S.M.E. Handbook *Metals Engineering—Design* (1953) 112.

144. R. L. TEMPLIN, F. M. HOWELL and J. O. LYST, "Fatigue Properties of Cast Aluminium Alloys". *Prod. Engng.* **23** (May 1952) 119.

145. A. BECK, *Technology of Magnesium and its Alloys.* Transl. from the German. F. A. Hughes & Co. Ltd. London. 3rd edition (1943).

146. P. H. FRITH, *Properties of Wrought and Cast Aluminium and Magnesium Alloys at Room and Elevated Temperatures.* H.M.S.O. (1956).

147. H. L. BURGHOFF and A. I. BLANK, "Fatigue Properties of Some Coppers and Copper Alloys in Strip Form". *Proc. Amer. Soc. Test. Mat.* **48** (1948) 709.

148. G. M. SINCLAIR and W. J. CRAIG, "Influence of Grain Size on Work Hardening and Fatigue Characteristics of α-Brass". *Trans. Amer. Soc. Met.* **44** (1952) 929.

149. A. R. ANDERSON, E. F. SWAN and E. W. PALMER, "Fatigue Tests of Some Additional Copper Alloys". *Proc. Amer. Soc. Test. Mat.* **46** (1946) 678.

150. H. L. BURGHOFF and A. I. BLANK, "Fatigue Characteristics of Some Copper Alloys". *Proc. Amer. Soc. Test. Mat.* **47** (1947) 695.

151. A. R. ANDERSON and C. S. SMITH, "Fatigue Tests on Some Copper Alloys". *Proc. Amer. Soc. Test. Mat.* **41** (1941) 849.

152. H. L. BURGHOFF and A. I. BLANK, "Fatigue Tests on Some Copper Alloys in Wire Form". *Proc. Amer. Soc. Test. Mat.* **43** (1943) 774.

153. G. R. GOHN and S. M. ARNOLD, "Fatigue Properties of Beryllium–Copper Strip". *Proc. Amer. Soc. Test. Mat.* **46** (1946) 741.

154. G. R. GOHN and W. C. ELLIS, "Fatigue Characteristics of Copper–Nickel–Zinc and Phosphor-Bronze Strip". *Proc. Amer. Soc. Test. Mat.* **47** (1947) 713.

155. J. N. Kenyon, "Fatigue Properties of Some Cold-Drawn Nickel Alloy Wires". *Proc. Amer. Soc. Test. Mat.* **43** (1943) 765.

156. D. N. Williams, "Hydrogen in Titanium and Titanium Alloys". *Titanium Metallurgical Lab. Ohio TML Rpt.* No. 100 (1958).

157. L. W. Berger, W. S. Hyler and R. I. Jaffee, "Effect of Hydrogen on the Fatigue Properties of Titanium and Ti-8 percent Mn Alloy". *Trans. Amer. Inst. Min. and Met. Engrs.* **212** (1958) 41.

158. L. M. T. Hopkin and C. J. Thwaites, "Creep and Fatigue Properties of Lead and Lead Alloys". *J. Inst. Met.* **82** (1953) 181.

159. E. C. Ellwood and R. Duckett, "Fatigue Strength of Pure Tin at Room Temperature". *Nature, Lond.* **173** (1954) 497.

160. W. L. Bruckart and W. S. Hyler, "Room Temperature Fatigue Properties of Molybdenum". *Trans. Amer. Inst. Min. and Met. Engrs.* **203** (1955) 287.

161. M. H. Weisman and M. H. Kaplan, "Fatigue Strength of Steel Through the Range from $\frac{1}{2}$ to 30,000 Cycles of Stress". *Proc. Amer. Soc. Test. Mat.* **50** (1950) 649.

162. P. P. Benham, "Fatigue of Metals Caused by a Relatively Few Cycles of High Load or Strain Amplitude". *Metal. Rev.* **3** (1958) No. 11, 203.

163. F. C. Smith, W. C. Brueggeman and R. H. Harwell, "Fatigue Strengths of Bare and Alclad 24S–T3 Aluminium Alloy Sheet Specimens Tested at 12 and 1000 Cycles per Minute". *Nat. Adv. Co. Aero. Tech. Note* 2231 (1950).

164. W. Illg, "Fatigue Tests on Notched and Unnotched Sheet Specimens of 2024–T3 and 7075–T6 Aluminium Alloys and of SAE 4130 Steel with Special Consideration of the Life Range from 2 to 10,000 Cycles". *Nat. Adv. Co. Aero. Tech. Note* 3866 (1956).

165. W. G. Finch, "Fatigue of Steels in the Finite Region of the S–N Curve". *Proc. Amer. Soc. Test. Mat.* **52** (1952) 759.

166. T. T. Oberg and W. J. Trapp, "High Stress Fatigue of Aluminium and Magnesium Alloys". *Prod. Engng.* **22** (Feb. 1951) 159.

167. T. T. Oberg and E. J. Ward, "Fatigue of Alloy Steels at High Stress Levels". *Wright Air Develop. Center Tech. Rpt.* **53**-256 (1953).

168. G. Sachs, B. B. Muvdi and E. P. Klier, "Fatigue of High Strength Steels". *Amer. Soc. Test. Mat. Spec. Publ.* **196** (1957) 77.

169. A. C. Low, "Short Endurance Fatigue". *Int. Conf. on Fatigue, Instn. Mech. Engrs.* (1956) 206 and page 899 (discussion).

170. L. F. Kooistra, "Effect of Plastic Fatigue on Pressure-Vessel Materials and Design". *Welding J.* **36** (1957) 120S.

171. L. F. Coffin, "Cyclic Straining—Fatigue". Symp. "*Internal Stresses and Fatigue in Metals*". General Motors U.S.A. (1958). Elsevier Amsterdam and London (1959) 363.

172. E. L. Layland, "How Metals Perform Under Repeated Impact". *Materials and Methods* **44** (July 1956) 104.

173. T. E. Stanton and L. Bairstow, "Resistance of Materials to Impact". *Proc. Instn. Mech. Engrs.* (1908) 889.

174. D. J. McAdam, "Endurance Properties of Steels". *Proc. Amer. Soc. Test. Mat.* **23** II (1923) 56.

175. G. A. Hankins and H. R. Mills, "Resistance of Spring Steels to Repeated Impact Stresses". *J. Iron and Steel Inst.* **131** (1935) 165.

176. H. C. O'Connor and J. L. M. Morrison, "Effect of Mean Stress on the Push-Pull Fatigue Properties of an Alloy Steel". *Int. Conf. on Fatigue, Instn. Mech. Engrs.* (1956) 102.

177. W. J. Trapp and R. T. Schwartz, "Elevated Temperature Fatigue Properties of SAE 4340 Steel". *Proc. Amer. Soc. Test. Materials* **53** (1953) 825.

178. H. J. Gough and W. A. Wood, "Deformation and Fracture of Mild Steel Under Cyclic Stresses". *Proc. Inst. Mech. Engrs.* **141** (1939) 175.

179. A. Pomp and M. Hempel, "Fatigue Strength–Tensile Strength Diagrams for Steels". *Mitt aus dem Kaiser Wilhelm Inst. fur Eisenforschung.* **18** (1936) 1.

180. A. R. Woodward, K. W. Gunn and G. Forrest, "Effect of Mean Stress on the Fatigue of Aluminium Alloys". *Int. Conf. on Fatigue, Instn. Mech. Engrs.* (1956) 158.

181. F. M. Howell and J. L. Miller, "Axial Stress Fatigue Strengths of Several Structural Aluminium Alloys". *Proc. Amer. Soc. Test. Mat.* **55** (1955) 955.

182. F. W. de Money and B. J. Lazan, "Dynamic Creep and Rupture Properties of an Aluminium Alloy". *Proc. Amer. Soc. Test. Mat.* **54** (1954) 769.

183. Anon. *Fatigue Characteristics of Ti–6Al–4V* Titanium Metals Corp. New York (1957).

184. F. H. Vitovec and B. J. Lazan, "Fatigue, Creep and Rupture Properties of Heat Resistant Materials". *Wright Air Develop. Center. Tech. Rpt.* 56-181 (1956). See also *ibid.* 58-340 (1958) and *Amer. Soc. Test. Mat. Spec. Tech. Publ.* 196 (1956).

185. Anon. "Co-operative Investigation of Static and Fatigue Properties of Wrought N-155 Alloy at Elevated Temperatures". *Nat. Adv. Co. Aero. Report* 1288 (1956).

186. M. Kawamoto and K. Nishioka, *Memoirs Faculty of Engng. Kyoto Univ.* **16** (1954) 228.

187. H. J. Grover, S. M. Bishop and L. R. Jackson, "Axial Load Fatigue Tests of Unnotched Sheet Specimens of 24S–T3 and 75S–T6 Aluminium Alloys and of SAE 4130 Steel". *Nat. Adv. Co. Aero. Tech. Note* 2324 (1951).

188. G. Sines, "Failure of Materials under Combined Repeated Stresses with Superimposed Static Stresses". *Nat. Adv. Co. Aero. Tech. note* 3495 (1955).

189. J. O. Smith, "Effect of Range of Stress on Fatigue Strength". *Univ. Illinois Engg. Expt. Station Bulletin* 334 (1942).

190. W. T. Chodorowski, "Fatigue Strength in Shear of an Alloy Steel". *Int. Conf. on Fatigue, Instn. Mech. Engrs.* (1956) 122.

191. A. Pomp and M. Hempel, "The Fatigue Behaviour of Cast Iron and Malleable Iron". *Mitt. Kaiser-Wilhelm Inst. fur Eisenforschung* **22** (1940) 169.

192. H. Majors, B. D. Mills and C. W. MacGregor, "Fatigue under Combined Pulsating Stresses". *J. Appl. Mech.* **16** (1949) 269.

193. R. W. Bundy and J. Marin, "Fatigue Strength of 14S–T4 Aluminium Alloy Subjected to Biaxial Stresses". *Proc. Amer. Soc. Test Mat.* **54** (1954) 755.

194. G. K. Morikawa and Le Van Griffis, "Biaxial Fatigue Strength of Low Carbon Steels". *Welding J.* **24** (1945) 167s.

195. P. Ludwik, "Notch and Corrosion Fatigue Strength". *Metall.* **10** (1931) 705.

196. P. H. Frith, "Fatigue Tests on Crankshaft Steels". *J. Iron and Steel Inst.* **159** (1948) 385.

197. T. Nishihara and M. Kawamoto, "Fatigue of Steel under Combined Bending and Torsion". *Trans. Soc. Mech. Eng.* (Japan) **6** (1940) S-2.

198. W. N. Findley, "Fatigue of Metals under Combinations of Stresses". *Trans. Amer. Soc. Mech. Engrs.* **79** (1957) 1337.

199. H. J. Gough and H. V. Pollard, "Properties of Some Materials for Cast Crankshafts with Special Reference to Combined Stresses'. *Proc. Inst. Auto. Engrs.* **31** (1937) 821.

CC

AA

200. T. NISHIHARA and M. KAWAMOTO, "The Strength of Metals under Combined Alternating Bending and Torsion with Phase Difference". *Memoirs Coll. Engg. Kyoto Univ. Japan* **11** (1945) 85.

201. K. MATTHAES, "Fatigue Strengths of Light Alloys". *Z. Metallkunde* **24** (1932) 176.

202. J. A. SAUER and D. C. LEMMON, "Effect of Steady Stress on Fatigue Behaviour of Aluminium". *Trans. Amer. Soc. Met.* **42** (1950) 559.

203. H. J. GOUGH, "Engineering Steels under Combined Cyclic and Static Stresses". *J. Appl. Mech.* **17** (1950) 113.

204. H. L. COX, "Four Studies in the Theory of Stress Concentrations". *Aero. Res. Council Monograph R and M No.* 2704 (1953).

205. R. C. A. THURSTON and J. E. FIELD, "Fatigue Strength under Bending, Torsional and Combined Stresses of Steel Test-Pieces with Stress Concentrations". *Proc. Instn. Mech. Engrs.* **168** (1954) 785.

206. H. L. COX, "Fatigue". *J. Royal Aero Soc.* **57** (1953) 559.

207. R. E. PETERSON, "Torsion and Tension Relations for Slip and Fatigue", *Colloquium on Fatigue, Stockholm* (1955). Springer-Verlag, Berlin (1956) 186.

208. G. STANFIELD, *Proc. Inst. Mech. Engrs.* **131** (1935) 93.

209. F. B. STULEN and H. N. CUMMINGS, "A Failure Criterion for Multi-Axial Fatigue Stresses". *Proc. Amer. Soc. Test. Mat.* **54** (1954) 822.

210. W. N. FINDLEY, "Theories Relating to Fatigue of Materials under Combinations of Stress", *Colloquium on Fatigue, Stockholm* (1955). Springer-Verlag, Berlin (1956) 35.

211. W. N. FINDLEY, J. J. COLEMAN and B. C. HANLEY, "Theory for Combined Bending and Torsion Fatigue". *Int. Conf. on Fatigue, Inst. Mech. Engrs.* (1956) 150.

212. A. PALMGREN, "Endurance of Ball-Bearings", *Z. Ver. Dtsch. Ing.* **68** (1924) 339.

213. M. A. MINER, "Cumulative Damage in Fatigue". *J. Appl. Mech.* **12** (1945) A-159.

214. T. F. ROYLANCE, "Review of Cumulative Damage in Fatigue". *M.O.S. S. and T* Memo. 8/57 (1957).

215. J. SCHIJVE and F. A. JACOBS, "Cumulative Damage in Fatigue of Riveted Aluminium Alloy Joints". *Nat. Aero. Res. Inst. Amsterdam* 20 (1956) *N.L.L. Report* M 1999.

216. J. B. KOMMERS, "Effect of Overstress in Fatigue on the Endurance Life of Steel". *Proc. Amer. Soc. Test. Mat.* **45** (1945) 532.

217. J. A. BENNETT, "Damaging Effect of Fatigue Stressing on X4130 Steel". *Proc. Amer. Soc. Test. Mat.* **46** (1946) 693.

218. BATTELLE MEMORIAL INSTITUTE, *Prevention of the Failure of Metals under Repeated Stress.* John Wiley, New York. Chapman and Hall, London (1941).

219. J. C. LEVY, "Cumulative Damage in Fatigue". *Engineering* **179** (1955) 724.

220. F. E. RICHART and N. M. NEWMARK, "An Hypothesis for the Determination of Cumulative Damage in Fatigue". *Proc. Amer. Soc. Test. Mat.* **48** (1948) 767.

221. S. M. MARCO and W. L. STARKEY, "A Concept of Fatigue Damage". *Trans. Amer. Soc. Mech. Engrs.* **76** (1954) 627.

222. G. E. DIETER, G. T. HORNE and R. F. MEHL, "Statistical Study of Overstressing in Steel". *Nat. Adv. Co. Aero. Tech. Note* 3211 (1954).

223. ANON. "Recovery and Permanent Damage to Metals under Fatigue Conditions". *Fulmer Res. Inst. Rpt. R* 94/8 (1957).

224. E. W. C. WILKINS, "Cumulative Damage in Fatigue", *Colloquium on Fatigue, Stockholm* (1955). Springer-Verlag, Berlin (1956).

225. D. Webber and J. C. Levy, "Cumulative Damage in Fatigue with Reference to the Scatter of Results". *M.O.S. S & T Memo. No.* 15/58 (1958).

226. T. J. Dolan, F. E. Richart and C. E. Work, "Influence of Fluctuations in Stress Amplitude on the Fatigue of Metals. *Proc. Amer. Soc. Test. Mat.* **49** (1949) 646.

227. H. T. Corten, G. M. Sinclair and T. J. Dolan, "The Influence of Fluctuating Stress Amplitude on Fatigue Life of 75S–T6 Aluminium". *Proc. Amer. Soc. Test. Mat.* **54** (1954) 737.

228. T. J. Dolan and H. F. Brown, "Effect of Prior Repeated Stressing on the Fatigue Life of 75S–T Aluminium". *Proc. Amer. Soc. Test. Mat.* **52** (1952) 733.

229. I. Smith, D. M. Howard and F. C. Smith, "Cumulative Damage of Axially Loaded Alclad 75S–T6 and Alclad 24S–T3 Aluminium Alloy Sheet". *Nat. Adv. Co. Aero. Tech. Note* 3293 (1955).

230. F. J. Plantema, "Some Investigations on Cumulative Damage". *Coll. on Fatigue, Stockholm* (1955). Springer-Verlag, Berlin (1956) 218.

231. J. B. Kommers, "Overstressing and Understressing in Fatigue". *Proc. Amer. Soc. Test. Mat.* **43** (1943) 749.

232. H. F. Moore, S. W. Lyon and N. P. Inglis, "Fatigue Strength of Cast Iron". *Univ. Illinois Engg. Expt. Station Bull. No.* 164 (1927).

233. G. N. J. Gilbert and K. B. Palmer, "The Influence of Understressing on the Fatigue Properties of Flake Graphite and Nodular Graphite Cast Irons". *Brit. Cast Iron Res. Assoc. J. Res. and Development* **6** (1956) 410.

234. K. B. Palmer, "The Effect of Understressing on the Fatigue Properties of Coarse Flake Graphite Cast Iron". *Brit. Cast Iron Res. Assoc. J. Res. and Development* **6** (1957) 660.

235. F. Bollenrath and H. Cornelius, "Effect of Rest Periods on Endurance and Fatigue Strength of Metals". *Z. Ver. Dtsch. Ing.* **84** (1940) 295. Transl. *Bull. British Non-Ferrous Metals Res. Assoc.* **135** (1940) 264.

236. G. M. Sinclair, "Coaxing Effect in Fatigue of Metals". *Proc. Amer. Soc. Test Mat.* **52** (1952) 743.

237. J. Holden, "Fundamental Considerations on the Fatigue of Metals". Chapter in *The Fatigue of Metals.* Inst. Metallurgists (1955) 3.

238. R. B. Heywood, "Effect of High Loads on Fatigue". *Coll. on Fatigue, Stockholm* (1955). Springer-Verlag, Berlin (1956) 92.

239. E. Gassner, "Effect of Variable Load and Cumulative Damage on Fatigue in Vehicles and Airplane Structures". *Int. Conf. on Fatigue, Inst. Mech. Engrs.* (1956) 304.

240. E. Gassner, "Performance Fatigue Testing with Respect to Aircraft Design". *Int. Conf. on Fatigue in Aircraft Structures.* Academic Press, New York (1956) 178.

241. A. M. Freudenthal and R. A. Heller, "Accumulation of Fatigue Damage". *Int. Conf. on Fatigue in Aircraft Structures.* Academic Press, New York (1956) 146.

242. H. F. Hardrath and E. C. Utley, "Behaviour of 24S–T4 Aluminium Alloy Subjected to Repeated Stresses of Constant and Varying Amplitudes". *Nat. Adv. Co. Aero. Tech. Note* 2798 (1952).

243. A. M. Freudenthal, "A Random Fatigue Testing Procedure and Machine". *Proc. Amer. Soc. Test. Mat.* **53** (1953) 896.

244. G. Wallgren, "Fatigue Tests with Stress Cycles of Varying Amplitudes". *FFA Report* No. 28 (1949).

245. A. K. HEAD and F. H. HOOKE, "Random Noise Fatigue Testing". *Int. Conf. on Fatigue, Instn. Mech. Engrs.* (1956) 301.

246. W. A. P. FISHER, "Programme Fatigue Tests on Notched Bars to a Gust Load Spectrum". *R.A.E. Tech. Note Struct.* 236 (1958).

247. R. A. CARL and T. J. WEGENG, "Fatigue of Aircraft Structures". *Proc. Amer. Soc. Test. Mat.* **54** (1954) 903.

248. H. W. LIU and H. T. CORTEN, "Fatigue Damage During Complex Stress Histories". *Nat. Aero. and Space Admin. Tech. Note* D-256 (1959).

249. N. M. NEWMARK, "Review of Cumulative Damage in Fatigue". *Symp. Fatigue and Fracture of Metals. M.I.T.* (1950). John Wiley and Sons, New York, Chapman and Hall, London (1952) 197.

250. T. WYSS, "Influence of Testing Frequency on the Fatigue Strength of Steels and Light Alloys". *Amer. Soc. Test. Mat. Bull.* **188** (1953) 31.

251. N. STEPHENSON, "A Review of the Literature on the Effect of Frequency on the Fatigue Properties of Metals and Alloys". *National Gas Turbine Establishment Memo M* 320 (1958).

252. C. E. INGLIS, "Stresses in a Plate due to the Presence of Cracks and Sharp Corners". *Engineering* **95** (1913) 415.

253. R. E. PETERSON, *Stress Concentration Design Factors*. J. Wiley, New York. Chapman and Hall, London (1953).

254. J. R. LINGE, "Brittle Lacquers". *Research Applied in Industry* **13** (Jan. 1960) 18.

255. M. M. FROCHT, *Photoelasticity*. J. Wiley, New York. Chapman and Hall, London. Vol. 1 (1941), Vol. 2 (1948).

256. R. B. HEYWOOD, *Designing by Photoelasticity*. Chapman and Hall (1952).

257. E. G. COKER and L. N. G. FILON, *Photoelasticity*, revised by H. T. Jessop. Cambridge Univ. Press (1957).

258. C. S. YEN and T. J. DOLAN, "A Critical Review of the Criteria for Notch-Sensitivity in Fatigue of Metals". *Univ. Illinois Bull.* 398 (1952).

259. P. KUHN, "Influence of Size on the Fatigue of Notched Specimens". *Rev. Met.* **55** (1958) 860.

260. M. HEMPEL, "Effect of Specimen Size on Fatigue Strength". *Draht* **8** (1957) 385.

261. C. E. PHILLIPS and R. B. HEYWOOD, "Size Effect in Fatigue of Plain and Notched Steel Specimens Loaded under Reversed Direct Stress". *Proc. Inst. Mech. Engrs.* **165** (1951) 113.

262. C. MASSONNET, "Effect of Size, Shape and Grain Size on the Fatigue Strength of Medium Carbon Steel". *Proc. Amer. Soc. Test. Mat.* **56** (1956) 954.

263. H. F. MOORE, "Size Effect and Notch Sensitivity in Fatigue". *Proc. Amer. Soc. Test. Mat.* **45** (1945) 507.

264. D. MORKOVIN and H. F. MOORE, "The Effect of Size of Specimens on Fatigue Strength of Three Types of Steel". *Proc. Amer. Soc. Test. Mat.* **44** (1944) 137.

265. R. E. PETERSON and A. M. WAHL, "Two and Three Dimensional Cases of Stress Concentrations and Comparison with Fatigue Tests". *Trans. Amer. Soc. Mech. Engrs.* **58** (1936) A.15.

266. O. J. HORGER and J. L. MAULBETSCH, "Increasing the Fatigue Strength of Press-Fitted Axle Assemblies by Surface Rolling". *Trans. Amer. Soc. Mech. Engrs.* **58** (1936) A91.

267. H. MAJORS, "Dynamic Properties of Nodular Cast Iron". *Trans. Amer. Soc. Mech. Engrs.* **74** (1952) 365.

268. W. BUCHMANN, "Influence of Notch Size on Endurance Limit". *Z. Ver. Dtsch. Ing.* **87** (1943) 325.

269. R. MAILANDER and W. BAUERSFELD, "Effect of Diameter of Testpiece on Alternating Torsional Fatigue Strength of Steel". *Krupp. Mitt.* **2** (1943) 143.

270. O. J. HORGER and H. R. NEIFERT, "Fatigue Strength of Machined Forgings 6 to 7 inches in Diameter". *Proc. Amer. Soc. Test. Mat.* **39** (1939) 723.

271. F. C. Eaton, "Fatigue Tests of Large Alloy Steel Shafts". *Amer. Soc. Test. Mat. Spec. Tech. Publ.* **216** (1957) 96.

272. T. W. BUNYAN, "Fatigue Performance of Marine Shafting". *Amer. Soc. Test. Mat. Spec. Tech. Publ.* **216** (1957) 59.

273. E. J. ECKERT, "Torsional Fatigue Testing of Axle Shafts". *Amer. Soc. Test. Mat. Spec. Tech. Publ.* **216** (1957) 21.

274. E. LEHR and F. RUEF, "Fatigue Strength of Crankshafts of Large Diesels". *Engineers Digest* **5** (1944) 285.

275. C. E. PHILLIPS and A. J. FENNER, "Some Fatigue Tests on Aluminium Alloy and Mild Steel Sheet With and Without Drilled Holes." *Proc. Instn. Mech. Engrs.* **165** (1951) 125.

276. G. FORREST, "The Effect on Fatigue of Notches, Surface Finishes etc." Chapter in *The Fatigue of Metals*. Inst. Metallurgists (1955) 40.

277. H. L. Cox, "Stress Concentration in Relation to Fatigue". *Int. Conf. on Fatigue, Instn. Mech. Engrs.* (1956) 212.

278. R. E. PETERSON, "Methods of Correlating Data from Fatigue Tests of Stress Concentration Specimens". *Stephen Timoshenko 60th Anniversary Vol.* Macmillan (1938) 179.

279. R. W. KARRY and T. J. DOLAN, "Influence of Grain Size on Fatigue Notch Sensitivity". *Proc. Amer. Soc. Test. Mat.* **53** (1953) 789.

280. N. E. FROST, "A Relation Between the Critical Alternating Propagation Stress and Crack Length for Mild Steel". *Proc. Instn. Mech. Engrs.* **173** (1959) 811.

281. N. E. FROST, "Notch Effects and the Critical Alternating Stress Required to Propagate a Crack in an Aluminium Alloy Subject to Fatigue Loading". *J. Mech. Engng. Science* **2** (1960) 109.

282. J. A. BENNETT, "The Distinction Between Initiation and Propagation of a Fatigue Crack". *Int. Conf. on Fatigue. Instn. Mech. Engrs.* (1956) 548.

283. P. KUHN and H. F. HARDRATH, "An Engineering Method for Estimating Notch Size Effect in Fatigue Tests on Steel". *Nat. Adv. Co. Aero. Tech. Note* 2805 (1952).

284. R. B. HEYWOOD, "Stress Concentration Factors". *Engineering* **179** (1955) 146.

285. R. E. PETERSON, "Relation Between Life Testing and Conventional Tests of Materials". *Amer. Soc. Test. Mat. Bull.* No. 133 (1945) 9.

286. A. POMP and M. HEMPEL, "Unnotched and Notched Fatigue Strengths of Unalloyed and Alloyed Structural Steels Between +20° and −78 °C. *Arch. Eisenhuttenw.* **21** (1950) 53.

287. F. KÖRBER and M. HEMPEL, "Axial Loading, Bending and Torsional Fatigue Tests of Steel Specimens with Holes and Notches". *Mitt. aus dem Kaiser-Wilhelm Inst. fur Eisenforschung* **21** (1939) 1.

288. S. F. DOREY and G. P. SMEDLEY, "The Influence of Fillet Radius on the Fatigue Strengths of Large Steel Shafts". *Int. Conf. on Fatigue. Instn. Mech. Engrs.* (1956) 247. (See also discussion on pages 750 and 881).

289. T. T. OBERG and J. B. JOHNSON, "Fatigue Properties of Metals at 3450 and 10,600 Cycles per Minute". *Proc. Amer. Soc. Test. Mat.* **37II** (1937) 195.

290. S. B. BAILEY, "Nodular Cast Iron". *Proc. Instn. Mech. Engrs.* **168** (1954) 643.

291. H. W. RUSSELL and W. A. WELCKER, "Damage and Overstress in the Fatigue of Ferrous Materials". *Proc. Amer. Soc. Test. Mat.* **36II** (1936) 118.

292. P. KUHN, "Effect of Geometric Size on Notch Fatigue". *Colloquium on Fatigue, Stockholm* (1955). Springer-Verlag, Berlin (1956) 131. (And see discussion by R. E. Peterson).

293. G. H. FOUND, "The Notch Sensitivity in Fatigue Loading of Some Magnesium-Base and Aluminium-Base Alloys". *Proc. Amer. Soc. Test. Mat.* **46** (1946) 715.

294. J. C. McDONALD, "Tensile, Creep and Fatigue Properties at Elevated Temperatures of Some Magnesium Base Alloys". *Proc. Amer. Soc. Test. Mat.* **48** (1948) 737.

295. D. J. McADAM and R. W. CLYNE, "Influence of Chemically and Mechanically Formed Notches on Fatigue of Metals". *J. Res. Nat. Bureau Standards* **13** (1934) 527.

296. H. R. OGDEN, F. C. HOLDEN and R. I. JAFFEE, "Mechanical Properties of Titanium–Chrome–Molybdenum Alloys". *Trans. Amer. Soc. Met.* **48** (1956) 627.

297. H. V. KINSEY, "The Mechanical and Engineering Properties of Commercially Available Titanium Alloys". *N.A.T.O. Adv. Group for Aero. Res. and Devel. Report* 100 (1957).

298. C. B. DITTMAR, C. W. BAUER and D. EVERS, "Fatigue Behaviour of Titanium and Titanium Alloys". *Wright Air Development Center. Tech. Report* 56-304 (1957).

299. H. F. HARDRATH, C. B. LANDERS and E. C. UTLEY, "Axial Load Fatigue Tests on Notched and Unnotched Specimens of 61S–T6 Aluminium Alloy, Annealed 347 Stainless Steel and Heat-Treated 403 Stainless Steel". *Nat. Adv. Co. Aero. Tech. Note* 3017 (1953).

300. K. GUNN, "Effect of Yielding on the Fatigue Properties of Testpieces Containing Stress Concentrations". *Aero. Quarterly* **6** (1955) 277.

301. H. J. GROVER, S. M. BISHOP and L. R. JACKSON, "Axial Load Fatigue Tests on Notched Sheet Specimens of 24S–T3 and 75S–T6 Aluminium Alloys and of SAE 4130 Steel with Stress Concentration Factors of 2 and 4". *Nat. Adv. Co. Aero. Tech. Note* 2389 (1951).

302. J. SCHIJVE, "Fatigue Crack Propagation in Light Alloys". National Luchtvaar and Laboratorium Amsterdam. *NLL-TN M* 2010 (1956).

303. L. J. DEMER, "Interrelation of Fatigue Cracking, Damping and Notch Sensitivity". *Wright Air Development Center Rpt.* 56-408 (1957).

304. P. J. E. FORSYTH and D. A. RYDER, "Fatigue Fracture". *Aircraft Engng.* **32** (1960) 96.

305. N. E. FROST and D. S. DUGDALE, "The Propagation of Fatigue Cracks in Sheet Specimens". *J. Mech. Phys. Solids* **6** (1958) 92.

306. N. E. FROST, "Propagation of Fatigue Cracks in Various Sheet Materials". *J. Mech. Engng. Science* **1** (1959) 151.

307. A. J. McEVILY, W. ILLG and H. F. HARDRATH, "Static Strength of Aluminium Alloy Specimens Containing Fatigue Cracks". *Nat. Adv. Co. Aero. Tech. Note* 3816 (1956).

308. P. G. FORREST, "The Measurement of Fatigue Damage in Mild Steel". *Engineering* **182** (1956) 266.

309. J. A. KIES and W. L. HOLSHOUSER, "Fatigue Damage of Steels by Supplementary Tension–Impact Tests". *Proc. Amer. Soc. Test. Mat.* **42** (1942) 556.

310. E. R. GADD, "Fatigue from the Metallurgists Viewpoint". *J. Roy. Aero. Soc.* **57** (1953) 565.

311. E. R. GADD, "Fatigue in Aero-Engines". *Int. Conf. on Fatigue. Instn. Mech. Engrs.* (1956) 658.

312. G. FORREST, "Internal or Residual Stresses in Wrought Aluminium Alloys". *J. Royal Aero. Soc.* **58** (1954) 261.

313. *Internal Stresses in Metals and Alloys.* Symp. Inst. of Metals, Monograph No. 5 (1948).

314. O. J. HORGER, "Residual Stresses". *Amer. Soc. Mech. Engrs. Handbook "Metals Engineering—Design."* (1953) 42.

315. *Residual Stresses in Metals and Metal Construction.* Reinhold, New York (1954).

316. Symposium *Internal Stresses and Fatigue in Metals.* General Motors U.S.A. 1958. Elsevier, Amsterdam, London, New York (1959).

317. H. BÜHLER and H. BUCHHOLTZ, "The Effect of Residual Stresses on Fatigue Strength". *Mitt. Forsch. Inst. Dortmund* **3** (1933) 235. *Stahl und Eisen* **53** (1933) 1330.

318. D. ROSENTHAL and G. SINES, "Effect of Residual Stress on the Fatigue Strength of Notched Specimens". *Proc. Amer. Soc. Test. Mat.* **51** (1951) 593.

319. D. S. DUGDALE, "Effect of Residual Stress on Fatigue Strength". *Welding J.* **38** (1959) 45 s.

320. M. L. BECKER and C. E. PHILLIPS, "Internal Stresses and their Effect on the Fatigue Resistance of Spring Steels". *J. Iron and Steel Inst.* **133** (1936) 427.

321. G. FORREST, "Some Experiments on the Effect of Residual Stresses on the Fatigue of Aluminium Alloys". *J. Inst. Met.* **72** (1946) 523.

322. R. L. MATTSON and J. G. ROBERTS, "Effect of Residual Stresses Induced by Strain Peening upon Fatigue Strength". Symp. *Internal Stresses and Fatigue*, General Motors (1958). Elsevier (1959) 337.

323. G. M. SINCLAIR, H. T. CORTEN and T. J. DOLAN, "Effect of Surface Finish on the Fatigue Strength of Titanium Alloys RC. 130B and Ti 140A. *Trans. Amer. Soc. Mech. Engrs.* **79** (1957) 89.

324. B. C. HANLEY and T. J. DOLAN, "Surface Finish". *Amer. Soc. Mech. Engrs. "Metals Engineering—Design".* (1953) 100.

325. O. J. HORGER and H. R. Neifert, "The Effect of Surface Conditions on Fatigue Properties". Symp. *Surface Treatment of Metals. Amer. Soc. Met.* (1941).

326. G. A. HANKINS, M. L. BECKER and H. R. MILLS, "The Effect of Surface Conditions on the Fatigue of Steels". *J. Iron and Steel Inst.* **133** (1936) 399.

327. E. SIEBEL and M. GAIER, "The Influence of Surface Roughness on the Fatigue Strength of Steels and Non-Ferrous Alloys". *Z. Ver. Dtsch. Ing.* **98** (1956) 1715. Transl. *Engineers Digest* **18** (1957) 109.

328. N. J. F. GUNN, "The Effect of Surface Finish on the Fatigue Resistance of Two Aluminium Alloys". *R.A.E. Tech. Note Met.* 196 (1954).

329. E. HOUDREMONT and R. MAILÄNDER, "Bending Fatigue Tests on Steels". *Stahl und Eisen* **49** (1929) 833.

330. M. HEMPEL, "The Problem of Specimen Size in Fatigue". *Arch. Eisenhutten.* **22** (1951) 425.

331. B. CINA, "The Effect of Surface Finish on Fatigue". *Metallurgia* **55** (1957) 11.

332. D. N. CLEDWYN-DAVIES, "Effect of Grinding on the Fatigue Strength of Steels". *Proc. Instn. Mech. Engrs.* **169** (1955) 83.

333. G. A. HANKINS and M. L. BECKER, "The Fatigue Resistance of Unmachined Forged Steel". *J. Iron and Steel Inst.* **126** (1932) 205.

334. J. F. WATKINSON, "The Influence of Some Surface Factors on the Torsional Fatigue Strength of Spring Steels". *Int. Conf. on Fatigue. Instn. Mech. Engrs.* (1956) 445.

335. J. G. BROOKMAN and L. KIDDLE, "Prevention of Fatigue Failures by Shot-Peening". *Symp. Failure of Metals by Fatigue. Melbourne* (1946) 395.

336. B. Iones, "Shot Peening". *Steels in Modern Industry*. Iliffe & Sons, London (1951) 501.

337. Anon. *Shot Peening*. Wheelabrator Corp. U.S. 5th Ed. (1956).

338. S. Takeuchi and T. Homma, "Effect of Shot-Peening on the Fatigue Strength of Metals". *Sci. Reports Tokhoku Univ.* **10** (1958) 426. **11** (1959) 48 and 94.

339. J. M. Lessells and R. F. Brodrick, "Shot-Peening as Protection of Surface-Damaged Propeller-Blade Materials". *Int. Conf. on Fatigue. Instn. Mech. Engrs.* (1956) 617.

340. J. O. Almen, "Shot Blasting to Increase Fatigue Resistance". *Trans. Soc. Auto Engrs.* **1** (1943) 248.

341. J. O. Almen, "Fatigue Weakness of Surfaces". *Prod. Engineering* **21** (November 1950) 117.

342. A. G. H. Coombs, F. Sherratt and J. A. Pope, "The Effects of Shot-Peening on the Fatigue Strength of Hardened and Tempered Spring Steel". *Int. Conf. on Fatigue. Instn. Mech. Engrs.* (1956) 227. See also discussion by J. F. Watkinson, page 755.

343. G. H. Found, "Increasing the Endurance of Magnesium Castings by Surface Work". *Metal Progress* **60** (August 1951) 51.

344. A. W. Demmler, M. J. Sinnott and L. Thomassen, "Fatigue Properties of Some Titanium Alloys". *Proc. Amer. Soc. Test. Mat.* **55** (1955) 981.

345. R. J. Love, "Fatigue in Automobiles". *Int. Conf. on Fatigue. Instn. Mech. Engrs.* (1956) 570.

346. G. N. J. Gilbert and K. B. Palmer, "Influence of Surface Rolling on the Fatigue Strength of Cast Iron". *Brit. Cast Iron Res. Ass. J. Res. and Develop.* **5** (1953–4) 71 and 447.

347. G. Sachs, "Improving Aircraft Propellers by Surface Rolling". *Metals and Alloys* **10** (1939) 19.

348. F. H. Vitovec, "Effect of Static Prestrain on Fatigue Properties". *Proc. Amer. Soc. Test. Mat.* **58** (1958) 552.

349. J. O. Almen, "Some Needed Precautions when Induction and Flame Hardening". *Metal Progress* **46** (1944) 1263.

350. R. J. Brown, *Sheet Metal Industries* **24** (1947) 795.

351. *Steels in Modern Industry*. Iliffe & Sons (London) 1951.

352. F. C. Lea, "Effect of Discontinuities and Surface Conditions on Failure under Repeated Stress". *Engineering* **144** (1937) 87, 140.

353. R. A. F. Hammond and C. Williams, "The Effect of Electroplating on Fatigue Strength". *Metal. Rev.* **5** (1960) 165.

354. T. C. deK Kuun, "The Fatigue Strength of Chromium-Plated Steel". *South African Mech. Engr.* **9** (1960) 139.

355. H. L. Logan, "Effect of Chromium Plating on the Endurance Limit of Steels used in Aircraft". *National Bureau of Standards. J. Research* **43** (1949) 101.

356. R. H. D. Barklie and H. J. Davies, "Effect of Surface Conditions and Electrodeposited Metals on the Resistance of Materials to Repeated Stresses". *Proc. Inst. Mech. Engrs.* **1** (1930) 731. Summary in *Engineering* **150** (1930) 670.

357. R. R. Moore, "Metallic Coatings". *Amer. Soc. Mech. Engrs. Metals Engineering—Design* (1953) 148.

358. J. O. Almen, "Fatigue Loss and Gain by Electroplating". *Prod. Engineering* **22** (June 1951) 109.

359. C. F. Williams and R. A. F. Hammond, "Effect of Chromium Plating on the Fatigue Strength of Steel". *Trans. Inst. Met. Finish* **32** (1955) 85.

360. J. S. Jackson, "Hydrogen Occlusion and its Effect on the Fatigue Properties of Plain Carbon Spring Steels". *Int. Conf. on Fatigue. Instn. Mech. Engrs.* (1956) 500.

361. D. Birchon, "Metal Spraying—Effect of a Molybdenum Deposit on Adhesion and on Fatigue of Ferritic Steels". *Metallurgia* **58** (1958) 273.

362. J. M. Finney, "Effect of Pickling and Anodising on the Fatigue Properties of 2L40 and DTD683 aluminium alloys". *Metallurgia* **60** (1959) 93.

363. E. G. Savage, E. G. F. Sampson and J. K. Curran, "The Effect of Hard Anodic Coatings on the Fatigue Strength of DTD 364 B Aluminium Alloy". *R.A.E. Tech. Note Met.* 200 (1954).

364. H. J. Gough, "Corrosion Fatigue of Metals". *J. Inst. Met.* **49** (1932) 17.

365. P. T. Gilbert, "Corrosion Fatigue". *Metal. Rev.* **1** (1956) 379.

366. A. J. Gould, "Corrosion Fatigue". *Iron and Steel* **24** (1951) 7; *Int. Conf. on Fatigue. Instn. Mech. Engrs.* (1956) 341.

367. U. R. Evans, *The Corrosion and Oxidation of Metals.* Edward Arnold, London (1960).

368. T. W. Bunyan, "Service Fatigue Failures in Marine Machinery". *Int. Conf. on Fatigue. Instn. Mech. Engrs.* (1956) 713.

369. H. J. Gough and D. G. Sopwith, "Some Comparative Corrosion Fatigue Tests employing two types of Stressing Action". *J. Iron and Steel Inst.* **127** (1933) 301.

370. D. J. McAdam and G. W. Geil, "Pitting and its Effect on the Fatigue Limit of Steels Corroded under Various Conditions". *Proc. Amer. Soc. Test. Mat.* **41** (1941) 696. *J. Res. Nat. Bureau Standards* **24** (1940) 685.

371. D. J. McAdam, "Corrosion Fatigue of Metals". *Trans. Amer. Soc. Steel Treating* **11** (1927) 355.

372. N. P. Inglis and G. F. Lake, "Corrosion Fatigue Tests of Steels in River Tees Water". *Trans. Faraday Soc.* **27** (1931) 803; **28** (1932) 715.

373. S. Hara, "Corrosion Fatigue of Marine Propeller Shafts". *Int. Conf. Fatigue. Instn. Mech. Engrs.* (1956) 348.

374. H. E. Haven, "Corrosion Fatigue on Streamline Wire for Aircraft". *Trans. Amer. Soc. Mech. Engrs.* **54** (1932) AER109.

375. B. B. Wescott, "Fatigue and Corrosion Fatigue of Steels". *Mech. Eng.* **60** (1938) 813.

376. T. S. Fuller, "Endurance Properties of Steel in Steam". *Trans. Amer. Inst. Min. and Met. Engrs.* **90** (1930) 280. *Trans. Amer. Soc. Steel Treat.* **19** (1931) 97.

377. J. W. Martin and G. C. Smith, "Fatigue of Metals in Liquid Metal Environments". *Metallurgia* **54** (1956) 227.

378. D. J. McAdam, "Corrosion Fatigue of Non-Ferrous Metals". *Proc. Amer. Soc. Test. Mat.* **27**II (1927) 102. Also *Int. Congress Testing Materials*, Amsterdam (1927) Vol. 1, p. 305.

379. H. J. Gough and D. G. Sopwith, "Resistance of Some Special Bronzes to Fatigue and Corrosion Fatigue". *J. Inst. Met.* **60** (1937) 143.

380. D. G. Sopwith, "The Resistance of Aluminium and Beryllium Bronzes to Fatigue and Corrosion Fatigue". *Aero. Res. Council R. and M.* 2486 (1950).

381. C. A. Subbington and P. J. E. Forsyth, "Some Corrosion Fatigue Observations on Aluminium–Zinc–Magnesium Alloys". *RAE Tech. Note Met.* 289 (1958).

382. R. Sterner-Rainer and W. Jung-Konig, "Corrosion Fatigue Strength of some Aluminium Alloys". *Korrosion u. Metallschutz* **18** (1942) 337.

383. D. J. MACK, "Corrosion Fatigue Properties of Some Hard Lead Alloys in Sulphuric Acid". *Proc. Amer. Soc. Test. Mat.* **45** (1945) 629.

384. N. P. INGLIS, "Titanium Research and Development". *Metal Industry* **90** (1957) 185.

385. H. A. LEYBOLD, H. F. HARDRATH and R. L. MOORE, "The Effects of Atmospheric Corrosion on the Fatigue Life of Aluminium Alloys". *Nat. Adv. Co. Aero. Tech. Note* 4331 (1958).

386. ANON. *Corrosion Prevention and Control.* **2** (Dec. 1955) 37.

387. I. CORNET and S. GOLAN, "Influence of Temperature on Corrosion Fatigue". *Corrosion* **15** (1959) 262t.

388. H. J. GOUGH and D. G. SOPWITH, "Influence of Mean Stress on the Resistance of Metals to Corrosion Fatigue". *J. Iron and Steel Inst.* **135** (1937) 293.

389. T. J. DOLAN, "Simultaneous Effects of Corrosion and Abrupt Changes in Section on the Fatigue Strength of Steel". *J. Appl. Mech.* **5** (1938) A 141.

390. W. L. COLLINS and J. O. SMITH, "Notch Sensitivity of Alloyed Cast Irons Subjected to Repeated and Static Loads". *Proc. Amer. Soc. Test. Mat.* **42** (1942) 639.

391. K. ENDO and Y. MIYAO, "Effects of Cycle Frequency on the Corrosion Fatigue Strength". *Bull. Japan Soc. Mech. Engrs.* **1** (1958) 374.

392. D. G. SOPWITH and H. J. GOUGH, "Effect of Protective Coatings on the Corrosion Fatigue Resistance of Steel". *J. Iron and Steel Inst.* **135** (1937) 315.

393. T. J. DOLAN and H. H. BENNINGER, "Effect of Protective Coatings on the Corrosion Fatigue Strength of Steel". *Proc. Amer. Soc. Test. Mat.* **40** (1940) 658.

394. W. E. HARVEY, "Protective Coatings against Corrosion Fatigue of Steels". *Metals and Alloys* **1** (1930) 458 and **3** (1932) 69.

395. B. B. WESCOTT, *Proc. Amer. Soc. Test. Mat.* **40** (1940) 667.

396. I. J. GERARD and H. SUTTON, "Corrosion Fatigue Properties of Duralumin with and without Protective Coatings". *J. Inst. Met.* **56** (1935) 29.

397. N. P. INGLIS and E. C. LARKE, "Corrosion Fatigue Properties of Aluminium–Magnesium–Silicon Alloy in the Unprotected, Anodized and Painted Conditions". *J. Inst. Met.* **83** (1954) 117.

398. J. A. BENNETT, "Effect of an Anodic (HAE) Coating on the Fatigue Strength of Magnesium Alloy Specimens". *Proc. Amer. Soc. Test. Mat.* **55** (1955) 1015.

399. A. J. GOULD and U. R. EVANS, "Effect of Shot-Peening on Corrosion Fatigue of a High Carbon Steel". *J. Iron and Steel Inst.* **160** (1948) 164.

400. J. N. KENYON, "A Corrosion Fatigue Test to Determine the Protective Qualities of Metallic Platings". *Proc. Amer. Soc. Test. Mat.* **40** (1940) 705.

401. A. ROYEZ and J. POMEY, "Protection against Corrosion Fatigue". *Rev. Met.* **56** (1959) 122.

402. O. FORSMAN and E. LUNDIN, "Influence of Surface Coatings on the Fatigue Strength of Steel". *Proc. 1st World Met. Congress. Amer. Soc. Met.* (1951) 606.

403. W. J. HARRIS, "Cyclic Stressing Frequency Effect on Fatigue Strength". *Aircraft Engineering* **31** (1959) 352.

404. H. J. GOUGH and D. G. SOPWITH, "Atmospheric Action as a Factor in Fatigue of Metals". *J. Inst. Metals* **49** (1932) 93.

405. H. J. GOUGH and D. G. SOPWITH, "Some Further Experiments on Atmospheric Action in Fatigue". *J. Inst. Metals* **56** (1935) 55.

406. H. J. GOUGH and D. G. SOPWITH, "Inert Atmospheres as Fatigue Environments". *J. Inst. Metals* **72** (1946) 415.

407. N. J. WADSWORTH and J. HUTCHINGS, "The Effect of Atmospheric Corrosion on Metal Fatigue". *Phil. Mag.* **3** (1958) 1154.

408. H. J. Gough and D. G. Sopwith, "The Behaviour of a Single Crystal of Aluminium under Alternating Torsional Stresses while Immersed in a Slow Stream of Tap Water". *Proc. Roy. Soc. A***135** (1932) 392.

409. U. R. Evans and M. T. Simnad, "The Mechanism of Corrosion Fatigue of Mild Steel". *Proc. Roy. Soc. A* **188** (1947) 372.

410. D. Whitwham and U. R. Evans, "Corrosion Fatigue—the Influence of Disarrayed Metal". *J. Iron and Steel Inst.* **165** (1950) 72.

411. K. H. R. Wright, "Fretting Corrosion as an Engineering Problem". *Corrosion, Prevention and Control* (Nov. 1957) 37.

412. A. J. Fenner, K. H. R. Wright and J. Y. Mann, "Fretting Corrosion and its Influence on Fatigue Failure". *Int. Conf. on Fatigue. Instn. Mech. Engrs.* (1956) 386.

413. J. R. McDowell, "Fretting Corrosion Tendencies of Several Combinations of Materials". *Amer. Soc. Test. Mat. Symp. on Fretting Corrosion. Spec. Tech. Publ.* **144** (1952) 24.

414. K. H. R. Wright, "Fretting Corrosion of Cast Iron". *Conf. on Lubrication and Wear. Instn. Mech. Engrs.* (1957) 628.

415. G. Sachs and P. Stefan, "Chafing Fatigue Strength of some Metals and Alloys". *Trans. Amer. Soc. Met.* **29** (1941) 373.

416. G. A. Tomlinson, P. L. Thorpe and H. J. Gough, "The Fretting Corrosion of Closely Fitting Surfaces". *Proc. Instn. Mech. Engrs.* **141** (1939) 223.

417. W. E. Campbell, "The Current Status of Fretting Corrosion". *Amer. Soc. Test. Mat. Symp. on Fretting Corrosion. Spec. Tech. Publ.* **144** (1952) 3.

418. A. J. Fenner and J. E. Field, "The Onset of Fatigue Damage due to Fretting". *N. E. Coast Inst. Engrs. and Shipbuilders.* **76** (1960) 183.

419. O. J. Horger, "Influence of Fretting Corrosion on the Fatigue Strength of Fitted Members". *Amer. Soc. Test. Mat. Symp. on Fretting Corrosion. Spec. Tech. Publ.* **144** (1952) 40.

420. O. J. Horger, "Fatigue of Large Shafts by Fretting Corrosion". *Int. Conf. on Fatigue. Instn. Mech. Engrs.* (1956) 352.

421. O. J. Horger and H. R. Neifert, "Fretting Corrosion of Large Shafts as Influenced by Surface Treatments". *Amer. Soc. Test. Mat. Spec. Tech. Publ.* **216** (1957) 81.

422. H. W. Liu, H. T. Corten and G. M. Sinclair, "Fretting Fatigue Strength of Titanium Alloy RC 130B". *Proc. Amer. Soc. Test. Mat.* **57** (1957) 623.

423. N. A. Scarlett, "Greases to Prevent Fretting Corrosion". *Engineering* **189** (1960) 424.

424. H. Wiegand, "Nitriding". *Rev. Metal* **45** (1948) 105.

425. P. L. Teed, *The Properties of Metallic Materials at Low Temperatures.* Chapman and Hall (1950).

426. M. Hempel and J. Luce, "Behaviour of Steel at Low Temperatures under Alternating Stress". *Mitt. Kaiser Wilhelm Inst. fur Eisenforschung.* **23** (1941) 53. *Transl. RAE No.* 303 (1949).

427. A. S. Kenneford and R. W. Nichols, "Fatigue Properties of Steels at Low Temperatures". *J. Iron and Steel Inst.* **194** (1960) 13.

428. A. H. Sully, *Metallic Creep.* Butterworths, London (1949).

429. W. Betteridge, *The Nimonic Alloys*, Edward Arnold, London (1959).

430. N. P. Allen and P. G. Forrest, "Influence of Temperature on the Fatigue of Metals". *Int. Conf. on Fatigue. Instn. Mech. Engrs.* (1956) 327.

431. J. E. Breen and J. R. Lane, "Effect of Grain Size on High Temperature Fatigue Properties of Alpha Brass". *Trans. Amer. Soc. Metals* **46** (1954) 1021.

432. P. R. TOOLIN and F. C. HULL, "Fatigue Strength of Refractaloy 26 as Affected by Temperature, Hardness and Grain Size". *Proc. Amer. Soc. Test. Mat.* **52** (1952) 791.

433. G. T. HARRIS and H. C. CHILD, "Statistical Study of Creep and Fatigue Properties of a Precision-Cast High Temperature Alloy". *J. Iron and Steel Inst.* **178** (1954) 284.

434. M. J. MANJOINE, "Effect of Pulsating Loads on the Creep of Aluminium Alloy 14S–T". *Proc. Amer. Soc. Test. Mat.* **49** (1949) 788.

435. H. J. TAPSELL, P. G. FORREST and G. R. TREMAIN, "Creep due to Fluctuating Stresses at Elevated Temperatures". *Engineering* **170** (1950) 189.

436. B. J. LAZAN, "Dynamic Creep and Rupture Properties under Tensile Fatigue Stress". *Proc. Amer. Soc. Test. Mat.* **49** (1949) 757.

437. F. H. VITOVEC, "Dynamic Creep". *Proc. Amer. Soc. Test. Mat.* **57** (1957) 977.

438. J. F. ECKEL, "Influence of Frequency on the Repeated Bending Life of Acid Lead". *Proc. Amer. Soc. Test. Mat.* **51** (1951) 745.

439. H. F. MOORE and C. W. DOLLINS, "Fracture and Ductility of Lead and Lead Alloys". *Univ. Illinois, Bulletin No.* 347 (1943).

440. G. R. GOHN and W. C. ELLIS, "Fatigue of Lead Cable Sheath". *Proc. Amer. Soc. Test. Mat.* **51** (1951) 721.

441. J. McKEOWN, "Fatigue Properties of some Non-Ferrous Metals excluding Light Alloys". *Int. Conf. on Fatigue. Instn. Mech. Engrs.* (1956) 432.

442. P. G. FORREST, "Speed Effect in Fatigue". *Proc. Roy. Soc. A.* **242** (1957) 223.

443. G. F. GUARNIERI, *Int. Conf. on Fatigue. Instn. Mech. Engrs.* (1956) 841.

444. W. L. COLLINS, "Fatigue Tests of an Austenitic Cast Iron at Elevated Temperatures". *Proc. Amer. Soc. Test. Mat.* **48** (1948) 696.

445. M. WEISZ and R. CAZAUD, "Influence of Temperature on the Notched Fatigue Strength of Steel". *Rev. Metal* **56** (1959) 299.

446. F. H. VITOVEC and B. J. LAZAN, "Creep Rupture and Notch Sensitivity Properties of S-816 Alloy up to 1650°F. under Fatigue and Static Stress". *Amer. Soc. Test. Mat. Spec. Tech. Publ. No.* 174 (1955).

447. R. L. FERGUSON, "Effect of Surface Finish on Fatigue Properties at Elevated Temperatures". *Nat. Adv. Co. Aero. Tech. Note* 3142 (1954).

448. W. E. JONES and G. B. WILKES, "Effect of Various Treatments on Fatigue Strengths at Elevated Temperatures". *Proc. Amer. Soc. Test. Mat.* **50** (1950) 744.

449. A. POMP and M. HEMPEL, "Fatigue Strength of Helical Springs at Elevated Temperatures". *Arch. Eisenhuttenw.* **21** (1950) 263.

450. F. P. BOWDEN, "The Experiments of Boas and Honeycombe on Internal Stresses due to Anisotropic Thermal Expansion of Pure Metals and Alloys". *Symposium on Internal Stresses in Metals and Alloys. Inst. Metals.* (1947) 275.

451. A. H. GOODGER, "Corrosion Fatigue Cracking Resulting from Wetting of Heated Metal Surfaces". *Int. Conf. on Fatigue. Instn. Mech. Engrs.* (1956) 394.

452. H. THIELSCH, "Thermal Fatigue and Thermal Shock". *Welding Research Council Bulletin Series No.* 10 (1952).

453. L. NORTHCOTT and H. G. BARON, "Craze-cracking in Metals". *J. Iron and Steel Inst.* **184** (1956) 385. See also *J. Iron and Steel Inst.* **197** (1961) 223.

454. J. R. JOHNSTON, J. W. WEETON and R. A. SIGNORELLI, "Engine Operating Conditions that cause Thermal Fatigue Cracks in Turbojet-engine Buckets". *National Aeronautics and Space Administration. Memo.* 4-7-59E. (1959). See also N.A.S.A. T.N. D-272 (1960).

455. M. J. WHITMAN, R. W. HALL and C. YAKER, "Resistance of Six Cast High-Temperature Alloys to Cracking Caused by Thermal Shock". *Nat. Adv. Co. Aero. Tech. Note* 2037 (1950).

456. H. E. LARDGE, "Thermal Fatigue Testing of Sheet Metal". *Amer. Soc. Test. Mat. Spec. Tech. Publ. No.* **174** (1955) 146.

457. E. GLENNY and T. A. TAYLOR, "The Thermal Fatigue Behaviour of Metals". *J. Inst. Metals* **88** (1960) 449. And see discussion **89** (1961) 428.

458. T. A. HUNTER, "Thermal Shock Testing of High-Temperature Metallic Materials". *Amer. Soc. Test. Mat. Spec. Tech. Publ.* No. **174** (1955) 164.

459. F. L. MUSCATELL, E. E. REYNOLDS, W. W. DYRKACZ and J. H. DALHEIM, "Thermal Shock Resistance of High-Temperature Alloys". *Proc. Amer. Soc. Test. Mat.* **57** (1957) 947.

460. P. A. HAYTHORNE, "Sheet Metals for High Temperature Service". *Iron Age* **162** (1948) 89.

461. S. S. MANSON, "Behaviour of Metals under Conditions of Thermal Stress". *Nat. Adv. Co. Aero. Report* 1170 (1954).

462. L. F. COFFIN and R. P. WESLEY, "Apparatus for the Study of the Effects of Cyclic Thermal Stresses on Ductile Metals". *Trans. Amer. Soc. Mech. Engrs.* **75** (1953) 923.

463. L. F. COFFIN, "Thermal-Stress Fatigue as Related to High-Temperature Piping Flexibility". *Trans. Amer. Soc. Mech. Engrs.* **79** (1957) 1637.

464. L. F. COFFIN, "Strain Cycling and Thermal Stress Fatigue". *Proc. 4th Sagamore Ordnance Materials Research Corp.* Syracuse University Res. Inst. New York (1957).

465. H. MAJORS, "Thermal and Mechanical Fatigue of Nickel and Titanium". *Trans. Amer. Soc. Met.* **51** (1959) 421.

466. F. J. CLAUSS and J. W. FREEMAN, "Thermal Fatigue of Ductile Materials". 1. *Nat. Adv. Co. Aero. Tech. Note* 4160 (1958). 2. *Nat. Adv. Co. Aero. Tech. Note* 4165 (1958). 3. *Nat. Aero. and Space Admin. Tech. Note* D-69 (1959).

467. R. W. SWINDEMAN and D. A. DOUGLAS, "The Failure of Metals Subjected to Strain Cycling". *Trans. Amer. Soc. Mech. Engrs.* **81** D (1939) 203.

468. F. J. MEHRINGER and R. P. FELGAR, "Low-Cycle Fatigue of Two Nickel-Base Alloys by Thermal-Stress Cycling". *Trans. Amer. Soc. Mech. Engrs.* **82** D (1960) 661.

469. L. F. COFFIN, "The Stability of Metals under Cyclic Plastic Strain". *Trans. Amer. Soc. Mech. Engrs.* **82** D (1960) 671.

470. S. M. ARNOLD, "Effect of Screw Threads on Fatigue". *Mechanical Engng.* **65** (1943) 497.

471. J. G. RITCHIE, "Fatigue of Bolts and Studs", Symp. *Failure of Metals by Fatigue*, (1946) Melbourne Univ. Press (1947) 260.

472. R. C. A. THURSTON, "The Fatigue Strength of Threaded Connections". *Trans. Amer. Soc. Mech. Engrs*, **73** (1951) 1085.

473. J. E. FIELD, "Fatigue Strength of Screw Threads". *Engineer* **198** (1954) 123.

474. D. G. SOPWITH and J. E. FIELD, "Unification of Screw Thread Practice". *Engineer* **203** (1957) 793.

475. H. F. MOORE and P. E. HENWOOD, "The Strength of Screw Threads under Repeated Tension". *Univ. Illinois Eng. Expt. Station Bull. No.* 264 (1934).

476. R. T. ALLSOP and J. A. FOWLER, "Development of Aircraft Fasteners by G.K.N.". *G.K.N. Report No. 524* (1960).

477. H. DINNER and W. FELIX, "Rolling of Screw Threads". *Engineers' Digest,* **6** (1945) 332.

478. J. O. ALMEN, "On the Strength of Highly Stressed, Dynamically Loaded Bolts and Studs". *Trans. Soc. Automotive Engrs.* **52** (1944) 151.

479. W. A. P. FISHER, R. H. CROSS and G. M. NORRIS, "Pre-Tensioning for Preventing Fatigue Failure in Bolts". *Aircraft Engng.* **24** (1952) 160.

480. P. B. WALKER, "Fatigue of a Nut and Bolt". *J. Royal Aero. Soc.* **62** (1958) 395.

481. A. ERKER, "Design of Screw Fastenings, Subject to repeated Stress". *Int. Conf. on Fatigue, Inst. Mech. Engrs.* (1956) 290.

482. D. G. SOPWITH, "The Distribution of Load in Screw Threads". *Proc. Inst. Mech. Engrs.* **159** (1948) 373.

483. H. WIEGAND, "Effect of the nut material on the fatigue strength of bolts". *Z. Ver. Dtsch. Ing.* **83** (1939) 64.

484. R. B. HEYWOOD, "Longer Fatigue Life for Nuts and Bolts. *Engineering* **189** (1960) 494.

485. F. KAUFMANN and W. JANICHE, "Fatigue Strength of Steel Bolts and Studs Fitted with Steel or Magnesium Alloy Nuts". *Z. Ver. Dtsch. Ing.* **85** (1941) 504.

486. R. H. CROSS and G. M. NORRIS, "Preventing Fatigue Failure of Steel Bolts". *Engineer* **198** (1954) 410.

487. M. HETENYI, "A Photoelastic Study of Bolt and Nut Fastenings". *Trans. Amer. Soc. Mech. Engrs.* **65** (1943) A93.

488. A. F. C. BROWN and W. McCLIMONT, "Fatigue Strength of Five Types of Stud". *Engineering* **189** (1960) 430.

489. R. B. HEYWOOD, "The Strength of Lugs in Fatigue". *Royal Aircraft Est. Tech. Note Struct.* **182** (1956).

490. J. SCHIJVE and F. A. JACOBS, "The Fatigue Strength of Aluminium Alloy Lugs". *Nat. Lucht. Lab. TN. M.*2024 (1957).

491. A. C. LOW, "The Fatigue Strength of Pin-Jointed Connections in Aluminium Alloy BS.L 65". *Proc. Inst. Mech. Engrs.* **172** (1958) 821 (and see discussion).

492. W. A. P. FISHER and W. J. WINKWORTH, "Improvements in the Fatigue Strength of Joints by the Use of Interference Fits". *Aero. Res. Council. R. & M.* 2874. H.M.S.O. (1955).

493. W. M. WILSON and F. P. THOMAS, "Fatigue Tests of Riveted Joints". *Univ. Illinois, Eng. Expt. Station, Bull.* No. 302 (1938).

494. W. H. MUNSE, D. T. WRIGHT and N. M. NEWMARK, "Laboratory Tests of Bolted Joints". *Trans. Amer. Soc. Civil Engrs.* **120** (1955) 1299.

495. S. KELSEY and J. B. SPOONER, "Direct Stress Fatigue Tests on Redux-Bonded and Riveted Double Strap Joints in 10 S.W.G. Aluminium Alloy Sheet". *Aero. Res. Council, Current paper* 353 (1957).

496. A. HARTMAN and W. KLAASSEN, "The Fatigue Strength of Single Lap Joints of Clad 24 S–T and 75 S–T Aluminium Alloy with Two Rows of 17S Rivets". *Nat. Lucht. Lab. TN M.*2011 (1956).

497. H. W. RUSSELL, L. R. JACKSON, H. J. GROVER and W. W. BEAVER, "Fatigue Characteristics of Sheet and Riveted Joints of 0·040". 24 S–T, 75 S–T and R 303–T 275, Aluminium Alloys". *Nat. Adv. Co. Aero. Tech. Note* 1485 (1948).

498. L. R. JACKSON, W. M. WILSON, H. F. MOORE and H. J. GROVER, "The Fatigue Characteristics of Bolted Lap Joints of 24S–T Alclad Sheet Material". *Nat Adv. Co. Aero. Tech. Note* 1030 (1946).

499. F. A. JACOBS and A. HARTMAN, "The Fatigue Strength of Redux-Bonded 75 S–T Clad Simple Lap Joints". *Nat. Lucht. Lab. Report M.*1969 (1954).

500. A. HARTMAN, "The Fatigue Strength of Riveted Single Lap Joints of 24 S–T Alclad Sheet and 17S Rivets". *Nat. Lucht. Lab. TN. M.*1943 (1954).

501. H. BURNHEIM, "The Endurances of Riveted Joints in Light Metal Sheets". *Aluminium* **28** (1952) 140 and 222.

502. W. A. P. FISHER and W. J. WINKWORTH, "The Effect of Tight Clamping on the Fatigue Strength of Joints". *Aero. Res. Council. R. & M.* 2873, H.M.S.O. (1955).

503. R. B. HEYWOOD, "Correlated Fatigue Data for Aircraft Structural Joints". *Aero. Res. Council. Current Paper* 227 (1955).

504. E. C. HARTMANN, M. HOLT and I. D. EATON, "Static and Fatigue Strengths of High-Strength Aluminium Alloy Bolted Joints". *Nat. Adv. Co. Aero. T.N.* 2276 (1951), T.N. 3269 (1954).

505. R. B. HEYWOOD, "Simplified Bolted Joints for High Fatigue Strength", *Engineering* **183** (1957) 174.

506. B. E. STEPHENSON, "Fatigue Properties of Joints", Chapter in *Metal Fatigue*, Chapman & Hall (1959) 283.

507. E. H. SPAULDING, "Detail Design for Fatigue in Aircraft Wing Structures". Chapter in *Metal Fatigue*. McGraw Hill, New York (1959) 325.

508. R. WECK, "Fatigue of Welded Structures". *Struct. Engr.* **32** (1954) 115.

509. R. WECK, "The Fatigue Problem in Welded Construction". *Int. Conf. on Fatigue. Instn. Mech. Engrs.* (1956) 704.

510. *Conference on Fatigue of Welded Structures.* Cambridge (1960). *Brit. Welding J.* **7** (1960) 161, 281, 472, 513, 577.

511. W. SPRARAGEN and G. E. CLAUSSEN, "Fatigue Strength of Welded Joints". *J. Amer. Welding Soc.* **16** (Jan. 1937) 1-s.

512. W. SPRARAGEN and D. ROSENTHAL, "Fatigue Strength of Welded Joints". *Welding J.* **21** (1942) 297-s.

513. J. G. WHITMAN, "Fatigue Properties of Welds". Chapter in *Metal Fatigue*. Chapman and Hall (1959) 295.

514. R. P. NEWMAN and T. R. GURNEY, "Fatigue Tests on Mild Steel Butt Welds". *Brit. Welding J.* **6** (1959) 569.

515. L. A. HARRIS, G. E. NORDMARK and N. M. NEWMARK, "Fatigue Strength of Butt Welds in Structural Steels". *Welding J.* **34** (1955) 83-s.

516. J. E. STALLMEYER and W. H. MUNSE, "Fatigue of Welded Joints in High-Strength Steels". *Brit. Welding J.* **7** (1960) 281.

517. H. DE LEIRIS and H. DUTILLEUL, "Fatigue Test of Arc-Welded Joints". *Welding J.* **31** (1952) 104-s.

518. W. D'ORVILLE DOTY, "Properties and Characteristics of a Quenched and Tempered Steel for Pressure Vessels". *Welding J.* **34** (1955) 425-s.

519. H. J. GROVER, R. W. BENNETT and G. M. FOLEY, "Fatigue Properties of Flash Welds". *Welding J.* **24** (1945) 599-s.

520. E. P. UNKSOV, "Fatigue Endurance of Large Parts with Electro-Slag Welds". *Int. Conf. on Fatigue. Instn. Mech. Engrs.* (1956) 727.

521. R. P. NEWMAN, "Fatigue Strength of Butt Welds in Mild Steel". *Brit. Welding J.* **7** (1960) 169.

522. *Steel Girder Bridges.* Part 3B Stresses. *British Standard* **153** (1958).

523. R. P. NEWMAN. "Effect on Fatigue Strength of Internal Defects in Welded Joints". *Brit. Welding J.* **6** (1959) 59.

524. R. P. NEWMAN, "The Influence of Weld Faults on Fatigue Strength". *Trans. Inst. Marine Engrs.* **68** (1956) 153.

525. J. Y. MANN, "Fatigue Properties of Welded Low ⊥ lloy Structural Steels". *Aero. Res. Labs. Australia. Tech. Memo.* SM/87 (1960).

526. J. E. BREEN and A. S. DWYER, "The Fatigue Strength of Magnesium Alloy HK.31, As Modified by a Weld Joint". *Amer. Soc. Test. Mat. Bull.* No. 234 (1958) 60.

527. R. P. NEWMAN, "Fatigue Tests on Butt-Welded Joints in Aluminium Alloys, H.E.30 and NP.5/6". *Brit. Welding J.* **6** (1959) 324.

528. K. W. GUNN and R. MCLESTER, "Fatigue Properties of Aluminium Alloy Butt-Welded Joints". *Brit. Welding J.* **7** (1960) 201.

529. J. L. Wood, "Flexural Fatigue Strength of Butt Welds in NP.5/6 Type Aluminium Alloy". *Brit. Welding J.* **7** (1960) 365.

530. R. L. Templin and M. Holt, "Static and Fatigue Strengths of Welded Joints in Aluminium–Manganese Alloy Sheet and Plates". *Welding J.* **26** (1947) 705-s.

531. E. C. Hartmann, M. Holt and I. D. Eaton, "Fatigue Strength of Butt Joints in ⅜in. Thick Aluminium Alloy Plates". *Welding J.* **33** (1954) 21-s.

532. *Welding Handbook*, Part 1, Amer. Welding Soc. (1957).

533. W. H. Munse and J. E. Stallmeyer, "Influence of Weld Details on Fatigue of Welded Beams and Girders". *Brit. Welding J.* **7** (1960) 188.

534. I. V. Kudryavtsev, "The Influence of Internal Stresses on the Fatigue Endurance of Steel". *Int. Conf. on Fatigue. Instn. Mech. Engrs.* (1956) 317.

535. T. R. Gurney and L. N. Trepka, "Influence of Local Heating on Fatigue Behaviour of Welded Specimens". *Brit. Welding J.* **6** (1959) 491.

536. G. Welter, "Fatigue of Spot Welds". *Welding J.* **34** (1955) 153-s.

537. G. Welter and A. Choquet, "Internal Stress Distribution of Single Spot Welds in Relation to their Fatigue Life". *Welding J.* **38** (1959) 145-s.

538. G. Hansel, "Mechanical Properties of Brazed Butt Joints". *Welding J.* **35** (1956) 211-s.

539. C. H. Chatfield and S. Tour, "Fatigue Strength of Silver-Alloy Brazed Joints in Steel". *Welding J.* **37** (1958) 37-s.

540. R. G. Aspden and W. Feduska, "Fatigue Characteristics of Joints Brazed with a Ni–Cr–Si–B–C Alloy". *Welding J.* **37** (1958) 125-s.

541. R. W. K. Honeycombe, "Conditions Leading to Fatigue Failure in Sleeve Bearings". *Symp. on Failure of Metals by Fatigue. Melbourne* (1946) 362.

542. J. W. Cuthbertson, "The Fatigue Properties of Brasses, Bronzes and Bearing Metals" and "Fatigue Testing of Bearings", Chapters in *Metal Fatigue*. Chapman and Hall (1959), 249 and 339.

543. W. E. Duckworth and G. H. Walter, "Fatigue of Plain Bearings", *Int. Conf. on Fatigue. Instn. Mech. Engrs.* (1956) 585.

544. P. G. Forrester, "How to Choose Materials for Bearing Surfaces". *Eng. Materials and Design* **2** (1959) 494.

545. *Symposium on Testing of Bearings*. Amer. Soc. Test. Mat. (1946).

546. R. H. Butler and T. L. Carter, "Stress-Life Relation of the Rolling-Contact Fatigue Spin Rig". *Nat. Adv. Co. Aero. Tech. Note* 3930 (1957).

547. F. T. Barwell and D. Scott, "Effect of Lubricant on Pitting Failure of Ball Bearings". *Engineering* **182** (1956) 9.

548. J. Lieblein and M. Zelen, "Statistical Investigation of the Fatigue Life of Deep-Groove Ball Bearings". *J. Res. Nat. Bureau Standards* **57** (1956) 273.

549. W. Coleman, "Improved Method for Estimating Fatigue Life of Bevel and Hypoid Gears". *Soc. Automotive Engrs. Quarterly Trans.* **6** (1952) 314.

550. H. B. Knowlton and E. H. Snyder, "Selection of Steel and Heat Treatment for Spur Gears". *Trans. Amer. Soc. Met.* **28** (1940) 687.

551. M. R. Gross, "Laboratory Evaluation of Materials for Marine Propulsion Gears". *Proc. Amer. Soc. Test. Mat.* **51** (1951) 701.

552. D. G. Sopwith, "The Production of Favourable Internal Stresses in Helical Compression Springs by Pre-stressing". *Symp. Internal Stresses in Metals and Alloys, Inst. Metals* (1947) 195.

553. W. E. Bardgett and F. Gartside, "Fatigue of Coiled Springs". *Iron and Steel* **24** (1951) 375, 411 and 454.

554. R. C. Coates and J. A. Pope, "Fatigue Testing of Compression-Type Coil Springs". *Int. Conf. on Fatigue, Instn. Mech. Engrs.* (1956) 604.

555. R. L. Rickett and A. O. Mason, "Fatigue Properties of Springs". *Metal Progress* **63** (March 1953) 107.

556. H. C. Burnett, "Torsional Fatigue Properties of Small Diameter High-Carbon Steel Wire". *Proc. Amer. Soc. Test. Mat.* **58** (1958) 515.

557. "Design of Helical Compression Springs". *Design Data Sheets*, M.O.S., H.M.S.O., London (1951).

558. J. O. Almen, "Torsional Fatigue Failures". *Product Engineering* **22** (Sept. 1951) 167.

559. T. Baldwin, "Significance of the Fatigue of Metals to Railways", *Int. Conf. on Fatigue. Instn. Mech. Engrs.* (1956) 695.

560. R. E. Peterson, "Fatigue of Shafts having Keyways", *Proc. Amer. Soc. Test. Mat.* **32** II (1932) 413.

561. C. G. Williams and J. S. Brown, "Fatigue Strength of Crankshafts". *Engineering* **154** (1942) 58.

562. R. J. Love, "Cast Crankshafts". *J. Iron and Steel Inst.* **159** (1948) 247.

563. C. W. Gadd and N. A. Ochiltree, "Full-Scale Fatigue Testing of Crankshafts". *Proc. Soc. Exp. Stress Analysis* **2II** (1944) 150.

564. H. R. Mills and R. J. Love, "Fatigue Strength of Cast Crankshafts". *Proc. Inst. Mech. Engrs., Automobile Division* (1948–49) 81.

565. C. W. Gadd, J. O. Anderson and D. Martin, "The Fatigue Strength of Steel Members". *Trans. Soc. Automotive Engrs.* **63** (1955) 362.

566. A. R. C. Markl, "Fatigue Tests of Piping Components". *Trans. Amer. Soc. Mech. Engrs.* **74** (1952) 287.

567. A. R. C. Markl, "Piping-Flexibility Analysis". *Trans. Amer. Soc. Mech. Engrs.* **77** (1955) 127.

568. P. H. R. Lane, "Fatigue Tests on Seamless Mild-Steel Pipe Bends". *Int. Conf. on Fatigue. Instn. Mech. Engrs.* (1956) 687, also see Discussion, page 869.

569. H. J. Gough, H. L. Cox and D. G. Sopwith, "Design of Crane Hooks and other Components of Lifting Gear". *Proc. Instn. Mech. Engrs.* **128** (1934) 253.

570. H. O'Neill, "Failures of Railway Materials by Fatigue". *Symp. on Fatigue, Melbourne* (1946) 416.

571. W. M. Keller and G. M. Magee, "Fatigue in Railroad Equipment". *Int. Conf. on Fatigue. Instn. Mech. Engrs.* (1956) 677.

572. A. O. Payne and others, "Fatigue Characteristics of a Riveted 24S–T Aluminium Alloy Wing". *Aero. Res. Labs., Melbourne*, SM.246, 247, 248 (1956), SM.263 (1958), SM.268 (1959)—Discussion of Results and Conclusions.

573. K. R. Raithby and J. Longson, "Some Fatigue Characteristics of a Two-Spar Light Alloy Structure". *H.M.S.O. Aero. Res. Council, Current Paper* 258 (1956).

574. R. E. Whaley, "Variable-Amplitude Tests of Full-Scale Transport-Airplane Wings". *Nat. Adv. Co. Aero. T.N.* 4132 (1957).

575. O. Foppl, "The Practical Importance of Damping Capacity of Metals". *J. Iron and Steel Inst.* **134** (1936) 393.

576. B. J. Lazan, "Fatigue Failure under Resonant Vibration Conditions". Chapter in *Fatigue*, ASM (1953).

577. R. L. Schleicher, "Practical Aspects of Fatigue in Aircraft Structures". *Fatigue in Aircraft Structures*. Academic Press, New York (1956), 376 (and see Appendix, Page 423).

578. W. Tye, "The Outlook on Airframe Fatigue". *J. Royal Aero. Soc.*, **59** (1955) 339.

579. R. H. SANDIFER, J. K. WILLIAMS, H. GIDDINGS, P. B. WALKER and A. J. BARRETT, "Aircraft Design Philosophy". *J. Royal Aero. Soc.* **60** (1956) 301.

580. *Fatigue in Aircraft Structures.* Academic Press, New York (1956).

581. J. TAYLOR, "Fatigue Loading Actions on Transport Aircraft". *Int. Conf. on Fatigue. Instn. Mech. Engrs.* (1956) 650.

582. J. TAYLOR, "Fatigue Loads and Their Effect on Aircraft Structures". Chapter in *Metal Fatigue*, Chapman and Hall, London (1959) 308.

583. R. J. ATKINSON, "Fatigue Testing in Relation to Transport Aircraft". *Fatigue in Aircraft Structures*, Academic Press, New York (1956) 279.

584. BO. K. O. LUNDBERG, "Fatigue Life of Airplane Structures". *J. Aero. Sci.* (1955) 349, and *Aero. Res. Inst., Sweden, FFA Rpt.* 60 (1955), see also *FFA Rpt.* 76 (1958).

585. E. H. SPAULDING, "Design of Fatigue-Resistant and Fail-Safe Aircraft Structures". *Int. Conf. on Fatigue. Instn. Mech. Engrs.* (1956) 628.

586. J. Y. MANN, "The Historical Development of Research on Fatigue". *J. Australian Inst. Metals* **3** (1958) 51.

587. N. THOMPSON and N. J. WADSWORTH, "Metal Fatigue". *Advanc. Phys.* **7** (1958) 72.

588. W. RANKINE, "On the Causes of Unexpected Breakage of the Journals of Railway Axles". *Proc. Inst. Civil Engrs.* **2** (1843) 105.

589. E. A. HODGKINSON, "Report of the Commissioners Appointed to Enquire into the Application of Iron to Railway Structures". *H.M.S.O. Command Paper* No. 1123 (1849).

590. W. FAIRBAIRN, "Experiments to Determine the Effect of Impact, Vibratory Action and Long-Continued Changes of Load on Wrought Iron Girders. *Phil. Trans. Roy. Soc.* **154** (1864) 311.

591. J. A. EWING and J. C. W. HUMFREY, "The Fracture of Metals under Repeated Alternations of Stress". *Phil. Trans. Roy. Soc.* A**200** (1903) 241.

592. H. J. GOUGH and D. HANSON, "Behaviour of Metals Subjected to Repeated Stresses". *Proc. Roy. Soc.* A**104** (1923) 539.

593. H. J. GOUGH, "Crystalline Structure in Relation to Failure of Metals— Especially by Fatigue". *Proc. Amer. Soc. Test. Mat.* **33** II (1933) 3.

594. E. OROWAN, "Theory of the Fatigue of Metals". *Proc. Roy. Soc.* A**171** (1939) 79.

595. W. A. WOOD, "Failure of Metals Under Cyclic Strain". *Int. Conf. on Fatigue Instn. Mech. Engrs.* (1956) 531.

596. W. A. WOOD, "Basic Studies of Fatigue in Metals". Int. Conf. on *Fracture.* Swampscott, Massachusetts (1959) Technology Press M.I.T. and John Wiley, New York; Chapman and Hall, London (1959) 412.

597. T. BROOM and R. K. HAM, "The Hardening and Softening of Metals by Cyclic Stressing". *Proc. Roy. Soc.* A**242** (1957) 166. See also **251** (1959) 186.

598. F. P. BULLEN, A. K. HEAD and W. A. WOOD, "Structural Changes During the Fatigue of Metals". *Proc. Roy. Soc.* A**216** (1953) 332.

599. P. J. E. FORSYTH, "Slip-Band Damage and Extrusion". *Proc. Roy. Soc.* A**242** (1957) 198.

600. P. J. E. FORSYTH, "Fatigue Crack Formation in Silver Chloride". *Amer. Soc. Test. Mat. S.T.P.* No. 237 (1958) 21.

601. A. H. COTTRELL and D. HULL, "Extrusion and Intrusion by Cyclic Slip in Copper". *Proc. Roy. Soc.* A**242** (1957) 211.

602. D. HULL, "Surface Structure of Slip Bands on Copper Fatigued at 293°, 90°, 20° and 4·2°K". *J. Inst. Met.* **86** (1958) 425.

603. N. THOMPSON, N. J. WADSWORTH and N. LOUAT, "The Origin of Fatigue Fracture in Copper". *Phil. Mag.* **1** (1956) 113.

604. N. Thompson, "Some Observations on the Early Stages of Fatigue Fracture". Int. Conf. on *Fracture*, Swampscott 1959. Tech. Press M.I.T. and John Wiley, New York, Chapman and Hall, London (1959) 354.

605. G. C. Smith, "The Initial Fatigue Crack". *Proc. Roy. Soc.* A**242** (1957) 189.

606. M. S. Hunter and W. G. Fricke, "Effect of Alloy Content on the Metallographic Changes Accompanying Fatigue". *Proc. Amer. Soc. Test. Mat.* **55** (1955) 942.

607. M. Hempel, "Metallographic Observations on the Fatigue of Steels". *Int. Conf. on Fatigue. Instn. Mech. Engrs.* (1956) 543.

608. W. J. Craig, "An Electron Microscope Study of the Development of Fatigue Failures". *Proc. Amer. Soc. Test. Mat.* **52** (1952) 877.

609. G. M. Sinclair and T. J. Dolan, "Use of a Recrystallization Method to Study the Nature of Damage in Fatigue of Metals". *Proc. First U.S. National Congress Appl. Mech.* (1951) 647.

610. G. F. Modlen and G. C. Smith, "Changes Occurring in the Surfaces of Mild Steel Specimens During Fatigue Stressing. *J. Iron and Steel Inst.* **194** (1960) 459.

611. B. P. Haigh, "Hysteresis in Relation to Cohesion and Fatigue". *Trans. Faraday Soc.* **24** (1928) 125.

612. C. S. Barrett, *The Structure of Metals.* McGraw Hill. 2nd Edition (1953).

613. H. J. Gough and W. A. Wood, "Fatigue of Metals Using X-ray Methods". *Proc. Roy. Soc.* A**154** (1936) 510. See also *ibid.* **165** (1938) 358.

614. C. S. Barrett, "The Application of X-ray Diffraction to the Study of Fatigue in Metals". *Trans. Amer. Soc. Met.* **25** (1937) 1115.

615. L. M. Clarebrough, M. E. Hargreaves, G. W. West and A. K. Head, "The Energy Stored in Fatigued Metals". *Proc. Roy. Soc.* A**242** (1957) 160.

616. A. H. Cottrell, *Dislocations and Plastic Flow in Crystals.* Clarendon Press, Oxford (1953).

617. H. A. Lipsitt and G. T. Horne, "The Fatigue Behaviour of Decarburized Steel". *Proc. Amer. Soc. Test. Mat.* **57** (1957) 587.

618. A. M. Freudenthal, "The Statistical Aspect of Fatigue of Materials". *Proc. Roy. Soc.* A**187** (1946) 416. See also **216** (1953) 309.

619. R. N. Wilson and P. J. E. Forsyth, "Some New Observations on Fatigue Damage". *J. Inst. Met.* **87** (1959) 336.

620. P. B. Hirsch, P. G. Partridge and R. L. Segall, "An Electron Microscope Study of Stainless Steel Deformed in Fatigue and Simple Tension". *Phil. Mag.* **4** (1959) 721.

621. A. K. Head, "The Growth of Fatigue Cracks". *Phil. Mag.* **44** (1953) 925.

622. A. K. Head, "The Propagation of Fatigue Cracks". *J. Appl. Mech.* **78** (1956) 407.

623. H. L. Cox, "Fracture under Fatigue Conditions". "The Fracture of Metals". *Inst. Metallurgists* (1950) 42.

624. W. C. Lewis, "Fatigue of Wood and Glued-Wood Constructions". *Proc. Amer. Soc. Test. Mat.* **46** (1946) 814.

625. F. B. Fuller and T. T. Oberg, "Fatigue Characteristics of Natural and Resin-Impregnated Compressed Laminated Woods". *J. Aero. Sci.* **10** (1943) 81.

626. W. J. Kommers, "Effect of 5,000 cycles of Repeated Bending Stresses on 5-ply Sitka Spruce Plywood". *U.S. Forest Products Lab. Rpt.* 1305 (1943).

627. W. C. Lewis, "Fatigue of Wood and Glued Joints Used in Laminated Construction". *Forest Prodcuts Res. Soc. Proc.* **5** (1951) 221.

628. W. C. Lewis, "Fatigue Resistance of Quarter-Scale Bridge Stringers of Green and Dry Southern Pine". *Amer. Railway Engg. Ass.* **59** (1958) 363.

629. A. G. H. Dietz and H. Grinsfelder, "Behaviour of Plywood Under Repeated Stresses". *Trans. Amer. Soc. Mech. Engrs.* **65** (1943) 187.

630. A. C. Horner, W. C. Lewis, E. J. Ruble and L. W. Wood, "Duration of Load and Fatigue in Wood Structures". *Proc. Amer. Soc. Civil Engrs.* 83 ST 5 (1957) No. 1361.

631. J. L. Leggett, "Fatigue Strength of Rail-Road Timber Bridge Stringers". *Amer. Railway Engng. Ass. Bull* **55** (1953) 161.

632. R. B. Heywood, "Present and Potential Fatigue and Creep Strengths of Reinforced Plastics". *R.A.E. Tech. Note Chem.* 1337 (1958). *British Plastics Federation Reinforced Plastics Tech. Conf.* (1958).

633. R. C. Hooper, "Fatigue of Glass-Reinforced Polyester Resins". *Plastics Technology* **3** (1957) 644.

634. K. H. Boller, "Fatigue Properties of Fibrous Glass-Reinforced Plastics Laminates". *Modern Plastics* **34** (June 1957) 163.

635. W. N. Findley and O. E. Hintz, "Relation Between Results of Repeated Blow Impact Tests and of Fatigue Tests". *Proc. Amer. Soc. Test. Mat.* **43** (1943) 1226.

636. L. S. Lazar, "Accelerated Fatigue of Plastics". *Amer. Soc. Test. Mat. Bull.* **220** (Feb. 1957) 67.

637. J. M. Zarek, "Accelerated Fatigue Testing of Polymethyl Methacrylate". *British Plastics* **30** (1957) 399.

638. S. M. Cadwell, R. A. Merrill, C. M. Sloman and F. L. Yost, "Dynamic Fatigue Life of Rubber". *Ind. & Engng. Chem. Analytical Ed.* **12** (1940) 19.

639. A. E. Moulton and P. W. Turner, "Influence of Design on Rubber Springs". *Trans. Inst. Rubber Industry* **26** (1950) 86.

640. A. E. Moulton and P. W. Turner, "Rubber Springs for Vehicle Suspension". *Inst. Mech. Engrs. Proc. Automobile Division* (1956) 17.

641. C. Gurney and S. Pearson, "Fatigue of Mineral Glass under Static and Cyclic Loading". *Proc. Roy. Soc.* A**192** (1948) 537.

642. G. M. Nordby, "Fatigue of Concrete—A Review". *J. Amer. Concrete Inst.* **55** (1958) 191.

643. S. C. C. Bate, "The Strength of Concrete Members Under Dynamic Loading". Proc. Symp. on *The Strength of Concrete Structures.* London (1956). Cement & Concrete Association (1958), p. 487.

644. J. W. Murdock and C. E. Kesler, "Effect of Range of Stress on Fatigue Strength of Plain Concrete Beams". *J. Amer. Concrete Inst.* **55** (1958) 221.

645. "Portland Cement (Ordinary and Rapid Hardening)". B.S. No. 12 (1947). British Standards Inst., London.

646. S. C. C. Bate, "The Relative Merits of Plain and Deformed Wires in Prestressed Concrete Beams Under Static and Repeated Loading". *Proc. Inst. Civil Engineers* **10** (1958) 473.

647. G. A. Hankins, D. Hanson and G. W. Ford, "The Mechanical Properties of Four Heat-Treated Spring Steels". *J. Iron and Steel Inst.* **114** (1926) 265.

648. J. W. Grant, "Notched and Unnotched Fatigue Tests on Flake and Nodular Cast Irons". *J. Res. & Development. Brit. Cast Iron Res. Ass.* **3** (1950) 333.

649. J. L. Zambrow and M. G. Fontana, "Mechanical Properties, including Fatigue, of Aircraft Alloys at Very Low Temperatures". *Trans. Amer. Soc. Met.* **41** (1949) 480.

650. J. W. SPRETNAK, M. G. FONTANA and H. E. BROOKS, "Notched and Un-notched Tensile and Fatigue Properties of Ten Alloys at 25 and —196°C". Trans. Amer. Soc. Met. **43** (1951) 547.

651. N. J. F. GUNN, "Fatigue Properties at Low Temperatures on DTD 363A Aluminium Alloy". R.A.E. Tech. Note Met. 163 (1952).

652. S. M. BISHOP, J. W. SPRETNAK and M. G. FONTANA, "Mechanical Properties, including Fatigue, of Titanium-Base Alloys at Very Low Temperatures". Trans. Amer. Soc. Met. **45** (1953) 993.

653. P. L. THORPE, G. R. TREMAIN and R. W. RIDLEY, "Mechanical Properties of Some Wrought and Cast Aluminium Alloys at Elevated Temperatures". J. Inst. Met. **77** II (1950) 111.

654. J. McKEOWN, D. E. DINEEN and L. H. BACK, "Fatigue Properties of Four Cast Aluminium Alloys at Elevated Temperatures". Metallurgia **41** (1950) 393.

655. J. J. CARTER, D. N. MENDS and J. McKEOWN, "Creep and Fatigue Properties of Two Commercial Aluminium Bronzes at 500°C". Metallurgia **45** (1952) 273.

656. W. D. BIGGS, The Brittle Fracture of Steel. Macdonald & Evans, London (1960).

657. T. R. G. WILLIAMS and D. H. HUGHES, "The Development of Programmed Fatigue Testing". Engineer **210** (1960) 703.

658. P. L. TEED, "Fretting". Metal. Rev. **5** (1960) 267.

659. S. S. MANSON and W. F. BROWN, "A Survey of the Effects of Non-Steady Load and Temperature Conditions on the Creep of Metals". Amer. Soc. Test. Mat. Spec. Tech. Publ. 260 (1959).

660. Symposium on Acoustical Fatigue. Amer. Soc. Test. Mat. (1960).

661. J. I. FISHER and J. P. SHEEHAN, "Effect of Metallurgical Variables on the Fatigue Properties of AISI 4340 Steel". Wright Air Development Center Tech. Rpt. **58**-289 (1959).

662. M. ATKINSON, "Influence of Non-Metallic Inclusions on Fatigue Properties". J. Iron and Steel Inst. **195** (1960) 64.

663. H. JIRO and A. JUNICH, "Studies on Rotating Beam Fatigue of Large Mild Steel Specimens". Proc. 9th Japan. National Congress Appl. Mech. (1959) 149.

664. E. AGERMAN, "Notch Sensitivity in Steel". Allmanna Svenska Elektriska Akticbolaget Res. No. 4 (1960) 5.

665. S. OKAMOTO and H. KITAGAWA, "Behaviour of Structural Steels Subjected to Corrosion Fatigue". Proc. 7th Jap. National Congress Appl. Mech. (1957) 27; ibid. 8th (1958) 187; ibid. 9th (1959) 153.

666. H. E. FRANKEL, J. A. BENNETT and C. M. CARMAN, "Fatigue Properties of Some High-Strength Steels". Nat. Bureau of Standards Tech. News Bull. **44** (1960) 174. Amer. Soc. Test. Mat. (1960) Preprint 65.

667. M. RIDDIHOUGH, "A Thermal Cracking Test for Steels and Alloys". Metallurgia **62** (1960) 53.

668. K. W. GUNN, Private communication.

669. S. WISE, D. LINDSAY and I. G. T. DUNCAN, "The Strength of Rails with Particular Reference to Rail Joints". Proc. Instn. Mech. Engrs. **174** (1960) 371.

670. N. J. PETCH, "The Lowering of Fracture Stress Due to Surface Adsorption". Phil. Mag. **1** (1956) 331.

671. P. R. WEDDEN and W. E. COOPER, "The Effect of Some Metallic Surface Protection Procedures on the Fatigue Properties of High and Ultra-High Strength Steels". Min. of Aviation S & T Memo. 13/60 (1960).

672. S. S. MANSON, "Thermal Stresses in Design". 22 articles published in Machine Design between 12/6/58 and 18/8/60. See also Ref. 680.

673. L. W. DERRY and S. R. HOUSE, "A Survey of Data on the Fatigue Strength of Riveted Lap Joints in Aluminium Alloy Sheet". *Min. of Aviation S & T Memo.* 4/60 (1960).

674. W. WEIBULL (Ed.) *Fatigue Testing and Analysis of Results.* Pergamon Press (1961).

675. P. H. ARMITAGE, "Statistical Aspects of Fatigue". *Metal. Rev.* **6** (1961) 353.

676. H. T. ANGUS, *Physical and Engineering Properties of Cast Iron.* Brit. Cast Iron Res. Ass., Brimingham (1960).

677. N. E. FROST, "A Note on the Behaviour of Fatigue Cracks". *J. Mech. Phys. Solids* **9** (1961) 143.

678. *Symposium on Crack Propagation*, Cranfield, 1961. To be published.

679. W. J. HARRIS, *Metallic Fatigue: with particular reference to the significance of certain standard aircraft fabrication and finishing processes.* Pergamon Press (1961).

680. DORN (Ed.), *Mechanical Behaviour of Materials at Elevated Temperatures.* McGraw Hill, New York (1961).

681. E. GLENNY, "Thermal Fatigue". *Metal. Rev.* **6** (1961) 387.

682. A. DEARDEN, "Residual Thermal Stress in Compression Ignition Engines". *J. Brit. Cast Iron Res. Ass.* **9** (1961) 540.

683. P. G. FORREST and A. B. PENFOLD, "New Approach to Thermal Fatigue Testing". *Engineering* **192** (1961) 522.

684. Symposium. *Fatigue of Aircraft Structures.* Amer. Soc. Test. Mat. S.T.P. 274 (1959).

685. Symposium. *Full-Scale Testing of Aircraft Structures*, Amsterdam (1959). Pergamon Press (1961).

86. P. J. E. FORSYTH, "A Two-Stage Process of Fatigue Crack Growth". *Symposium on Crack Propagation*, Cranfield, 1961. To be published.

# AUTHOR INDEX

The figures in bold type are reference numbers and each is followed by the page number or numbers on which it is quoted.

# SUBJECT INDEX